"Though lacking widespread agreement, evangelicals currently abound with origins books from young- and old-earth creationists, theistic evolutionists/evolutionary creationists, and intelligent design proponents. No origins question dominates this scene more than 'who was Adam?' The updated edition, then, of *Who Was Adam?* by Fazale Rana and Hugh Ross arrives just in time to continue setting the bar in scholarship and amicable tone. A decade after the important first edition, the revision maintains its stance on biblical inerrancy and a specially created historical Adam as the first human. But now Rana and Ross test their original scientific model against a further decade of discoveries, refreshingly admitting they were wrong about some details. With added treatments of difficult subjects such as the origin of races and diseases, and human-Neanderthal interbreeding, the new edition is a must read for those who take the Bible and science seriously."

—Ted Cabal, professor of philosophy and apologetics,
Southern Baptist Theological Seminary, editor, *The Apologetics Study Bible*

"In the ten years since *Who Was Adam?* was first published, an exciting explosion of scientific discoveries has occurred in the fields of paleoanthropology and genetics. In this updated edition, Rana shows where the RTB model has been supported by these new discoveries. He also explains where the RTB model of Adam's special creation by God has had to be refined, fine-tuned, and, where necessary, adjusted. Not only is the amount of research exhibited in this book truly remarkable, Rana presents the material clearly in a way that is accessible to the non-specialist. Bottom line, the RTB model continues to serve as a testable hypothesis of how God acted to create the original couple."

—Ken Keathley, professor of theology, director of the L. Russ Bush Center
for Faith and Culture, Southeastern Baptist Theological Seminary

"This is a scholarly, in-depth scientific treatment of the origin of human beings from an old-earth creationist point of view that is based on a belief in the historicity and reliability of the Genesis record."

—Norman Geisler, PhD, dean, Southern Evangelical Seminary

"This is the most careful analysis of human origins I have seen. Rana and Ross have treated the scientific evidence fairly without imposing upon that evidence an atheistic worldview."

—Henry F. Schaefer III, fellow, American Academy of Arts and Sciences

"Every thinking Christian must read this book. Evangelicals have dismissed or avoided the scientific findings relating to human origins for too long; this book opens that door and shows that there is nothing to fear: God's Word is still true, and His world still reveals His handiwork."

—John A. Bloom, PhD, professor of physics, director of the master's degree program in science and religion, Biola University

"As a nonscientist who is deeply interested in science, I have learned from and been challenged by this book, which is the reaction I have expected from RTB's books since *The Creator and the Cosmos*. *Who Was Adam?* is one of the most fascinating books that I have read in a long time."

—Craig Keener, professor of New Testament, Palmer Seminary; author of *The IVP Bible Background Commentary: New Testament*

"*Who Was Adam?* addresses a generation with the gospel of creation, which will open many thoughtful minds and needy hearts to the gospel of salvation."

—Jack W. Hayford, PhD, founder and chancellor, The Kings College and Seminary

"Rana and Ross have taken us carefully and thoughtfully through the biology and the fossils and have shown how to read them properly. Their willingness to put their biblical model to the test of science is invigorating."

—C. John "Jack" Collins, PhD, professor, chairman of the Department of Old Testament, Covenant Theological Seminary

"If you want evidence from genetics, biology, archeology, paleontology, and astronomy that points to the conclusion that the human race came into existence a relatively short time ago, read this book."

—John F. Ankerberg, MA, DMin, apologist; host of *The John Ankerberg Show*

God actioned to act over billions (13.8 billion of years may have used some evolution, but guided

FAZALE RANA WITH HUGH ROSS

WHO

was

ADAM?

Modern man was a special creation

Believe in evolution from beginning of life • of man after special creation

SECOND EXPANDED EDITION

Some think 1st Adam + Eve were first evo-organism. + 2nd Adam + Eve had souls, but could interbreed

A CREATION MODEL APPROACH

TO THE ORIGIN OF HUMANITY

Sort of half way between Theistic evolution and Intelligent design

RTB Model ~ pp. 55-56

modern humans originate 200,000 - 100,000 ~150,000 years ago

rtb
PRESS

Covina, CA

Believe in guided evolution but special creation of humans progressive Old Earth Creationism OEC very similar to intelligent design. Prog/Age OEC

ISBN 978-1-886653-11-5

Cover design by 789 Inc.

Some of the anecdotal illustrations in this book are true to life and are based on information available in the public domain. All other illustrations are composites of real situations, and any resemblance to people living or dead is coincidental.

All epigraphs are taken from *The Riverside Shakespeare*, ed. G. Blakemore Evans (Boston: Houghton Mifflin, 1974). Unless otherwise identified, all Scripture quotations taken from the Holy Bible, NEW INTERNATIONAL VERSION®, NIV® Copyright © 1973, 1978, 1984, 2011 by Biblica, Inc.® Used by permission. All rights reserved worldwide.

Rana, Fazale, 1963-
    Who was Adam? : a creation model approach to the
origin of man / Fazale Rana ; with Hugh Ross. -- Second
expanded edition. -- 10-year update.
    pages cm
    Includes bibliographical references and index.
    ISBN 978-1-886653-11-5

    1. Human evolution--Religious aspects--Christianity.
    2. Human evolution. 3. Religion and science.
    I. Ross, Hugh (Hugh Norman), 1945- II. Title.

BT712.R36 2015   233ʼ.11
                            QBI15-600090

For Amy Rana and Kathy Ross

Contents

List of Figures

Acknowledgments

Many people worked hard and made sacrifices to get both the first and second editions of this book into print. First and foremost we appreciate the love and encouragement of our wives, Amy Rana and Kathy Ross.

The Reasons to Believe team (staff and volunteers) dedicated themselves to this book as if it was their own. We are grateful to Kathy Ross, Patti Townley-Covert, and Tani Trost who gave expert editorial guidance for the first edition. Joe Aguirre, Sandra Dimas, and Maureen Moser served as editors for the second edition. We are grateful for their help. Our thanks go to Jonathon Price and Phillip Chien for designing the tables and many figures that enhanced the first edition's clarity. Marj Harman and Colleen Wingenbach deserve special thanks for preparing the manuscript of the first edition and taking care of the multitude of details that go into each book project. We also want to express gratitude to Diana Carrée, who has the thankless task of managing our schedules so that we would have the time to write.

Valuable interactions took place with scholars Kenneth Samples, David Rogstad, Krista Bontrager, C. John Collins, Robert Bowman, Virgil Robertson, Richard Deem, Sue Dykes, Kevin Birdwell, Jeff Schloss, Darrel Falk, and AJ Roberts. These conversations improved the quality of both the first and second editions. We appreciate the expertise displayed in their manuscript reviews. Of course, we assume responsibility for any errors found herein.

Warm thanks to our friends at NavPress for their contributions to the first edition, particularly Rachelle Gardner.

Preface

Welcome to this expanded edition of *Who Was Adam?* In 2005, when this book was first published, our goal was to show that the biblical account of human origins possessed scientific credibility. To do this, we proposed a scientifically testable, biblically derived creation model for humanity's origin and early history. We then evaluated the predictions that logically flowed from our model based on what we knew about the origin of humanity from scientific studies. We also discussed the limitations of evolutionary explanations for the hominid fossil record and humanity's genesis.

A lot has happened in the last ten years. New scientific insights into humanity's origin are legion. In this ten-year update we left the original work intact and discuss the new advances in Part III. We also respond to critics' challenges and even add to our original model based on questions we've received from audiences.

If you have already read *Who Was Adam?* (2005), go to Part III of the book and start there. If not, start at the beginning. Much of the original content found in the first edition is still relevant. After you read a section, you may want to go to the corresponding section in Part III to see how that part of our model performs today.

When it comes to science-faith issues, I can think of no more important topic than human origins. What we believe about our beginnings has profound implications about how we view others and ourselves and how we function as societies. Does the biblical account of human origins withstand the scrutiny of scientific testing? Dive in and see for yourself.

—Fazale Rana, 2015

Who Am I?

What does it mean to be human? Over the centuries, a significant amount of scholarship, art, and literature has been dedicated to making sense of the human experience and illuminating the human condition.

My first real appreciation of this quest came during my senior year in high school. Kathryn Hodges, my English teacher, was a true champion of the arts. She sought to foster a love for good literature in her students. Unfortunately, I worked hard to resist Mrs. Hodges' best efforts. She and I frequently clashed in and out of the classroom. Even though I was one of the valedictorians, Mrs. Hodges threatened to keep me from graduating because of an off-color answer I wrote on my final exam.

I still remember the phone call my father received from Mrs. Hodges a few days later. I also remember my father's pleas on my behalf. And, as much as I'd like to forget it, I remember the conversation I had with my father after he hung up the phone.

Somehow, in the midst of our battles that year, Mrs. Hodges ignited in me a love of Shakespeare. I spent hours memorizing (for fun) passages from his plays and sonnets. Even though I studied chemistry and biology as an undergraduate, I crossed over and took advanced courses in Shakespeare—much to the bewilderment of my fellow science students and science professors.

The thing that fascinates me most about this master playwright is the insight he offers into the complexities of human nature—a depth of insight rarely presented since his time. One question Shakespeare never addressed, however, was "Why are humans the way they are?" As a biochemist, I'm now convinced that science, in particular the study of humanity's origin, is a good place to start the search for answers.

The Quest Begins

Most people take one of two positions on the topic of human origins. David regarded humanity as God's ultimate creation. His thoughts are recorded in the Bible. Charles Darwin reasoned that man evolved. He wrote a book about his position.[1]

Though you likely agree with one of these men, or wonder if they could somehow both be right, the mainstream scientific community accepts only Darwin's view. Scientists tend to believe biological evolution offers the best explanation for humanity's origin, and within their circles the idea of creation is widely rejected and ridiculed.

However, many people (including some credible scientists) agree with the biblical perspective on human origins. Yet this view rarely receives attention in a classroom or a serious examination in scientific debate. Why?

The problem doesn't lie with the scientific evidence, but largely with the approach some creationists take. (In this book, "creationist" refers to anyone who believes in the existence of a supernatural Creator.) People who accept creation often attack human evolutionary models. They quickly point out the model's deficiencies but seldom offer a viable theory of their own—one open to critique by evolutionary biologists and anthropologists. Even worse, some creationists call the integrity of scientists into question with accusations of deception and conspiracy theories.

Personal attacks destroy the possibility for dialogue. They erect barriers. Such methods will never gain creationist ideas a fair hearing. And these efforts repeatedly fail to convince the scientific community of the Bible's scientific merits. So do grassroots political efforts designed to force the opposition to acquiesce to creationist demands, while condemning the scientific community for dogmatic naturalism.

Although materialism is the reigning worldview in science, Christians must realize that the scientific community's resistance to creation stems largely from the view that the biblical perspective represents a religion, not science. Biologists Brian Alters and Sandra Alters, in their book *Defending Evolution in the Classroom*, make this point in arguing against the teaching of biblical creation alongside evolutionary theory.

The fairness question is still faulty because it mixes apples and oranges. A federal judge has ruled (young-earth) creation science to be "not science" but a religious concept. Therefore, presenting both sides does not mean including various scientific theories but rather including religious ideas, or at least non-scientific ideas, alongside scientific theories in science instruction.[2]

When creation is presented strictly as a religious idea, scientists are left to conclude that the theory's sole basis is blind faith. By contrast, scientific ideas gain acceptance only when they withstand the rigors of ongoing experimental and observational evaluation. For scientists, faith has no place in science. Testing does.

Whenever scientists make statements about the physical and biological world, these statements must be tested. In addition, logical consequences follow from these statements—consequences that lead to predictions. If past and future experimental and observational work matches these predictions, then the scientific statements gain credibility. For scientists, no idea escapes challenge, whereas religious ideas are often considered sacred and beyond the reaches of testing. Because of this perception, biblical ideas seldom influence classroom instruction or debates that take place at the cutting edge of science. Researchers typically don't see religious ideas, including creation, as testable and therefore meaningful to the scientific enterprise.

Alters and Alters also make the important point that the classroom isn't where crucial debate about scientific ideas should take place. Rather, they argue, these discussions belong at the highest levels:

> Creationists must first change the construct of the scientific community; then science instructors will teach intelligent design because it's part of the construct. Until that day, instructors cannot honestly teach it as science.[3]

Putting Creation to the Test

Many Christians trained in the sciences, including my colleagues at Reasons to Believe (RTB), agree with Alters and Alters on these points. We observe the harmony between God's revelation in the words of the Bible and the facts of nature. Establishment of this relationship in a testable framework is the core of our research, and it *can* change the construct of the scientific community.

Development of RTB's testable creation model has already made important strides toward this end. Drawing from biblical texts, we have advanced detailed scientific models for the universe's beginning, age, and characteristics as well as life's origin. Each model (while still open to refinement) has successfully withstood significant testing, with more rounds to come.[4] The scientific creation model for human origins presented in this book continues in this vein.

About This Book

This book focuses on human origins. Traditional evolutionary thinking expresses Darwin's view and an approach to science based on naturalism (or materialism). The RTB human origins model represents David's view and reflects the science of nature (creation) based on a biblical description. (This book describes one biblical creation model. Alternate interpretations of biblical creation texts may produce slight variants.) Both views are put to the test for scientific viability. By using a testable framework, this book places creation in the realm of science.

For the sake of simplicity, this work follows a precedent established in the Bible. Genesis 5:1–2 says, "When God created man, he made him in the likeness of God. He created *them* male and female and blessed them. And when *they* were created, he called them '*man*'" (emphasis added). Rather than denoting gender, the words "Adam," "he," and "man" in this book at times signify all humanity—women and men equally. In this usage, no offense is intended to anyone.

The material in this book unfolds in what we hope is an intriguing manner. Chapter 1 contrasts David's and Darwin's views on man's significance. Chapter 2 takes a look at the hominid fossil record and at the current evolutionary models to explain humanity's origin.

Chapter 3 presents the RTB model for human origins using testable methodology and delineating key predictions.

Chapters 4 and 5 discuss advances in genetics, archeology, and paleontology and show how discoveries in these areas impact both models. Chapter 6 analyzes the timing of humanity from an astronomical perspective. Chapter 7 explores how the long life spans recorded in Genesis can be accounted for scientifically. Chapter 8 examines genetic evidence from human populations that maps the surprising pattern of humanity's spread from the Middle East. A look at the geological research and archeological record helps identify the timing of humanity's migration throughout the world.

Chapter 9 addresses the question, can human evolution be declared a fact? Questions about the origin of bipedalism and humanity's large brain size are examined in chapter 10, while chapters 11 and 12 discuss *Homo erectus* and Neanderthals. Chapter 13 takes a look at the genetic similarities and differences between humans and chimpanzees and shows how this comparison (often cited as evidence for evolution) fits within the biblical framework and RTB's model. Chapter 14 provides a response to what many consider the greatest challenge to biblical creation: junk DNA. Chapter 15 reflects on the significance of the latest advances in human origins research.

Scripture references have been placed in the endnotes so readers can easily examine what the Bible says. Scientific references and additional reading material can also be found in the notes.

While I have written most of its contents, this book equally represents the work of Hugh Ross. Over the last decade or so, the two of us have contemplated and probed the question of humanity's origin. For the last five years, we have vigorously pursued answers to this question as a multidisciplinary quest. Though each of us has made original and unique contributions to this book, it is difficult, in many instances, to know where one's contribution begins and the other's ends.

Understanding the differences between David's and Darwin's perspectives on human origins impacts every important decision an individual can make. *Do I have value and purpose, or am I an accident of nature?* The answer to this question carries life-changing implications.

Fazale Rana

PART I

WHAT
IS
MAN?

Chapter 1

The Differences between David and Darwin

What is a man,
If his chief good and market of his time
Be but to sleep and feed? A beast, no more.
Sure He that made us with such large discourse,
Looking before and after, gave us not
That capability and godlike reason
To fust in us unus'd.
—*Hamlet* Act 4, scene 4

Is man merely a physical being, the sum of his parts? Can those parts be dissected and used at society's discretion? Or is there more to human beings than their physical makeup? Does human life possess innate worth and significance that establish inviolable boundaries? These questions lead to the most crucial one of all—what is man?

A picture of Earth recorded by *Voyager 1* from 3.7 billion miles away emphasizes the profound nature of these questions. In the middle of this grainy photograph, produced by the spacecraft's instruments on Valentine's Day 1990, Earth appears as just a small, pale-blue dot—one tiny planet in the midst of the universe's great expanse (see figure 1).[1] For astronomer Carl Sagan, the stunning imagery magnified the reality that every part of human history that had ever been known occurred on this small dot. Every ancestor you ever had came from this tiny world. Every terrible crime and extraordinary invention, from the discovery of fire to the invention of spaceflight, has all occurred on this tiny little speck.[2]

Humanity's home, the Milky Way Galaxy, measures about 120,000 light-years across and consists of about 200 billion stars.[3] Yet our small spiral galaxy is only one in a collection of 27 galaxies spanning 3 million light-years. Together they comprise but a small fraction of the universe, which contains roughly 200 billion galaxies.[4] Each galaxy includes an average of about 100 billion stars, making a total of about 20 billion trillion stars.[5] As an infinitesimal part of the universe, Earth's smallness seems incomprehensible. But there, in its midst, stands man.

Most people don't need current astronomy facts to be spurred to consider humanity's insignificance. A contemplative gaze into a clear night sky is enough. In light of the vast cosmic expanse, humans just don't seem to matter at all.

David's Melody

About 3,000 years ago, a man named David wrote a song expressing his sense of human triviality as he looked up into the dark, jeweled expanse of about 6,500 visible stars.

> When I consider your heavens,
> the work of your fingers,
> the moon and the stars,
> which you have set in place,
> what is man that you are mindful of him,
> the son of man that you care for him?[6]

David saw evidence for God's existence. He believed the beauty and vastness of the heavens resulted from God's handiwork. In light of the universe's grandeur, David, a human being with a heart full of desires, struggled to think that God might take notice of any particular individual.[7]

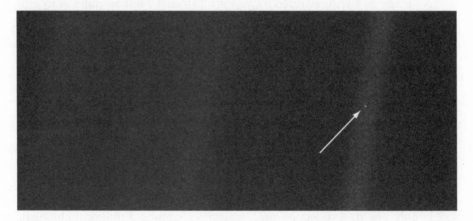

Figure 1: An Image of Earth Taken from the Edge of the Solar System

However, in the depths of his incredulity, David recalled the Genesis 1 creation account.[8]

> You made him [man] a little lower than the heavenly beings
> and crowned him with glory and honor.
> You made him ruler over the works of your hands;
> you put everything under his feet:
> all flocks and herds,
> and the beasts of the field,
> the birds of the air,
> and the fish of the sea,
> all that swim the paths of the seas.[9]

Based on ancient scrolls, David believed that God had created man and woman in His image and appointed them to take charge of Earth and all its other creatures. Even though humanity appeared to be a tiny part of the cosmos, God made people the pinnacle of His creation.[10]

David's view of humanity largely prevailed in the Judeo-Christian world until the early 1870s. Then publication of Charles Darwin's detailed work on human origins, *The Descent of Man, and Selection in Relation to Sex*, stopped the music.

Darwin's Discord

For evolutionists, the idea of man's inherent value and purpose no longer made sense. Darwin proposed that, like all species, humanity evolved through a process of descent with modification from an ancestor shared with apes. As Darwin put it, "In a series of forms graduating insensibly from some apelike creature to man as he now exists, it would be impossible to fix on any definite point when the term 'man' ought to be used."[11]

Darwin saw evidence that human beings are nothing more than animals—certainly not the direct product of divine activity. He believed man differs only in degree and not in kind from apes.

Charles Darwin did the unthinkable: He interpreted humanity in a fully mechanistic and materialistic fashion. According to this view, all of human nature, not just humanity's physical makeup, emerged under the auspices of natural selection. Darwin regarded humanity's mental powers and intellectual capacity, as well as moral sense and religious beliefs, as evolution's invention.

Only an Accident

The late Stephen Jay Gould, in his work *Wonderful Life* (written nearly 120 years after Darwin's *The Descent of Man*), drove home naturalism's claim: Man's appearance, self-awareness, intellect, and moral sensibility are not the inevitable product of an evolutionary process that marched inexorably toward increasingly sophisticated organisms with advanced mental capacity. Rather, humanity is nothing more than "a thing so small in a vast universe, a wildly improbable evolutionary event," that it must be a quirk of fate.[12]

Gould based his conclusion of "historical contingency" on the nature of the evolutionary process. Because chance governs biological evolution at its most fundamental level, repeated evolutionary events must result in dramatically different outcomes. According to Gould, "No finale can be specified at the start, none would occur a second time in the same way, because any pathway proceeds through thousands of improbable stages. Alter any early event ever so slightly, and without apparent importance at the time, and evolution cascades into a radically different channel."[13]

Gould asserted that if a person were to push the rewind button, erase life's history, and "replay life's tape," the results would be completely different.[14] The nature of the evolutionary process renders outcomes nonreproducible. Evolution has no tendencies. From this perspective, humanity might never have been.

Until recently, Gould's (and others') case for historical contingency was qualitative, based on the logical outworkings of evolution's observed mechanisms. New work by scientists from McGill University (Montreal, Canada) and Michigan State University provides quantitative support for historical contingency.[15] These researchers modeled the evolutionary process with computer simulations monitoring the behavior of autonomously replicating computer programs. These studies showed that biological evolution must take place along a unique pathway *each time*, if and when it occurs. In other words, evolution cannot repeat.

Historical contingency drives away any hope one might derive from thinking evolution "had humanity in mind" as it began its work 4 billion years ago. Evolution has no "mind," no direction, no tendency toward progressive advance. The evolutionary process, rightly understood, might not have produced human beings at all.

Accordingly, primates emerged through a lucky happenstance. Lucky happenstance caused bipedal primates to appear. Lucky happenstance brought primates with large brains into being. And, once lucky happenstance gave modern humans their start, only lucky happenstance kept them from suffering the fate of Neanderthals and *Homo erectus*.

Historical contingency dramatically amplifies man's insignificance in the cosmos.

Darwin's View

When Darwin wrote *The Descent of Man*, he lacked direct evidence for human evolution. He surmised that man must have evolved from an apelike animal based on anatomical comparisons among humans and other mammals, embryological similarities, and the existence of what he called "rudimentary," or vestigial, organs—biological structures found in humans that seemingly served little or no function but that appeared to be derived from fully functional ancestral forms.[16]

Darwin reasoned that natural selection and variation were at work in humans, just as in lower animals. He believed that after humans arose, several subspecies (races) evolved.[17] Darwin also provided an explanation as to why distinctly human features evolved and how these characteristics provided man's progenitors with an evolutionary advantage.[18]

Scientific Milestones

At the time Darwin wrote *The Descent of Man*, paleontologists had just discovered Cro-Magnon man fossils (1868), dated at 35,000 years of age, in the caves of France.[19] However, these human remains did little to support the notion of human evolution.

Paleontologists had also discovered the first fossil specimen to be assigned as a Neanderthal (in 1856) in the Neander Valley of western Germany.[20] These fossil remains, which dated anywhere from 40,000 to 100,000 years in age, bore many similarities to modern humans, yet they also possessed distinct features. For example, the skull displayed prominent bony ridges above the eyes, unusually large teeth, a chin that receded, and a forehead that sloped backward. Debate centered on Neanderthal's "human" status. Was he a primitive prehuman or simply a deformed human?

Because of their similarity to human beings, Neanderthals provided little fossil evidence for humanity's shared ancestry with the great apes. Paleontologists had yet to discover fossils for intermediate forms that could demonstrate the gradual transition of apelike creatures into humans—fossils that could powerfully corroborate Darwin's idea.

However, the Neanderthal fossils convinced many people that humanity's age far exceeded 6,000 years, the age espoused by many self-described biblical literalists, who viewed the Genesis 1 creation days as 24-hour time periods. For many people, this finding greatly diminished the credibility of the biblical account of Adam and Eve.

Though human evolution gained little direct support from Neanderthals, it indirectly gained favor. The scientific community seemed to have demonstrated biblical error regarding human origins.

"A Beast, No More"

The first ape-human "intermediate" interpreted from the fossil record was discovered around 1890 on the Indonesian island of Java by Dutch paleontologist Marie Eugène François Thomas Dubois.[21] This species, dubbed *Pithecanthropus erectus* (and later *H. erectus*), walked upright but had a brain size about 60 percent that of modern humans. While some anthropologists regarded "Java man" as one of humanity's ancestors, controversy surrounded this conclusion. Still, this evidence seemed to substantiate human evolution.

In 1924, anthropologist Raymond Dart uncovered a small skull in South Africa with a blend of ape and human features that represented (to the scientific community) humanity's most primitive predecessor.[22] This fossil, nicknamed the "Taung child," was formally classified as *Australopithecus africanus*. Dart reasoned that the Taung child must have walked erect based on the location of its foramen magnum (the opening in the skull's base that receives the spinal cord).[23] As with *Pithecanthropus*, however, controversy swirled around the status of the Taung child in relation to modern humans.

But then Louis Leakey uncovered stone tools in the early 1930s. This discovery drew him and his wife, Mary, back to Olduvai Gorge in Tanzania again and again in an attempt to find and identify the toolmaker. The turning point for human evolution finally came in the late 1950s. After nearly three decades of labor, Mary Leakey discovered the *Zinj* fossil in East Africa.[24] Almost immediately after this discovery (eventually classified as a robust *Australopithecus*), Louis Leakey unearthed the first *Homo habilis* specimen. Paleontologists considered this species the connection between the more primitive apelike australopithecines and *H. erectus*. These scientists also regarded *H. habilis* as the species responsible for the tools recovered in Olduvai Gorge and the first toolmaker in the human evolutionary pathway.[25]

These two discoveries opened the floodgates. In the decades since, paleontologists have uncovered a treasure trove of hominid fossils that encompass a wide range of species and their accompanying archeological remains. The discoveries occurred throughout eastern, central, and southern Africa; Asia; the Middle East; and Europe—and the riches continue to pour in. Each new hominid unearthed appears (to the general public) to fill in the evolutionary tree and clarify the course of human evolution over the last 6 million years.

For many people, genetic comparisons between humans and the great apes further fill in the fossil evidence for human evolution. Such studies indicate a high degree of genetic similarity (98 percent) between humans and chimpanzees, for example. To evolutionary biologists, this resemblance means humans and chimps must have shared a common ancestor roughly 5 to 6 million years ago.[26] Darwin's circumstantial case has apparently been substantiated by such compelling evidence that H. James Birx (a visiting professor at Harvard University) wrote in the introduction to a new edition of *The Descent of Man*, "The myth of Creation as espoused by religious creationists and biblical fundamentalists has been replaced by the fact of evolution....Despite the wishes of some to the contrary, the fact of evolution will not disappear."[27]

So, What's Left to Discuss?

These discoveries and their implications about humanity's origin and place in the universe continue to captivate the general public's interest. To satisfy this curiosity, reports about hominid finds and the latest ideas in human evolutionary theory permeate the popular media. Topics related to human origins are a programming staple for PBS and the Discovery Channel. The most recent fossil discoveries and their importance to human evolution are frequent topics in science periodicals such as *Scientific American*, *National Geographic*, and *Discover*.

In the last few years, *Time* magazine has published at least two cover stories about hominid fossil finds, and the recovery of a hominid fossil (dubbed the "Toumai man") even made the front page of *USA Today*.[28] Given the widespread media attention to these discoveries, it's no wonder that most people believe there is overwhelming evidence for human evolution.

The Ultimate Question

For Darwin, evidence of humanity's "lowly origin" came from the "indelible stamp" of evolution on "his bodily frame."[29] But was he right? And what about David? Does his view, expressed in the Bible, have any merit at all?

Is humanity a quirk of nature—a mere accident with no significance whatsoever? Or is man the crown of creation, made in the Creator's image?

Given the magnitude of these questions, one must carefully consider the data. Does the fossil record really support Darwin's view of the "indelible stamp"? Or does the record reveal the need for an alternative theory, one based on David's explanation—the biblical view of humanity's origin? Facts from the fossil record, as described in the next chapter, point toward some intriguing answers.

Chapter 2

Fossil Record Facts

All the world's a stage,
And all the men and women merely players;
They have their exits and
Their entrances,
And one man in his time plays many parts.
                    —*As You Like It* Act 2, scene 6

In 1912, Charles Dawson and Arthur Smith Woodward reported on fossils recovered from ancient gravels near Sussex, England. Pieces of a human-like cranium, a partial apelike jaw, and a few worn-down molars were interpreted to come from an individual hominid (deemed *Eoanthropus dawsoni*) that represented a transitional intermediate between apes and humans. Called "Piltdown man," the fragments displayed the very features that evolutionary biologists expected to see in the "missing link."

Based on other mammal fossils reported to be associated with these specimens, Dawson and Woodward dated their find at about 500,000 years old. Piltdown man's status as humanity's ancestor gained further credence with Dawson's report (in 1915) of a second specimen recovered near Sheffield Park.

However, after Raymond Dart discovered *Australopithecus* in 1924, some scientists began to think Dart's newly recognized hominids—not Piltdown man—were the ones that led to modern humans. In the 1930s, scientists further questioned Piltdown man's importance as a transitional form when paleoanthropologists discovered and confirmed *Pithecanthropus erectus* and *Sinanthropus pekinensis* (and later *Homo erectus pekinesis*) as ancient hominids. Piltdown man was relegated to a mere evolutionary side branch.

Better dating of the site of Piltdown man's discovery and careful chemical and morphological analysis of the fossil specimens ultimately exposed what Alexander Kohn (onetime editor of the *Journal of Irreproducible Results*) called "the most elaborate scientific hoax ever perpetuated."[1] The fossils were actually carefully doctored modern remains stained with a dye to make them appear old. The cranium pieces were human. The jawbone fragment came from an orangutan. The teeth were carefully filed to fit the mandible and make them appear more humanlike.

The legendary Piltdown man forgery went unrecognized for nearly 40 years before a team of scientists exposed it as a fraud in 1953.[2] Debate still continues as to the perpetrator's identity and the motivation for his or her actions. Science historians also discuss why the scientific community so readily accepted Piltdown man as authentic and why it took so long to recognize the discovery as a forgery, since (at least in retrospect) many indicators along this line were quite evident.

In part, the ready acceptance of Piltdown man stemmed from an eagerness to find the missing link that would support Darwin's model for human evolution with evidence from the fossil record. Piltdown man exactly fit the scientific community's preconceived ideas as to what the transitional intermediate between humans and apes must look like. According to Kohn:

> Scientists, contrary to lay belief, do not work by collecting only "hard" facts and fitting together information based on them. Scientific investigation is also motivated by pursuit of recognition and fame, by hope and by prejudice. Dubious evidence is strengthened by strong hope: anomalies are fitted into a coherent picture with the help of cultural bias.[3]

Scientists are human, and from time to time their fallibility or bias can influence the scientific process. However, the scientific enterprise eventually roots out error and exposes fraud, though not always as quickly as might be desirable.

Some creationists capitalize on the Piltdown man forgery (along with a few other examples of dubious paleoanthropological finds). They generalize that hominid fossils are either fictitious or fraudulent.[4] Others view the fossils as real but regard some to be apes (the australopithecines, for example) and some (such as *Homo erectus* and Neanderthals) as variants of modern humans.[5] Any dating of fossils as older than 10,000 years in age is disputed and dismissed.

However, these all too popular creationist views are not the only Christian views. A perspective consistent with the Bible can regard hominids in much the same way as the entire scientific community does—as real animals that existed in Earth's past. This interpretation also considers the dates assigned to hominid fossils as generally reliable within the limitations of the methods used to obtain them. (A note on nomenclature: In modern evolutionary biology, humans are classified as "hominids." This book uses that term to refer only to the bipedal primates that preceded "modern humans." The term "modern human" is used where appropriate for *Homo sapiens sapiens*, out of respect for contemporary nomenclature conventions, although neither the authors nor RTB believe that hominids prior to modern humans should be called human beings.)

"All the World's a Stage"

It's true that the hominid fossil record is incomplete, sometimes notoriously so. Debate rages among paleoanthropologists as to the proper classification of some fossils and as to the number of species that existed. Still, this debate does not preclude the fossil record—along with the accompanying archeological and geological records—from providing insight into hominid biology, behavior, culture, and life history. The scientific record also supplies information about the timing of the hominids' existence and the ecology of their environs. Fossil data provide the means to evaluate the relationships among hominids and assess their connections to modern humans.

Although a few instances of fraud and error have occurred in the history of paleoanthropology, this doesn't mean paleoanthropologists are dishonest or incompetent. In reality, most of these scientists, though typically committed to methodological naturalism (the notion that in science only mechanistic explanations based on the laws of physics and chemistry are permitted), display exemplary integrity and work hard at their discipline.

Familiarity with the hominid fossil and archeological records is the first step toward a full appreciation of the ideas and debates that are so much a part of the quest for humanity's origin. The overview that follows may seem tedious for some. However, those readers who take time to go through the brief descriptions will be rewarded with greater awareness of how the different hominids fit within the context of human origins. For readers who choose to skim the chapter, the contents are summarized in figures 2.1 and 2.2. These figures give a limited but helpful perspective on the hominid fossil record. Most readers will find it beneficial to refer to this chapter as they encounter later discussions about the various hominids.

What Do Anthropologists Mean by "Human"?

The nomenclature used by paleoanthropologists to discuss the hominid fossil record can be misleading for the uninitiated. Scientists often refer to members of the genera *Sahelanthropus, Orrorin, Ardipithecus, Australopithecus, Paranthropus,* and *Homo*—all primates that walked erect—as humans. People unfamiliar with this practice commonly misinterpret the term "human" to indicate that human beings (as colloquially understood) existed as far back as 5 to 6 million years ago. This choice of words ignores the marked morphological and behavioral differences between these extinct hominids and modern humans.

Equally confusing, some paleoanthropologists call hominids—those that existed between about 500,000 years ago and the appearance of modern humans—*Homo sapiens.* This list includes some specimens of *H. erectus, Homo antecessor, Homo heidelbergensis,* and *Homo neanderthalensis.* Sometimes paleoanthropologists use the term "archaic *Homo sapiens*" in reference to these hominids. Again, this practice overlooks the significant behavioral differences and unique morphological characteristics that distinguish these extinct hominids from modern man. When referring to human beings (as popularly understood), paleoanthropologists use the terms "modern human," "anatomically modern human," or "*Homo sapiens sapiens.*"

When newspaper headlines announce the finding of "human" fossils that date 3 million years old, paleoanthropologists have merely discovered the remains of an australopithecine or some other member of a related genus, not a modern human. In a similar vein, when the cover of a magazine features an article on the latest *H. sapiens* find, dated at 170,000 years in age, no doubt it's referring to an archaic *H. sapiens,* not a modern human (*H. sapiens sapiens*). Without an understanding of how paleoanthropologists use the terms "human" and "*H. sapiens,*" reports in the popular media that describe the latest hominid fossil finds can be misconstrued as evidence of humanity's great antiquity.

However, nearly all paleoanthropologists agree that anatomically modern humans (*H. sapiens sapiens*) appear in the fossil record not much earlier than 100,000 years ago.

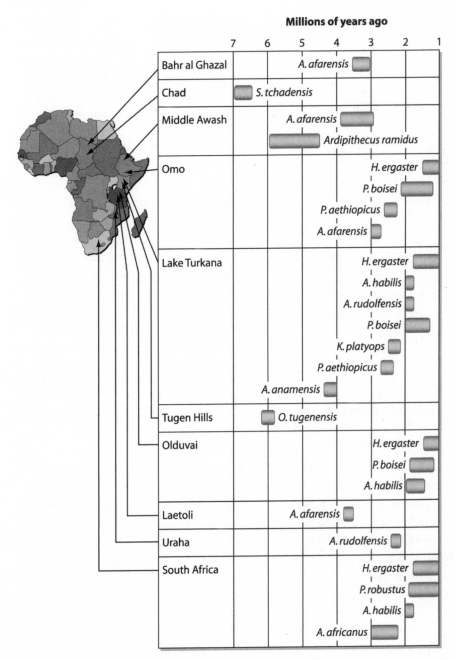

Figure 2.1: The Biogeographical Distribution of Hominid Species Found in the African Fossil Record

Figure 2.2: Different Modes of Technology Found in the Archeological Record

The Play Begins

Based on genetic comparisons between humans and great apes, most evolutionary biologists believe that the human lineage must have arisen from an apelike ancestor about 6 to 5 million years ago. In accord with this belief, paleoanthropologists have traditionally recognized that the oldest hominids in the fossil record (the australopithecines) date to about 4 million years of age. However, in recent years, a flurry of discoveries has pushed the hominid fossil record back to nearly 7 million years ago and indicates that a menagerie of hominids existed across a vast geographical region.[6]

The oldest hominid fossil (*Sahelanthropus tchadensis*) now dates about 7 million years in age. Older than expected, this remarkable find was made in the central African nation of Chad—an area previously thought to have been unoccupied by hominids. The fossil exhibits surprisingly modern features. It appears that this hominid walked erect and possessed a brain close in size to that of a chimpanzee. *S. tchadensis* lived in both woodlands and green savannas.

Orrorin tugenensis fossils, which date at 6 million years old, have been recovered in Kenya. Paleoanthropologists found partial jaws, teeth, and arm, finger, and thigh bones. Analysis of its femurs suggests *O. tugenensis* also walked erect. This creature lived in a mixed woodland and open plain habitat.

Ardipithecus ramidus fossils dating at 5.8, 5.6, 5.2, and 4.4 million years in age were discovered in Ethiopia. In fact, about 45 percent of a complete skeleton exists for *A. ramidus*, including hand, foot, arm, leg, pelvic, and skull bones. *A. ramidus* walked erect and lived in a forest environment. Recent analysis of *Ardipithecus* teeth, 5.6 million years old, indicates that *A. ramidus* may actually constitute two species.[7] This view assigns the 4.4-million-year-old specimens to *A. ramidus* and the older specimens to *Ardipithecus kadabba*.

Because of the limited number of available fossils, paleoanthropologists don't have a clear understanding of the biology of these earliest hominids. The current data indicate that all four hominids display many apelike morphological characteristics, but their anatomical features make them distinct from chimpanzees. In this sense, they can rightly be thought of as novel bipedal apes. Paleoanthropologists think these four hominids may represent only a small fraction of those that existed prior to 5 million years ago and expect future fieldwork to reveal this extensive early hominid diversity (see chapter 9).

Entrances and Exits

Between 4 million and 2 million years ago, at least 11 different hominid species existed in central, eastern, and southern Africa. These species fall into three genera: *Australopithecus*, *Paranthropus*, and *Kenyanthropus*. At any given time during this era, from four to seven different species existed simultaneously.[8]

Paleoanthropologists surmise that at least six of the hominids were *Australopithecus*. Like earlier hominids, australopithecines can be thought of as bipedal apes, distinct from chimpanzees.[9] The brain size of australopithecines (380 to 450 cm^3) was slightly larger than that of chimpanzees (300 to 400 cm^3). Though the cranium, facial features, and dental anatomy were apelike, they were distinct from the corresponding chimpanzee features.

The australopithecines stood about four feet tall and matured rapidly, like the great apes. Skull, pelvis, and lower limbs all display features that indicate these hominids walked erect. Still, the bipedalism, called facultative, was distinct from the obligatory bipedalism employed by *Homo* hominids. Some paleoanthropologists think the australopithecines could also climb and move effectively through trees. This idea is based on their relatively long upper arms, short lower limbs, and funnel-shaped torsos. Work published in 2000 indicates that some australopithecines might have knuckle-walked like the great apes.[10]

The earliest australopithecines lived either in a woodland environment or in a mixed habitat of trees and open savannas. Later australopithecines lived only on the grassy plains. Their capacity to climb and move through trees, as well as walk erect, gave these hominids easy mobility in their varied environment.

The oldest member of *Australopithecus*, *Australopithecus anamensis*, existed between 4.2 and 3.8 million years ago, based on fossils recovered near Lake Turkana in Kenya. *Australopithecus afarensis* fossils have been recovered in eastern Africa and date to between 4 and 3 million years old. "Lucy" (discovered in the early 1970s by Donald Johanson) is one of the best-known specimens. She is nearly 40 percent complete, with much of the postcranial skeleton intact.[11]

Remains of *Australopithecus bahrelghazali*, dated at 3.2 million years ago, have been recovered in Chad. Some paleoanthropologists think, however, that *A. bahrelghazali* is properly classified as an *A. afarensis*. *Australopithecus africanus* lived in South Africa between 3.0 and 2.2 million years ago, based on the fossil record. One of the best-known *A. africanus* specimens is the "Taung child" discovered in 1924 by Dart. The Taung child was the first australopithecine found.[12]

Australopithecus garhi lived in eastern Africa around 2.5 million years ago. The australopithecines, as a rule, did not use tools of any sort. However, some evidence indicates that *A. garhi* might have used crude implements to remove flesh from animal remains.[13]

Members of the genus *Paranthropus* were once included in the genus *Australopithecus*. They were referred to as the "robust" australopithecines. Other members of *Australopithecus* were labeled "gracile." Though their anatomy was similar, *Paranthropus* hominids were much hardier than these other australopithecines. Another distinguishing feature was their specialized dental and jaw anatomy, which permitted heavy chewing.[14]

Currently, paleoanthropologists recognize three *Paranthropus* species. *Paranthropus aethiopicus* fossils recovered in East Africa date at 2.5 million years old. *Paranthropus robustus* fossils found in South Africa date to between 1.8 and 1.0 million years in age. The most robust *Paranthropus* of all, *Paranthropus boisei*, existed in East Africa between 2.2 and 1.3 million years ago.[15]

Kenyanthropus is a newly recognized hominid genus and currently consists of one undisputed species, *Kenyanthropus platyops*. Fossil evidence places this hominid in eastern Africa between 3.5 and 3.2 million years ago. Like other australopithecines, *Kenyanthropus* possesses many apelike characteristics, though the limited number of fossil specimens available for study leaves much about its biology unknown. One defining feature is its remarkably flat face.[16]

Homo Takes Center Stage

According to the fossil record, the first hominid assigned to the genus *Homo* appeared just over 2 million years ago. Classified as *Homo habilis*, this hominid lived between about 2.4 and 1.5 million years ago. A closely related species, *Homo rudolfensis*, might have coexisted with *H. habilis*.[17] These two hominids lived in eastern and southern Africa and might have even migrated into southwest Asia.[18]

Paleoanthropologists estimate that *H. habilis'* brain size (650 to 800 cm^3)

was somewhat larger than that of the australopithecines, though many other features were quite apelike. In fact, some scientists think that *H. habilis* and *H. rudolfensis* are rightly classified as members of *Australopithecus*.[19]

H. habilis might have been the first hominid to use tools. Paleoanthropologists refer to this technology as Mode I (or Oldowan) technology.[20] Mode I tools consisted of rock flakes chipped away from a stone core by using a rock called a hammer stone. The archeological record shows that this technology persisted for at least a million years with no perceptible change.

Homo ergaster appeared in the fossil record about 1.8 million years ago in East Africa and showed up in Eurasia around 1.7 million years ago.[21] The body proportions of *H. ergaster* more closely resembled those of a modern human's than those of an australopithecine. This creature likely stood about five feet tall and possessed a brain size that ranged between 850 and 1,000 cm^3. One of the best-known *H. ergaster* specimens is "Turkana boy." This nearly complete skeleton, found in Kenya, dates about 1.8 million years old. Though still quite crude, *H. ergaster*'s technology was more sophisticated than that of *H. habilis*.

Mode II (or Acheulean) technology involved shaping stones into a variety of forms called bifaces: teardrop-shaped rocks (hand axes); rocks with a flat, sharp edge (cleavers); and triangular-shaped rocks (picks). Presumably, these bifaces were used to butcher animal remains. However, much debate centers on whether *H. ergaster* was a hunter or a scavenger. After these tools appeared, the technology apparently remained static for nearly a million years.[22]

Closely related to *H. ergaster*, *H. erectus* lived somewhere between 1.8 million and 100,000 years ago in Asia. Some paleoanthropologists refer to *H. ergaster* as the African *H. erectus*. "Java man" and "Peking man" are perhaps the two best-known *H. erectus* specimens. (See chapter 11 for a more detailed discussion of *H. ergaster* and *H. erectus* biology and culture.)

Around 900,000 years ago, a new type of hominid appeared. The spread of these hominids can be traced from Africa and into western and eastern Eurasia.[23] They possessed a large brain (about 1,200 to 1,300 cm^3 in size), but facial features such as a large, forward-projecting face, a chinless lower jaw, large brow ridges, and a low, flat forehead made them distinct from modern humans. Traditionally, paleoanthropologists referred to these hominids as archaic *H. sapiens*, but now few scientists consider them to be an early form of modern human beings. Most regard them as a separate species, *H. heidelbergensis*, although some think that a menagerie of species existed, including (among others) *H. antecessor*, *H. heidelbergensis*, and *H. sapiens idaltu*.

These hominids behaved in nonhuman ways. They used Mode III

technology (also referred to as Mousterian in some instances). Though more sophisticated than Mode II, this technology was vastly inferior to Mode IV, which appeared with the advent of modern humans (see chapters 5, 11, and 12).

Neanderthals (*H. neanderthalensis*) appeared in the fossil record around 130,000 years ago and persisted until about 30,000 years ago. Neanderthals were confined to Europe and western Asia. Like *H. heidelbergensis*, they employed Mode III technology.[24] Chapter 12 discusses Neanderthal biology and culture in some detail.

Human Origins Models

Paleoanthropologists typically interpret hominids in the fossil record within an evolutionary framework. They view hominids that existed from 7 million to 2 million years ago as transitional forms that gave rise to the *Homo* genus. Most think *A. ramidus* gave rise to *A. anamensis*, which in turn yielded *A. afarensis*. Some paleoanthropologists think *A. afarensis* then evolved to produce *A. africanus*. They suggest this hominid produced *H. habilis*. Others believe that *A. afarensis* was the ancestral species for *H. habilis*. Some paleoanthropologists regard *Kenyanthropus* as *H. habilis'* direct ancestor.

Almost all paleoanthropologists agree that *Paranthropus* represents an evolutionary side branch. Again, these scientists aren't clear whether *A. afarensis* or *A. africanus* produced *Paranthropus* (see figure 2.3). Most paleoanthropologists say *H. habilis* gave rise to *H. ergaster*. However, this is where agreement ends.

Multiregional Hypothesis

For nearly 50 years, the multiregional hypothesis was the mainstay explanation for humanity's origin. This model suggests that modern humans evolved roughly simultaneously around the world from different hominid populations.[25] According to this view, *H. erectus* in Asia gave rise to Asian and Oceanic peoples, *H. neanderthalensis* produced Europeans, and archaic *H. sapiens* in Africa evolved into Africans. Multiregionalists posit that gene flow among these different hominids kept *H. sapiens sapiens* a single species but that long-term geographical separation explains humanity's racial diversity. The multiregional hypothesis views all archaic *H. sapiens* as essentially a single species that collectively evolved toward modernity (see figure 2.4).

Out-of-Africa Hypothesis

An alternative model, which has emerged relatively recently, maintains that

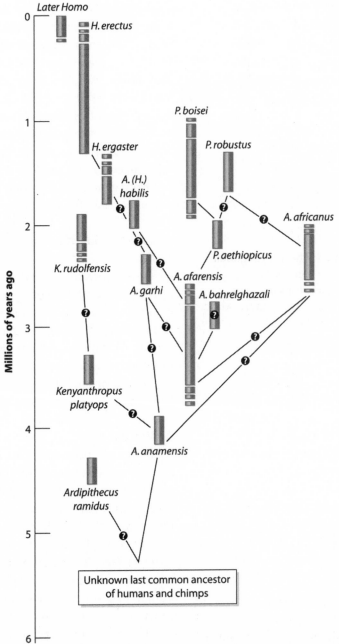

Figure 2.3: Presumed Evolutionary Relationships among the Australopithecines and Other Related Genera

Figure 2.4: The Multiregional Model
This model posits that modern humans evolved around the world from different hominid populations.

Figure 2.5: The Out-of-Africa Model
This model maintains that modern humans evolved from African "archaic" *H. sapiens* populations.

modern humans evolved exclusively from African archaic *H. sapiens* populations and then migrated around the world to replace preexisting hominids. This model is called the out-of-Africa hypothesis, or the replacement model. According to this view, *H. neanderthalensis* and *H. erectus* are evolutionary side branches and dead ends,[26] while racial differences among modern humans result from genetic drift and natural selection effects (see figure 2.5).

African Hybridization and Replacement Model
Given the current support for the out-of-Africa model, some paleoanthropologists have proposed a mostly out-of-Africa model. In this view, modern humans originated from African populations but interbred with hominids, such as *H. erectus* and *H. neanderthalensis*,[27] thus contributing to humanity's origin.

A Missed Cue
Even though paleontologists have discovered a menagerie of hominids, they cannot seem to establish evolutionary connections among them.[28] Without these connections, human evolution cannot be declared a fact but remains a theory (see chapter 9). Instead of solidifying evolutionary hypotheses about human origins, each new hominid find generates more turmoil.

The recent recovery of the "Toumai man" (*Sahelanthropus tchadensis*) skull in Chad raises many new questions. This specimen, uncovered in a surprising location (central Africa), was older than expected (about 7 million years in age) and possessed amazingly advanced features (see chapter 11).[29] According to science writer John Whitfield, the Toumai man discovery may be "the tip of that iceberg—one that could sink our current ideas about human evolution."[30]

Recent discoveries related to Neanderthals, *H. erectus*, and chimpanzees also have raised questions about traditional evolutionary ideas. These advances suggest an expanding base for Whitfield's iceberg. Is it possible that the case for human evolution may be sunk? Genetic studies on modern human population groups have yielded results with obvious biblical overtones. Could anthropologists have been too quick to dismiss the Bible's account of human origins?

Perhaps David was right. Maybe an alternative model, with predictions developed from the text of the Bible, can make better sense of the data on human origins. At the very least, the Reasons to Believe scientifically testable creation model described in the next chapter warrants consideration.

Chapter 3

A Scientific Creation Model

There is a play to-night before the King,
One scene of it comes near the circumstance
Which I have told thee of my father's death.
I prithee, when thou seest that act afoot,
Even with the very comment of thy soul
Observe my uncle. If his occulted guilt
Do not itself unkennel in one speech,
It is a damned ghost that we have seen,
And my imaginations are as foul
As Vulcan's stithy. Give him a heedful note,
For I mine eyes will rivet to his face,
And after we will both our judgment join
In censure of his seeming.
    —*Hamlet* Act 3, scene 2

Despite songs and sonnets that give voice to the human soul, despite human yearnings for something beyond this life, and despite fossil and genetic evidence suggesting that David's view of man might be correct, most scientists give little if any consideration to the possibility of humanity's creation. Many dismiss the biblical account of human origins because they assume it requires a young-earth interpretation of Genesis 1—a position that treats the creation days as six 24-hour days.

Clearly, any stance that regards the universe and Earth as merely 6,000 to 10,000 years old lacks scientific credibility. However, to discount the biblical explanation for humanity based on this one creationist perspective disregards all other theologically credible interpretations of Genesis 1.[1] As philosopher and theologian Norman Geisler wrote, "Indeed, many of the greatest champions of the highest view of Scripture have held divergent views regarding the age of the earth."[2]

Several positions, including the day-age interpretation adopted in this book, treat the biblical creation accounts as reliable (though not exhaustive) descriptions of Earth's and life's natural history. According to the day-age approach, the Creator repeatedly intervened in Earth's history, initiating new life-forms, including humans.

The day-age view considers the Genesis creation days to be long periods of time and readily accommodates, even anticipates, the scientific dates for the age of the universe and Earth. For a biblical and theological justification of the day-age interpretation of Genesis 1, see *A Matter of Days* (second expanded edition).[3] This interpretation is not a recent invention to accommodate scientific discoveries but a valid historical position.[4]

"Our Judgment Join"

The answer to David's question "What is man?" carries great significance for every human being. Can a scientifically testable model demonstrate the validity of his assertion—that man, although seemingly insignificant in the cosmos, is the crown of God's creation? Is the Bible's explanation consistent with nature's record when both are properly interpreted and understood?

Supernatural causes might have been operating, and the scientific method suffices to detect them, if and when they occurred. All assumptions must be challenged by both the scientific and Christian communities. Reliable human origins research places the same demand on naturalistic processes as it does on creation by supernatural intervention—the same as for any scientific idea. Each model must survive the rigors of testing and accurately predict (or account for) scientific discoveries—past, present, and future—to be considered valid.

For a biblical creation theory to be taken seriously by scientists (or by the general public), it must be framed in the form of a scientifically testable model that can be scrutinized. If the model's predictions have merit, cutting-edge researchers will be compelled to recognize them as part of the "construct of science."

Building the RTB Creation Model

The ongoing process of building Reasons to Believe's (RTB) model for humanity's origin begins with identification of all relevant Bible passages that describe God's creative work in bringing humans into existence, as well as those passages that recount early human history. Once all relevant Scripture is collated, sound exegetical techniques help form the most plausible interpretations (although for some passages several plausible interpretations exist). Using the historical-grammatical method, the origins passages are examined side by side with other relevant passages. All passages that deal with humanity's creation can then be integrated to form a comprehensive picture. The biblical scenario for humanity's origin and spread is then recast in scientific terms.

The results of this work thus far—the general features of the model and the scientific predictions that logically flow from it—are described in the next section. Subsequent chapters subject the RTB model to experimental and observational scrutiny.

However, before getting to the central ideas and predictions of the RTB model, a key point must be emphasized. With RTB's model, *creation is testable.* The concept of creation has entered the scientific domain.

Considerable freedom exists within the creation model's framework for adjustments and fine-tuning as scientists and theologians make new discoveries and gain fresh insight. The RTB model represents only one of many possible biblically derived models for humanity's origin. For many of the biblical passages used to develop the RTB model, a small range of interpretive options is possible. Different interpretations of the same passage will, of course, lead to slightly different models and predictions. Even though biblical texts inspire the framework and constrain RTB's model, opportunity abounds to advance a variety of models and new understandings.

The Model's Design
Detailed exegetical treatment of all the scriptural passages related to humanity's origin and early history is beyond the scope of this book. Substantial exegetical scholarship undergirds RTB's interpretations, but of course not all theologians agree in their understanding of the passages that inspire this particular model. The RTB model's central features, along with a brief description of the biblical and theological basis for each, appear in the following pages.

God created the first humans (Adam and Eve) both physically and spiritually through direct intervention.
Genesis 1:26–27 and 5:1–2 state that God created the first man and woman in His image. In these verses two different Hebrew verbs, *'āśâ* and *bārā'*, translate as "make" and "create," respectively. Both verbs communicate God's direct action in creating human beings.[5] Genesis 2:7 also describes God's formation of Adam from the dust of the earth. Then God breathed life into Adam. Genesis

2:22 explains Eve's creation from Adam's side. The text clearly teaches that God Himself created the first human pair.

These passages challenge most forms of theistic evolution (the idea that God exclusively used natural-process biological evolution to create new life-forms). According to that quasinaturalistic view, God played no direct role in humanity's origin. Rather, human beings evolved from hominids. Adam and Eve were simply literary figures representing humanity. Some theistic evolutionists believe God intervened to create Adam and Eve's spirit, though their physical makeup evolved from lower life-forms. Others say the human components—both body and spirit—evolved from earlier species.

Theistic evolution (as defined above) seems to contradict Genesis 1 and 2 as well as Mark 10:6 and Matthew 19:4, where Jesus states that God created the first humans to be male and female. These and other Bible passages indicate that God created the original human pair in a special and direct way. Thus RTB's model for humanity's origin must reject any form of theistic evolution that doesn't posit God's direct involvement. The RTB model asserts that attempts to establish evolutionary relationships among the hominids in the fossil record and to identify the evolutionary pathways to modern humans will ultimately prove unfruitful.

All humanity came from Adam and Eve.
The RTB model treats Adam and Eve as the first human beings in history. A careful reading of Genesis 2–4 supports the couple's historical existence. So does the inclusion of Adam in the Genesis 5 genealogy and in Luke's genealogy of Jesus.[6]

In addition to viewing Adam as part of human history, the genealogies treat Adam as the man who ultimately fathered all humanity. In a similar vein, Genesis 3:20 refers to Eve as the woman who became "the mother of all the living."

Based on these passages, the RTB model predicts that without scientific limitations, investigation can trace humanity's origin to one man and one woman. As a corollary to this prediction, the RTB model predicts that attempts to gauge humanity's original population size will, at minimum, indicate that it was initially small.

Humanity originated in a single geographical location (the Garden of Eden).
Genesis 2 teaches that after God created Adam, He placed him in the garden He'd planted in "the east, in Eden." Here, God made Eve. The author of Genesis

2 (presumed to be Moses) treated the Garden of Eden as a specific geographical location. He even named the four rivers that ran through it—the Pishon, Gihon, Tigris, and Euphrates. After Adam and Eve disobeyed God, they were banished from this garden. This consequence reinforces the idea that the Garden of Eden was an actual place. Cain's banishment to the land of Nod, said to be "east of Eden," also indicates a specific location.[7]

Because the RTB model describes all humanity as coming from Adam and Eve, their early life and subsequent ejection from the Garden of Eden mean that humanity's origin should be traceable to a single region. The best scholarship places the garden's location in Mesopotamia, with the possibility that it extended into northern and eastern Africa (see "Where Was the Garden of Eden?").

Where Was the Garden of Eden?

The Garden of Eden's location has been the subject of endless debate throughout history. While the debate is not fully resolved, most theologians agree that the garden was located in one of two adjacent regions. With the land later called Israel as the frame of reference, Genesis 2:8 describes the garden's location as "east, in Eden." This implies that the garden was contained within a larger region called Eden.[8]

The mention of the Tigris and Euphrates rivers indicates the garden's location within Mesopotamia (Genesis 2:14). However, the Pishon and Gihon rivers (also noted) are unknown. They might have been smaller river channels or part of the Tigris and Euphrates systems,[9] or they might have disappeared becoming dry riverbeds.[10] Along these lines, Old Testament archeologist K. A. Kitchen argues that these four rivers came together in Mesopotamia to form a single stream that ran into the Garden of Eden. Based on Kitchen's analysis, the rivers are listed starting with the Pishon, located in a southwesterly direction and proceed in a counterclockwise fashion across the east to the Gihon, north to the Tigris, and finally northwest to the Euphrates. Kitchen proposes that the Garden of Eden was located at the northern end of the Persian Gulf and is now submerged under water.[11]

Alternatively, the Pishon and Gihon may be the Blue and White Niles. Part of the support for this view comes from Genesis 2:13, which states that the Gihon "winds through the entire land of Cush." In the Old Testament, the land of Cush equates to Ethiopia. However, "Cush" can also refer to the Kassites, descendants of the patriarch Cush. The Kassites lived in Mesopotamia.[12]

It's probable that the Garden of Eden was somewhere within Mesopotamia, but its boundaries might have extended into northern and eastern Africa.

God created Adam and Eve relatively recently, between 10,000 and 100,000 years ago.

Genesis 1 and 2 teach that making humans was God's last creative act on the sixth creation day. From a scientific standpoint, this chronology indicates a relatively recent appearance of humanity on Earth—after the appearance of other land and sea animals in the fossil record. However, precisely dating the creation of Adam and Eve from the biblical text is not possible.

Gaps in the genealogies and the ambiguity of key words in the original Hebrew text render the best attempts at a biblical date for Adam and Eve as estimates only. If few gaps exist, the date calculates to around 10,000 years ago. If many gaps occur, the date falls closer to 100,000 years ago.[13] It may be possible to limit the date for Adam and Eve's creation, at least to some extent, by using extrabiblical sources to calibrate the Genesis 5 and 11 genealogies.

Some theologians treat the genealogies in Genesis 5 (Adam to Noah) and Genesis 11 (Noah to Abraham) as exhaustively complete chronologies and have attempted to determine the date for Adam and Eve's creation from them. This approach, however, is questionable for several reasons.

First, the Genesis 5 and 11 genealogies were not intended as chronometers but instead (like all genealogies found in Scripture) were meant to communicate theological truths.[14] For example, the Genesis 5 genealogy begins with a reminder that Adam was created by God in His image. The genealogy then teaches that God's image was passed by procreation through Adam's lineage to Noah.[15]

The Hebrew words translated "father" (ʾāb) and "son" (bēn) can mean "ancestor" and "descendant," respectively.[16] Similarly, the Hebrew word translated as "begot" or "become the father of" can mean "to father an individual" or "to bring forth a lineage."[17] In Hebrew thought a father is not only the parent of his child but also the parent of all his child's descendants. According to Kitchen, the genealogies of Genesis 5 and 11 could be read as "A fathered [P, who fathered Q, who fathered R, who fathered S, who fathered T, who fathered...] B." As for the ages listed in Genesis 5 and 11, they could be read as "A fathered the lineage culminating in B, and after fathering the line A lived X years."[18]

Since conveying theological ideas was the chief aim of genealogies, biblical authors frequently abbreviated them by omitting theologically less important names. The genealogies of Genesis 5 and 11 were no exception.[19]

In addition, Bible authors organized genealogies according to patterns. This convention often necessitated dropping names. For example, Matthew 1 uses three sets of 14 names. To maintain this systematic approach, the author omits some names that are listed in 1 Chronicles 1–9. In like manner, Genesis 5 and 11 display a pattern that uses two sets of 10 names. In Genesis 5, the genealogy starts with one name, Adam, and 10 patriarchs later the passage ends with three sons: Shem, Ham, and Japheth. Genesis 11 begins with one name, Shem, and 10 patriarchs later terminates with three sons: Abram, Nahor, and Haran. In other words, gaps exist in the Genesis 5 and 11 genealogies. These gaps do not imply that Scripture is deficient; rather, they signify that biblical genealogies have theological (not timekeeping) importance.

Even so, it may be possible to calibrate the genealogies to some extent by using the accurate dates available for Abraham and Peleg. Biblical and extra-biblical historical records establish that Abraham lived about 4,000 years ago. Genesis 10:25 indicates that "in [Peleg's] time the earth was divided." If this refers to the breaking of land bridges that connected the western hemisphere continents to the eastern hemisphere, then an accurate date for Peleg can also be determined.

Radiocarbon dating places the breaking of the Bering Land Bridge at 11,000 years ago.[20] This event made human migration from Eurasia to North and South America virtually impossible until the development of modern ships. If life spans in the Genesis 11 genealogy are proportional to the passage of time (which may not be the case), then the dates for Abraham and Peleg place Noah's flood at roughly 20,000 to 30,000 years ago, and the creation of Adam and Eve at a few tens of thousands of years earlier.

Humanity's female lineage should trace back to an earlier date than the male lineage.
Though all humanity came from Adam and Eve, scientific dating of humanity's origin using genetic markers specific for the female lineage should measure older than those specific for the male lineage. This discrepancy results not because Eve came first but because the male line experienced a severe bottleneck at the time of the flood.

The Bible teaches that the flood destroyed all humanity except for Noah, his wife, his three sons (Shem, Ham, and Japheth), and their wives.[21] The four men on the ark were close blood relatives, but the women were not. Scientifically speaking, humanity's male lineage effectively traces back to Noah, whereas the female lineage traces back much farther, closer to Eve.[22]

God prepared the planet for humanity's advent, then created Adam and Eve at a special moment in Earth's history.

The Bible teaches the great significance of man, as David (among others) so eloquently expresses. Humanity is the crown of God's creation.[23] Of all His creatures, only human beings were made in God's image.[24] God gave humanity dominion over the earth and appointed people to be creation's caretakers.[25] Psalm 8 designates humanity's status:

> You made him a little lower than the heavenly beings
> and crowned him with glory and honor.
> You made him ruler over the works of your hands;
> you put everything under his feet.

God did not, however, create Adam and Eve first. Instead, He brought the pinnacle of His creative work into existence last.

Psalm 104, a creation song that mirrors Genesis 1, offers insight into why God made humanity when He did. While the Genesis passage outlines Earth's and life's natural history, this description extols and elaborates on the order of God's creative works. Each creation day set the stage for subsequent days. Psalm 104 communicates the purposeful progression of God's creative activity and His providential care in the process. God carefully shaped Earth to support life. Once life appeared, the planet was transformed (both naturally and supernaturally) to make it suitable for humanity. The RTB model predicts that humanity's advent coincides with a unique moment in Earth's history, the exact time when the planet was optimized to sustain human existence.

Human beings share physical characteristics with animals.

In Genesis 1:26–27 (and Genesis 5:1–2), the verbs *'āśâ* and *bārā'*—translated "make" and "create," respectively—describe the beginning of man and woman. In this context, *'āśâ* typically means to fashion an object from already existing materials. Apparently, Adam and Eve were shaped from an available substance or substances.[26]

Genesis 2:7 adds details. This text says that God "formed the man from the dust of the ground." The Hebrew verb *yāṣar* meaning "to form," "to fashion," and "to produce," is approximately synonymous with *'āśâ*.[27] When used to describe God's creative work, *yāṣar* emphasizes the forming and shaping of the object. This word choice emphasizes that God created Adam using preexisting materials. In Genesis 2:19, *yāṣar* expresses God's work in forming "out of the ground all the beasts of the field and all the birds of the air." Man, animals, and birds were all fashioned by the Creator from Earth's raw materials.

Being created from the same substances implies physical similarity between humans and animals. Comparative studies should uncover common anatomical, physiological, biochemical, and genetic characteristics.

Humanity, made in God's image, displays unique characteristics distinct from those of all other creatures.

While humanity shares physical qualities with animals, people stand alone in terms of their spiritual nature. *Bārā'*, used both in Genesis 1:26–27 and Genesis 5:1–2 with reference to humanity's creation, suggests God's origination of something new.[28] Not only were Adam and Eve fashioned (in an *'āśâ* manner) from preexisting material, but they were also created (*bārā'*) as something new—something that never before existed. Both passages identify human beings alone as creatures made in God's image. In this sense, people were made distinct from the animals God formed.

Who Were the Hominids?

RTB's model considers hominids to be animals created by God's direct intervention for His purposes. They existed for a time, then went extinct. These remarkable creatures walked erect. They also possessed limited intelligence and emotional capacity. Such characteristics allowed them to employ crude tools and even adopt a low level of "culture," much as baboons, gorillas, and chimpanzees do. But while the hominids were created by God's command, they were not spiritual beings made in His image. This status was reserved for human beings.

Furthermore, the RTB model treats hominids as analogous to, yet distinct from, the great apes. For this reason, the model predicts that anatomical, physiological, biochemical, and genetic similarities existed among hominids and human beings to varying degrees. But because the hominids were not made in God's image, they are expected to be noticeably different from humans, as reflected by their cognitive and communicative capacities, behavior, "technology," and "culture."

The RTB model maintains that while human beings reflect God's image in their activities, hominids did not. The model asserts that humans are uniquely spiritual and hominids were not. The archeological record associated with hominid fossils supplies key data to evaluate this prediction.

Other verses emphasize this point. Genesis 2:7 describes how God fashioned Adam and then breathed life into him. When God formed the animals and birds from the ground (Genesis 2:19), He did not impart to them this "breath of life."[29] People stand apart from animals in that humankind alone received spirit life from God.[30] Only humans contemplate morality, purpose, the afterlife, and God's existence.

Humanity's uniqueness is also implied in Genesis 1:28 and Psalm 8:6–8. These verses state that God made people His representatives on Earth, placing them as rulers over the animals. According to Genesis 2:19–20, God brought the animals and birds to Adam to name. In Hebrew thought, names can be conferred only by someone in a position of authority.[31] This act signifies Adam's sovereignty over them.

If only humans bear God's image, then culture and technology should make a dramatic appearance in the archeological record. As a corollary to this prediction, humans should be culturally and behaviorally distinct (in ways that reflect God's image) from all animals, including the extinct hominids observed in the fossil record.

Life spans of the first human beings were on the order of several hundred years and became significantly shorter after the flood.

The Genesis 5 genealogy indicates that some of humanity's patriarchs lived to be several hundred years old. The RTB model maintains that these ages are to be taken literally. Genesis 6:3 records that God deplored humanity's rampant sinful behavior and intervened to shorten the maximum human life span from about 900 years to about 120 years. According to the RTB model, the genealogy of Genesis 11 documents the effects of this intervention—life spans of the patriarchs from Noah to Abraham grew progressively shorter. RTB's model maintains that long life spans in the early era of human existence are scientifically possible.

A universal flood shaped early human history.

Genesis 6–9 describes a devastating flood ordained by God in response to man's wicked behavior. All human beings and the "soulish" animals (birds and mammals) they came into contact with were destroyed by this flood—except for Noah, his wife, his three sons, and their wives. Contrary to popular perception of the Genesis flood account, RTB's model for human origins posits that the flood was geographically limited (confined to the environs of Mesopotamia), not global. Still, the RTB model considers the extent of the flood to be "universal" in that *all* humanity was impacted by it.

Discussion of the flood is beyond this book's scope. A detailed treatment that expounds the biblical and theological case for a regional flood and its scientific plausibility can be found in the book *Navigating Genesis* (formally titled *The Genesis Question*).[32] Suffice it to say that this key component of RTB's human origins model finds significant scientific support.

Humanity spread around the world from somewhere in or near the Middle East. Genesis 11:8 describes God's intervention to force people to scatter all over the earth. Humanity had twice resisted God's command to multiply and fill the earth—once before the flood and then again after.[33] Finally, through God's prompting, human global migration began.

RTB's model predicts that the spread of people around the world radiated outward from or near the Middle East. This migration took place in recent history and occurred with relative rapidity. On this basis RTB's model also predicts that human civilization started primarily in the vicinity of the Middle East and spread from there around the world.

The Model's Predictions
The RTB model's predictions follow as reasonable outcomes of the model's central features. It is important to recognize that scientific predictions do not constitute prophecy; rather, they logically flow from the model's tenets. Once proposed, a model does not have to await future discovery for the evaluation process to begin. The model can be assessed to a significant degree by the data that already exist. The following list outlines the key predictions of RTB's creation model for humanity's origin and spread. More predictions are possible.

RTB's Human Origins Creation Model Predictions
1. Humanity traces back to one woman (Eve) and one man (Noah).
2. Humanity's early population size was relatively small.
3. Humanity originated in a single location in or near the Middle East.
4. Humanity's origin dates between 10,000 and 100,000 years ago.
5. The origin of the female lineage (Eve) predates the origin of the male lineage (Noah).
6. God created humanity at the "just-right" time in Earth's history.
7. Human culture appears and expands explosively in the archeological record since humanity's origin.
8. Humans share anatomical, physical, biochemical, and genetic

similarities with the extinct hominids as well as with great apes and other animals.

9. Humans are behaviorally distinct (in ways that reflect God's image) from the earlier hominids, the great apes, and other animals.

10. A universal but local flood, that impacted all of humanity, shaped human history.

11. Human life spans (once longer than 900 years) became progressively shorter after the flood.

12. Humanity spread around the world from in or near the Middle East relatively recently.

13. The seeds of human civilization and agriculture had their birth in or near the Middle East.

Some may disagree with one or more of the RTB model's predictions. The model's incompleteness and the possibility for disagreement are positive signs that RTB's model can serve as a framework for fertile scientific debate. It is poised to stimulate future scientific work.

For now, the following five chapters summarize recent advances in the study of human origins—discoveries that permit testing of the RTB model's predictions. Does currently available data validate a biblical view of human origins? How will David's position on man's significance fare? Chapter 4 subjects the theory of creation to a genetics test.

PART II

THE
SONG OF
SCIENCE

Chapter 4

It's All in the Genes

Full many a lady I have
Ey'd with best regard,
And many a time th' harmony
Of their tongues hath into
Bondage brought my too diligent ear.
For several virtues have I lik'd
Several women, never any with so
Full soul but some defect in her
Did quarrel with the noblest grace
She ow'd, and put it to the foil.
But you, so perfect and so
Peerless are created of every
Creature's best!
—*The Tempest* Act 3, scene 1

For nine years French paleontologist Michel Brunet led a team of scientists searching for fossils on a dry lakebed in the desert of Chad.[1] The team spent endless days sifting through sunbaked sands. They built "tents" out of sand dunes and frequently found themselves confined to quarters in the face of fierce desert winds. At times they barely had enough water to brush their teeth. Local warlords threatened Brunet's French and Chadian team at gunpoint. Land mines planted by warring factions made digging in the sand even more dangerous.

Finally, after sweltering through long, hot, and tedious days, weeks, months, and years, Brunet's team recovered perhaps one of the most important finds of the last century: a nearly complete hominid skull. This remarkable fossil dates back to between 6 and 7 million years ago. Nicknamed "Toumai man" by Chad's president, this hominid was classified as a new species, *Sahelanthropus tchadensis*. The remains came from an area of Africa previously thought uninhabited by hominids. The discovery made Brunet a celebrity in the scientific community.[2]

However extreme, the challenges faced by Brunet's team were not unusual. To recover hominid fossils (the chief source of data for paleoanthropology), paleontologists usually labor under harsh conditions in exotic and sometimes dangerous locations.

But times are changing. Many anthropologists have exchanged fieldwork for high-tech adventures with DNA in sterile laboratories. They sit in front of computers, carefully developing mathematical equations and computer algorithms. These scientists meticulously interrogate massive databases. And once in a while, after long hours, weeks, and sometimes years of labor, molecular discoveries appear like fossil finds—offering new ways to characterize humanity's origin. Unexpected results make the field of molecular anthropology every bit as thrilling as work in traditional paleoanthropology.

The emerging results provide a way to evaluate Reasons to Believe's (RTB) model. Insights from the developing discipline of molecular anthropology supply a powerful way to put the model's predictions to the test.

A Genetic Melody

Molecular anthropologists scrutinize variations in DNA sequences among people who reside or originate in different geographical locations around the world. These variations reveal important clues about humanity's beginning. A little information about DNA's structure and biochemistry makes it possible to appreciate the stunning insights that come from these types of genetic studies.

DNA

DNA is an extremely large molecular complex consisting of two parallel chains or strands (see figure 4).[3] These paired chains twist around each other to form the widely recognized DNA double helix. To form DNA's molecular chains, the cell's machinery links together subunit molecules called nucleotides. The cell uses four different nucleotides (abbreviated A, G, C, and T) to construct DNA's molecular chains.

These nucleotide sequences contain the information needed for the cell to make the myriad proteins required for life's operation. Proteins help form structures inside the cell and the surrounding matrix. These molecules also catalyze (assist) chemical reactions, store and transport molecules, harvest chemical energy, and assemble all of the cell's structures.[4]

Biochemists refer to the segments of DNA that contain the information needed to make proteins as genes. Each gene corresponds to a single protein.

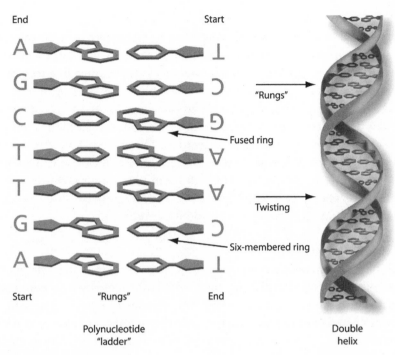

End   **Start**

"Rungs"

Fused ring

Start   "Rungs"   **End**

Twisting

Six-membered ring

Polynucleotide   Double
"ladder"   helix

Figure 4: DNA Structure
DNA is an extremely large molecule that consists of two molecular chains.

An organism's DNA does not consist of genes exclusively. Some of the DNA segments that lie within or between genes do not specify proteins. Biochemists call these DNA regions nongenic, or noncoding.[5]

Mutations
From time to time, physical and chemical events damage DNA's structure. Though the cell possesses machinery that can fix this damage, sometimes the repair is ineffective, or errors occur in the process. When this failure happens, the nucleotide sequence of DNA becomes permanently altered. These changes in DNA sequences (mutations) can also result from errors that occur when the cell's machinery replicates DNA just prior to cell division.[6]

Biochemists have identified numerous types of mutations. The term "substitutions" refers to mutations that replace one nucleotide in the DNA sequence with another. "Insertions" refers to mutations that add nucleotides to the DNA sequence, and "deletions" describes nucleotide losses from a DNA sequence.

Mutations that occur in genes are seldom beneficial. They alter information and cause the structure of the protein specified by that gene to become distorted. Because of the structure-altering effect of mutations, many are harmful or deleterious. However, sometimes mutations can be neutral in their effect. Biochemists tend to believe that mutations occurring in noncoding regions are mostly neutral, since these DNA regions don't specify proteins. (However, this idea is being challenged based on recent advances, as discussed in chapter 14.)

When deleterious mutations occur in genes, natural selection often prevents their propagation to the next generation. The altered DNA sequence often compromises the fitness and reproductive success of the organism. In other words, natural selection usually weeds out harmful mutations. However, neutral mutations readily pass from generation to generation because they don't impact the organisms' survival and reproductive prowess.[7]

DNA sequence genealogies
Mutations are the major source of DNA sequence variation in the different human population groups studied by molecular anthropologists. By comparing similarities and differences in corresponding regions of DNA among samples taken from people of different clans, scientists attempt to build gene genealogies for the groups. These genealogies are similar to family trees constructed by people interested in their heritage.[8]

Most DNA sequence variations result from mutations that have occurred throughout human history. These mutations are typically unique for populations that have been isolated for some time. This uniqueness allows molecular anthropologists to identify DNA sequences (and hence population groups) that came from the same ancestral sequence (and hence population). The researchers say these sequences coalesce. Once ancestral sequences and populations have been identified, repeating this process throughout the gene genealogy leads backward to the ultimate ancestor and population. Molecular anthropologists refer to this basal sequence and population as the most recent common ancestor (MRCA).

If researchers factor into the analysis the geographical location of each population group (assuming these locations are static or historic), the location of humanity's origin can be identified. The pattern of humanity's spread can also be discerned from gene genealogies when coupled with historical geographic information.

The shape of the gene genealogy also reflects humanity's population history and dynamics. And it provides clues as to humanity's original population size.

Molecular clocks
Molecular anthropologists believe that natural selection doesn't operate on neutral mutations. Therefore, over long periods of time, these changes in DNA sequences should accrue at a roughly constant rate (given that the neutral mutation rate does not vary). This constancy turns DNA sequence differences into a molecular clock.[9] When molecular anthropologists know the mutation rate (nucleotide substitutions per year), they can estimate the coalescence time— the time since the DNA sequences (and hence populations) diverged from the shared ancestral sequence (population). Molecular clock analysis estimates the timing of humanity's origin and spread around the globe.

"Created of Every Creature's Best"
Molecular anthropologists employ a variety of genetic techniques to study the origin of humankind. One relatively straightforward approach characterizes humanity's genetic (DNA sequence) diversity. This methodology measures the average number of sequence differences between various people groups for a particular DNA segment. The scientists determine the average genetic difference by making pair-wise comparisons of all the individual DNA sequences that comprise the sample.[10]

Whenever molecular anthropologists conduct these comparisons, they get the same result: human beings display much less genetic diversity than any other species. For example, several recent studies report a much more extensive genetic diversity for chimpanzees, bonobos, gorillas, and orangutans than for people (based on mitochondrial DNA, X-chromosome, and Y-chromosome sequence comparisons).[11] This means that when comparing DNA sequences for any two chimpanzees, any two bonobos, any two gorillas, or any two orangutans, a much greater genetic difference will be observed than for any two human beings compared.

The human similarity is observed worldwide, regardless of race or ethnicity. The limited geographical range of the great ape species, contrasted to the widespread geographical distribution and extensive biological variation of humans, makes this observation impressive.

More recent work (published in 2002) highlights this unusual genetic unity.[12] A comparison of 377 DNA regions for 1,056 individuals from 52 different population groups found that 93 to 95 percent of the (small) genetic variation occurs within all populations and only 3 to 5 percent of the genetic variability occurs between populations.

What do these finds indicate about humanity's natural history? Molecular anthropologists pose what they sometimes call the "Garden-of-Eden hypothesis" to explain the limited genetic diversity. This model maintains that humanity had a recent origin in a single location and the original population size must have been quite small. From this one location, humanity expanded rapidly to occupy all the geographical regions of the planet.[13]

This scenario closely resembles the biblical description of humankind's origin—hence the Garden-of-Eden label. Molecular anthropologists observe the greatest genetic diversity among African populations and conclude that these groups must be the oldest.[14] If these populations have always resided in Africa, humanity's origin would seem to have occurred there, specifically in East Africa.

The Human Genome
New insight into human origins and genetic diversity comes from the Human Genome Project (HGP). This collaborative international effort involving public and private laboratories allowed researchers to determine the DNA sequence for the entire human genome. (Geneticists refer to an organism's entire DNA content as its genome.) Biomedical scientists hope that the data from the HGP can be used to provide deeper insight into human biology, increase understanding of genetic disorders and diseases, develop new pharmaceuticals, and tailor drug therapies. To do all this, however, biomedical researchers need more than the genome's DNA sequence. They also must understand how the genome's DNA sequence varies from person to person.

Plans to comprehensively map the genetic variation of the human genome are just getting under way.[15] Biomedical scientists expect these projects to unleash the full potential of the HGP. But molecular anthropologists anticipate the project to be a valuable excavation site where they can mine significant information about humanity's origin and history.[16]

In 2001 scientists from Perlegen Science, Inc., demonstrated HGP's potential to characterize humanity's origin.[17] This team identified all the single nucleotide polymorphisms (SNPs) found on chromosome 21. An SNP refers to a single site in a DNA sequence that differs from other corresponding DNA sequences. SNPs result from mutations. Many SNPs exist throughout a DNA sequence. They often occur in characteristic combinations and patterns. A collection of SNPs is called a haplotype.

When the Perlegen Science team scanned the 32,397,439 nucleotides of chromosome 21 for two dozen individuals from African, Asian, and Caucasian backgrounds, they discovered 35,989 SNPs. This number meant the potential

The Location of Humanity's Origin

Does an African origin of humanity represent a problem for RTB's creation model? Not necessarily. Considering that some biblical scholars understand the Garden of Eden to extend from Mesopotamia and into Africa, Cush may well have been Ethiopia. If this identification is accurate, then there is no conflict between the data and RTB's model.

What if the Garden of Eden is rightly understood to be confined exclusively to Mesopotamia? The data that locate humanity's origin in Africa need not be seen as problematic for a biblical model. Without question, African populations are humanity's oldest (not only because of genetic diversity but also because African DNA sequences encompass DNA sequences from all other human population groups). This inclusion, however, does not mean these groups originated in Africa. When molecular anthropologists use genetic data to locate humanity's origin (and spread), they assume that the current location of population groups represents their location throughout human history. This supposition remains open to question, particularly because many human population groups have migrated as much as thousands of miles throughout their history. The Bible explicitly claims (Genesis 10–11) that God intervened early in human history to move some people groups great distances from their point of origin, while others remained fairly close to their starting place.

Moreover, the Bible teaches that, as a result of their sin, Adam and Eve were banished from the Garden of Eden. So humanity's population growth began *outside* the garden's confines.[18] An origin of humanity in East Africa could easily match this scenario.

for genetic diversity among humans is enormous (given that $2^{35,989}$ haplotypes can possibly exist). And yet the Perlegen scientists discovered that only three haplotypes describe 80 percent of the genetic diversity of chromosome 21. This result indicates a very limited genetic diversity among human populations. The conclusion, obtained from examining a vast DNA sequence, fully accords with other genetic diversity studies based on much smaller DNA segments.

Since this initial work, other research teams have probed the HGP data for SNP distributions and have confirmed that a limited number of haplotypes describe humanity's genetic diversity. These studies also indicate that the SNP haplotypes of non-African populations represent a subset of the African ones. This finding verifies that the African population groups are the oldest.[19]

In short, these studies agree with the genetic diversity studies—humanity had a recent origin from a single location (apparently Africa). Mankind indeed began with a small population that rapidly expanded. The accumulating data make this conclusion all the more secure, while other genetic techniques offer additional insights into humanity's origin.

A Mother's Legacy

One of the first and most widely used genetic techniques to study humanity's origin involves characterization of mitochondrial DNA (mtDNA). This circular piece of DNA resides inside mitochondria (organelles found in nearly all cells of the human body). Most human cells possess a large number of mitochondria, with muscle cells having the most. Molecular anthropologists find mtDNA nearly ideal for the study of human origins because of its relatively simple pattern of inheritance and its rapid mutation rate.[20]

Mitochondrial-DNA analysis produces genealogies that trace humanity's maternal lineage because this type of DNA is inherited exclusively from one's mother. All mitochondria in the human body derive from the egg cell; the sperm cell does not contribute any mtDNA during the fertilization process. After fertilization, the zygote (fertilized egg) undergoes several initial rounds of cell division. During this process, the resulting daughter cells divide up the egg cell's original population of mitochondria. Later, as the embryo's cells continue to undergo cell division and specialization, the egg's original mitochondria produce more mitochondria.

These mitochondria reproduce by a duplication and fission process that yields two "daughter" mitochondria from the "parent." During cell division, the daughter mitochondria become distributed among the daughter cells. All mitochondria found in the cells of the human body come from the mother's egg cell. The mother's mitochondria and mtDNA were inherited from her mother and grandmother and so forth.

In 1980, biochemist Wesley Brown conducted one of the first mtDNA studies designed to probe humanity's origin.[21] Limited in scope (only 21 samples from racially and geographically diverse sources), this study rather crudely characterized mtDNA sequences with provocative results—humanity originated recently (about 180,000 years ago) from a small original population.

Seven years later a team led by biochemist Allan C. Wilson carried out a much more extensive study using the same methodology. This time, however, the researchers analyzed mtDNA from 147 people taken from five geographical regions. The results led scientists to conclude that humanity originated from one woman. She came from a single location (apparently Africa) roughly

200,000 years ago.[22] The science community named her "mitochondrial Eve."

Controversy surrounded these results. Critics expressed concern with the crude technique used to assess the mtDNA sequence, the relatively small sample size, the use of African-Americans to represent African populations, and the methods used to construct the mtDNA genealogy.[23]

Wilson's team addressed these concerns in a 1991 study of mitochondrial DNA from 189 people. They included DNA samples from native Africans and used much more comprehensive sequencing techniques.[24] This study confirmed the earlier results. They pointed to a recent origin of humanity (between 249,000 and 166,000 years ago) from one location (apparently Africa) from a very small population of women. Since then, molecular anthropologists have conducted a number of mtDNA studies. All results square with the original research.[25]

A team of Swiss and German scientists conducted one of the most comprehensive studies.[26] These researchers examined the entire mtDNA sequences (16,500 base pairs) taken from 53 people representing a diversity of races and geographies. The results (reported in 2000) again placed humanity's origin in a single location, apparently Africa. This study indicates that women appear to have had a relatively recent beginning (171,500 ± 50,000 years ago) from a small population. The mtDNA genetic fingerprints paint a picture of humanity's origin consistent with the biblical account and RTB's model.

Keeping Time

Mitochondrial-DNA analysis is a popular method among biologists interested in constructing gene trees and determining origin dates. However, several recent lines of evidence call into question the reliability of molecular clocks based on mtDNA.[27] When researchers used these clocks to date humanity's origin, they assumed each individual in the study had only one type of mtDNA. (Scientists refer to this as homoplasmy.) But 10 to 20 percent of the population possesses two types of mtDNA—a condition called heteroplasmy.[28] Less than 1 percent of the human population possesses three types of mtDNA (triplasmy).[29]

Recent work demonstrates that heteroplasmy varies from tissue to tissue (with the greatest occurrence in muscle) and increases with age.[30] Sometimes this condition results from mutations in the egg cell and other times in the body's cells after fertilization. Researchers must pay careful attention to the source of mitochondria and hence of mtDNA. Hetero- and triplasmy make mtDNA mutation rates and molecular clocks appear to run faster than scientists originally thought.[31] Corrections to mtDNA mutation rates that factor

How Accurate Are Genetic Dates?

Though molecular clock analysis is relatively straightforward in principle, its application is problematic. One chief difficulty centers on the clock's calibration. In practice, calibration is extremely difficult, if not impossible, to accomplish.[32] Researchers simply cannot determine with any real accuracy mutation rates and the changes in these rates over time. Scientists typically must estimate the *likely* high and low values for mutation rates.

Other factors influence molecular clock analysis as well. These include: (1) the sample size; (2) the number of representative populations included in the study; and (3) the length of the DNA sequence analyzed. The dates for humanity's origin extracted from genetic data of human population groups must be regarded as ballpark estimates, not ironclad conclusions. One researcher noted that molecular clocks are best thought of as "sun dials," not "stopwatches."[33]

in heteroplasmy place mitochondrial Eve perhaps as recently as 50,000 years ago[34]—squarely within the range predicted by the RTB model (between 10,000 and 100,000 years ago).

Other factors complicate use of mtDNA molecular clocks. Researchers have discovered that mutation rates differ from region to region within mtDNA. These scientists also observed that mutations accumulate at a faster rate with age.[35] Both factors confuse calibration of mtDNA clocks. Age-accelerated mutation rates render genetic diversity artificially high.

The level of radioactivity in the environment also impacts mtDNA mutation rates and molecular clock analysis. A study reported in 2002 showed that mutation rates were much higher for people historically connected to the Indian state of Kerala than for people in nearby regions. It turns out that the people of Kerala receive about 10 times more natural radiation than the worldwide average because of high levels of the mineral monazite (which contains about 10 percent thorium phosphate) in their environment.[36] Such worldwide variations in mtDNA mutation rates create calibration challenges for mtDNA (and other) molecular clocks.

For molecular clocks to function reliably, mutations that accrue in the DNA sequence of interest must be neutral. If they impart a benefit, the mutations become fixed into the DNA sequence through natural selection's influence. Such sequences also throw off the accuracy of molecular clocks.

Natural selection has definitely influenced the mtDNA sequence that contains information necessary to produce proteins forming part of the electron transport chain.[37] The electron transport chain plays an important role in extracting energy from organic compounds. Mutations to the proteins of the electron transport chain reduce the efficiency of the energy-extraction process. As a consequence, heat is liberated. Researchers speculate that this liberated heat imparts an advantage for humans who have historically lived in cold-weather climates. The loss of efficient mutations to electron transport chain proteins benefited some human population groups. Though a benefit to humans, these mutations confound attempts to date humanity's origin, particularly for analysis that uses the entire mtDNA sequence.

Mitochondrial-DNA studies bear significance for RTB's model. They describe with some certainty humanity's origin from a single location and small population, traceable to one female. Age estimates for humanity's origin derived from mtDNA molecular clocks range from 150,000 to 200,000 years old. These assessments are likely to be high, but current methodology lacks the means to correct for the various complicating factors. However, when the complicating factors are qualitatively considered, it seems reasonable to conclude that the date for humanity's origin may come in under 100,000 years—consistent with the prediction made by RTB's human origins model.

From the Father

Molecular anthropologists also use DNA associated with the Y chromosome (the male sex chromosome) to characterize humanity's origin. Y-chromosomal DNA analysis serves as the counterpart to mtDNA analysis. This technique traces humanity's origin through the paternal (as opposed to the maternal) lineage because Y-chromosomal DNA passes exclusively from father to son. (Researchers regard this simple pattern of inheritance as ideal for studying human origins.)[38]

In the investigation of humankind's beginning, Y-chromosomal DNA offers advantages over mitochondrial DNA. Ongoing characterization gives researchers access to much longer sequences on the Y chromosome compared to mtDNA (which is limited to about 16,000 base pairs). The longer DNA sequence provides more opportunity to detect mutations. This extra sensitivity allows better resolution. In addition, Y-chromosome analysis doesn't suffer from the complications associated with hetero- and triplasmy. Still, as with all molecular-clock studies, this type of analysis has limitations that stem from inaccuracies and imprecisions associated with calibration (see "How Accurate Are Genetic Dates?" on page 68).

In 1995, one of the first Y-chromosomal DNA studies to probe humanity's origin examined a 729-base-pair DNA sequence in 38 men constituting a worldwide sample.[39] Researchers found, to their surprise, that the sequence displayed no variation at all. They concluded that men originated no more than 270,000 years ago from a small population.

Another study followed almost immediately. This second study examined a 2,600-base-pair segment of the Y chromosome. Again it indicated a recent origin for humanity (around 188,000 years ago) from a small population (less than 10,000).[40] More recent Y-chromosome studies indicate that humanity came from a single location (apparently Africa).[41] (See "The Location of Humanity's Origin" on page 65.)

These later studies used much more expansive regions of the Y chromosome. Their findings indicate that humanity's male lineage originated around 40,000 to 60,000 years ago.[42] They also verify that humanity's origin traces to one location and to a small population. The results fall in line with yet another study that placed humanity's origin between 35,000 and 47,000 years ago.[43]

As with the studies on genetic diversity and mtDNA, Y-chromosome analysis of humanity's history fully concurs with the RTB model predictions for humanity's origin. The astonishing agreement among these three genetic techniques provides powerful evidence for the reliability of the biblical creation account. And these three methods are not the only ones used to investigate humanity's origin. As molecular anthropologists expand their repertoire beyond mitochondrial and Y-chromosomal DNA, additional approaches offer insights into humanity's start.

Why Eve Might Have Been an Older Woman

Molecular anthropologists find the large discrepancy between the dates for mitochondrial Eve (150,000 to 200,000 years ago) and "Y-chromosomal Adam" (40,000 to 60,000 years ago) perplexing. To explain this difference, scientists suggest that males living prior to Y-chromosomal Adam failed to pass along their genes and hence their genetic fingerprint. This lack of inheritance could occur if all their descendants had died out. As a lone survivor, Y-chromosomal Adam, born around 50,000 years ago, thus happened to have his genetic fingerprint take over the entire human population.[44]

RTB's human origins model actually predicts this discrepancy between the maternal and paternal dates. The most recent common ancestor for men traces to Noah, not Adam, because of the flood. In contrast, women's common ancestor traces further back, closer to Eve, because the wives of Noah and his sons were probably not directly related to one another (see page 51).

A recent study, reported in 2004 by molecular anthropologists from the University of Arizona, offers another explanation for the differences between the mitochondrial and Y-chromosomal dates for humanity's origin.[45] These researchers noted that the mtDNA dates were consistently twice those measured using Y chromosomes for three population groups (Khoisan, Mongolians, and Papua New Guineans). This constant difference goes beyond mere coincidence and reveals a pattern in the data. They also failed to detect any evidence in the Y-chromosomal data for the so-called selective sweep that would have occurred if Y-chromosomal Adam were a lone survivor among many different males.

The researchers suggested that mitochondrial Eve and Y-chromosomal Adam lived at the same time and that the disparity in the mitochondrial and Y-chromosomal dates is not real. Rather this difference reflects a larger effective population size for females than for males.

This explanation makes sense in light of the flood account because Noah and his sons would represent a single Y-chromosome sequence. The wives of Noah and his sons would have had up to four different mtDNA sequences, making it appear as if the effective population size of the female lineage was larger than the male lineage.

One final note: the differences in mitochondrial and Y-chromosomal DNA dates are not as great as they may seem. As already discussed, when heteroplasmy is factored in, the mitochondrial Eve date may well come in under 100,000 years ago (see page 67–69). In addition, some of the differences could reflect methodological differences between the two techniques. A study that examined the paternal and maternal ancestry of all 131,060 Icelanders born since 1972 attests to this idea.[46] Based on the research, it appears that mtDNA manifests a greater microevolutionary rate than Y-chromosomal DNA. This difference is due in part to a 10 percent shorter generation time for the maternal line. Still, once methodological differences are accounted for, there seems to be a difference between the maternal and paternal dates for humanity's origin, as predicted and explained by RTB's model.

An Inheritance Divine

The success and the limitations of mitochondrial and Y-chromosomal DNA studies have spurred researchers to explore the use of other genetic markers to characterize humanity's origin.

Nuclear genes

A 1986 study looked beyond mtDNA and the Y chromosome to a small DNA segment of the β-globin gene cluster. Investigators used genetic material from 601 individuals of European, Indian, Asian, and African descent. These scientists also reached the conclusion that humanity began from a small population living in one location (apparently Africa) and that from there people rapidly moved around the world.[47]

Similar outcomes arise from more recent work. In 2001, a Swedish research team determined that humanity must have originated from a small population in a single location (Africa). Their conclusion was based on the genetic variation of the monoamine oxidase A and B genes found on the X chromosome.[48] Likewise, in 2003, investigators from the University of Utah observed the genetic variation of the *CYP1A2* cytochrome P450 gene (a gene that plays a role in metabolizing drugs and toxins) in 113 individuals. They found it to be consistent with an origin of humanity from a single location.[49]

Pseudogenes

Scientists generally consider pseudogenes to be nonfunctional DNA and therefore free of natural selection's influence. Because mutations are expected to accrue in them at an approximately constant rate, pseudogenes may be ideal markers for the study of human origins. (Chapter 14 discusses how pseudogenes fit into RTB's model.)

Two studies conducted in 2001 illustrate the potential of pseudogenes to illuminate early human history. These studies examined the glucocerebrosidase pseudogene and the Type I keratin pseudogene (φhHaA), respectively, and concluded that humanity's origin occurred in a single location around 200,000 years ago.[50]

Endogenous retroviruses

Biochemists view endogenous retroviruses in the same vein as pseudogenes— nonfunctional DNA that accumulates mutations at a constant rate. For anthropologists the clocklike mutation rate of endogenous retroviral DNA makes them ideal to study human origins. (Chapter 14 discusses endogenous retroviruses and describes their place in the RTB model.)

A study reported in 2004 indicates that endogenous retroviral DNA sequences found in the human genome provide important insight into the human genetic diversity and consequently the origin of humanity.[51] This work focused on the HERV-K (HML2) family of endogenous retroviruses. Researchers screened seven HERV-K sequences from 109 DNA samples collected from people in Africa, Europe, Asia, and Southeast Asia. The genetic diversity of these DNA sequence elements indicates that humanity had a recent origin from a single location (Africa).

Microsatellite DNA

Researchers recently turned their attention toward another class of noncoding DNA, called microsatellite DNA or short tandem repeats. These DNA segments consist of numerous repeating di-, tri- and tetra-nucleotides distributed throughout the human genome. A Russian and US research team examined these short tandem repeats. After analyzing 377 locations in the human genome of 1,056 individuals representing 52 population groups, the researchers concluded that humanity originated from one place (apparently Africa). Human beings came from a small population (about 2,000 or less) between 71,000 and 142,000 years ago.[52] These conclusions corroborate an earlier study of short tandem repeats that showed humanity originated roughly 60,000 years ago with about 500 individuals in one location.[53]

Minisatellite DNA

Researchers interested in the question of humanity's origin have examined minisatellite DNA as well. Like microsatellite DNA, these DNA elements consist of repeating nucleotides, but they tend to be longer, on the order of 25 to 30 base pairs in length. Minisatellite DNA occurs with much lower frequency in the human genome than does microsatellite DNA. As a demonstration of this technique's potential usefulness, scientists from the United Kingdom examined minisatellite DNA associated with the human insulin gene and interpreted its genetic variation to indicate a start for humanity from a single location and a small population.[54]

SINE DNA

Recently, a large team of collaborators from around the world focused their attention on short interspersed nuclear elements (SINE) DNA as a probe for early human history. SINE DNA is a class of noncoding DNA generally thought to be nonfunctional and thus free from natural selection's influence. (See chapter 14 for a discussion of SINE DNA in light of RTB's model.) Scientists think SINE DNA experiences only neutral mutations and, therefore, it serves as a potential marker for humanity's origin.

SINE DNA consists of anywhere from 130 to 300 base pairs and occurs in multiple copies throughout the human genome. In fact, SINE DNA makes up about 10 percent of the human genome. When the international team of investigators conducted a genome-wide probe for a particular category of SINE DNA (referred to as *Alu* sequences), they noted that its genetic variation could be explained only if humanity began from a small population in one (apparently) African location.[55]

Linkage disequilibrium

Some researchers have recognized the potential of linkage disequilibrium to answer questions about human origins. Linkage disequilibrium involves the association of genes with one another along a chromosome's length. When genes are associated, scientists refer to them as being linked. Genes can lose their linkage with one another when recombination occurs during meiosis—the cell division process that produces gametes (sperm and egg cells).

During recombination, sister chromosomes align and swap segments with one another. The farther apart genes are on the chromosome, the more likely they are to become unlinked during recombination. Over time, however, even closely juxtaposed genes become unlinked.[56] For this reason, researchers find linkage disequilibrium to be a potent tool for measuring humanity's age.

In a 1996 study researchers demonstrated the effectiveness of linkage disequilibrium as a way to characterize human origins. They examined the linkage disequilibrium of the CD4 locus and in doing so dated humanity's origin as occurring about 100,000 years ago in a single location.[57] Other linkage disequilibrium studies since then have supported this conclusion.[58] One of the most extensive such research projects to date (published in 2003) measured humanity's start at about 173,500 years ago from an extremely small population apparently located in Africa.[59]

Currently techniques using genes, pseudogenes, micro- and minisatellite DNA, SINEs, and linkage disequilibrium as tools to learn about humanity's origin are less developed than those involving mitochondrial and Y-chromosomal DNA. Still, these emerging methods provide a remarkably consistent picture of early human history. This scientifically satisfying agreement provides researchers with a high degree of confidence that molecular anthropologists are well on their way to establishing the correct understanding of human origins.

"Several Virtues Have I Lik'd"

The origin and spread of disease-causing pests interest scientists for obvious health-related reasons. Understanding the timing and location of these microbes' origin, the historical pattern of their spread, and the current distribution of their genetic variation helps biomedical researchers develop effective treatments against disease. In the process of studying the origin and natural history of these microbes, molecular geneticists have stumbled upon an intriguing new way to investigate humanity's origin (and migrations around the world).

Their intimate association with humans allows parasites to act as surrogates for their human hosts in scientific investigations. Researchers believe that the time and place these parasites started—as well as their spread around the world—mirrors the timing, location, and spread of humanity. Therefore, the worldwide genetic variation of these infectious agents can be used in the same way molecular anthropologists use human genetic variation to gain understanding about humanity's past.

Tapeworms

In 2001, an international research team characterized the genetic variation of the cytochrome c oxidase gene for 35 species of tapeworms that belong to the genus *Taenia*. These tapeworms are transferred to humans through the consumption of meat or visceral organs taken from cattle and swine. These herbivores serve as intermediate hosts in the tapeworm life cycle and became infected when they consumed tapeworm eggs.

Traditionally, the scientific community thought the tapeworms infested human populations about 10,000 years ago, after cattle and swine were domesticated. Genetic analysis, however, reveals a different story. It turns out that tapeworms began parasitizing humans between 90,000 and 160,000 years ago (depending on which mutation rate is used in the analysis).[60] Given the uncertainty associated with molecular clock analyses, these dates can be considered to coincide with humanity's origin. And based on these results, the researchers involved in the work speculated that the first humans became infected with tapeworms when they hunted and scavenged meat from wild herbivores.

Malaria

In 2002, a team from the National Institutes of Health (NIH) examined the genetic variation of 204 genes from a worldwide sampling of *Plasmodium falciparum* (the malaria parasite). Based on molecular analysis, the group concluded that this pathogen originated between 100,000 and 180,000 years ago. Again, given that this technique yields approximate dates, it can be argued that this parasite's origin coincides with humanity's.[61] A follow-up study in 2003 refined the earlier NIH results and demonstrated an African origin for *P. falciparum* between 50,000 and 100,000 years ago. The researchers also noted a subsequent genetic expansion about 10,000 years ago, when agricultural societies began to flourish and spread.[62]

Ulcers

Biomedical researchers now think that *Helicobacter pylori*, the stomach bacteria that causes gastric and duodenal ulcers, also holds the potential to shed light on humanity's natural history. Parents transmit this germ to their children in roughly the same way they transmit their genes. Because of this predominant transmission through families, *H. pylori* genetic variation likely reflects the genetic variation of human population groups.[63]

An international team of molecular geneticists tested this hypothesis in 2003 by using *H. pylori* recovered from 27 different human populations. They discovered that this bacterium clusters into seven subpopulations that correspond to distinct geographical locations of the human population. This distribution finds easy explanation if humanity originated recently in one region and then spread globally.[64]

Molecular geneticists are also focusing attention on the JC virus as a surrogate for early human history. This virus has a transmission similar to that of *H. pylori*. Essentially all human beings are infected with the JC virus. In adults this virus resides in the kidneys and its progeny are secreted in urine, making it easy for researchers to recover its genetic material from urine. Adults cannot transmit the virus to one another. Rather, transmission occurs exclusively from parent to child through prolonged contact. In 2003, an Italian investigator sampled the genetic material of 113 JC virus specimens recovered worldwide and showed that its pattern of genetic variation was consistent with an apparently African origin, followed by its spread into Europe and Asia as distinct events.[65]

Lice

Molecular anthropologists from the Max Planck Institute for Evolutionary Anthropology (in Germany) performed an elegant and highly original study in 2003. This research was designed to probe both humanity's early history and the beginning of clothing use.[66] To accomplish their objectives, the team traced the origin and spread of body lice. Biologists refer to this pest as an obligatory ectoparasite because body lice, which reside on the skin, can't survive long when separated from their human host. Body lice are a subspecies of head lice, which are also obligatory ectoparasites. Head lice live on the human scalp, whereas body lice prefer clothing. Biologists believe that body lice emerged (via a microevolutionary process) from head lice after clothing use became widespread.

When the German research team measured the genetic variation of a global sample of head and body lice, they concluded that body lice originated in Africa around 72,000 years ago (± 42,000 years). This result fits nicely with all the other genetic studies designed to probe humanity's origin and seems to suggest that clothing use came into vogue with the first humans. This suggestion implies that the hominids prior to humans in the fossil record did not wear clothes. If they had done so, then body lice's origin should predate humanity's origin.

More recently, an international research team produced data that corroborate the results obtained by anthropologists from the Max Planck Institute. These researchers demonstrated that human head lice have two genetic lineages. The major lineage has worldwide distribution and appears to have originated about 100,000 years ago.[67] The second lineage, confined to Native Americans, had its origin around 25,000 years ago.

The genetic variation observed in global samples of *Taenia*, *P. falciparum*, *H. pylori*, the JC virus, and *P. humanus* (body lice) all indicate, by proxy, that humanity had a relatively recent origin from one location (Africa). This finding fully squares with studies that directly examine human genetic variation.

Molecular Anthropology and RTB's Model
Over the years, molecular anthropologists and geneticists have used at least 14 different methods to probe humanity's origin and early history. Conclusions of these genetic studies align well (given each method's limitations and the uncertainties associated with molecular clock analysis). And they are remarkably consistent with RTB's creation model. The scientific evidence continues to indicate that humanity had a recent origin from a single location and involved a small population size.

The genetic fingerprint of all humanity traces to one man and one woman. The timing and location of humanity's origin are consistent with the predictions of RTB's human origins model. Humanity's population dynamics during its early history agree with the biblical account. By comparison, how does the evolutionary paradigm handle the results of these genetic studies?

Molecular Anthropology and Human Evolution
Anthropologists and evolutionary biologists are quick to accept the results of

genetic studies probing humanity's origin. However, they view these results as an awkward fit with the evolutionary framework. Based largely on the genetic studies, molecular anthropologists have formulated a new explanation for humanity's origin, called the "out-of-Africa hypothesis" (or in some cases, the "Garden-of-Eden hypothesis"). The chief features of the out-of-Africa hypothesis bear striking similarity to the central tenets of RTB's human origins model. In some respects the out-of-Africa hypothesis could be thought of as the biblical model shoehorned into an evolutionary framework.

The out-of-Africa hypothesis posits a recent origin for humanity in a single location, apparently Africa, and from a small population. This theory also recognizes that humanity's genetic fingerprint traces to one woman and one man. Based on the preponderance of evidence, many anthropologists consider this idea the best explanation for humanity's origin. And yet this conclusion is considered controversial because it stands in sharp contrast to traditional expectations concerning human evolution. The long-established multiregional hypothesis maintains that modern humans evolved over a span of 2 million years from different hominid populations.

To be clear, evolutionary biologists do not think humanity originated from one man and one woman. Rather, they maintain that large populations of either the hominid predecessors to modern humans or the first modern humans suffered a catastrophic collapse. When this occurred, scientists claim, genetic diversity was lost and the first humans went through a genetic bottleneck. After suffering the population collapse, the humans who supposedly endured the bottleneck are thought to have experienced rapid population growth and expansion to fill the planet.

According to evolutionary biologists and anthropologists, the genetic marker of the population collapse remains imprinted on today's human population groups in the form of limited genetic variation. They theorize that the passage of humanity through a genetic bottleneck, perhaps as recently as 100,000 years ago, creates the appearance that humanity arose from a small original population. The recent origin of humanity from a small population and a single location in Africa would merely reflect humanity's recovery from a population collapse.

This evolutionary explanation could perhaps account for the genetic pattern seen among modern human populations, but does it do a better job of deciphering the data than does the biblical account as set forth by RTB's model? Not likely. The out-of-Africa model ignores much of the research conducted by conservation biologists.

A Fatal Flaw

Both fieldwork and theoretical work demonstrate that population collapse leads relentlessly toward extinction rather than toward recovery and flourishing population growth. University of Oregon scientists theoretically explored the consequences of fragmenting a larger population into isolated subpopulations. The results showed that when subpopulations of a species become disconnected, extinction risks dramatically increase.[68] Fieldwork confirms this conclusion. Time and time again, conservation biologists have noted that habitat (and resultant population) fragmentation rapidly drives species toward extinction.[69] One 2004 study noted that when birds are introduced into a new habitat as part of conservation efforts, unless the initial populations exceed 600 individuals, the newly introduced species do not survive long. Genetic diversity and genetic bottleneck effects influence these results.[70]

High population numbers and extensive genetic diversity are necessary to dilute and wipe out the effects of harmful mutations. When population numbers are too low, these harmful mutations pass into subsequent generations and quickly accrue. The population then becomes fragile and susceptible to rapid extinction.

These field studies focused on reptiles and birds, but the conclusions of this work likely have broad applicability. The results may apply to primates and in particular to great apes—species on the cusp of extinction because of low population numbers.

A Simple Explanation

Though the RTB model predicts humanity's origin from two individuals, it doesn't suffer the same concerns that the evolutionary model does. RTB's model maintains that the first humans were created in a genetically pristine state. Under these conditions, genetic diversity was not necessary, because no harmful mutations yet existed.

Although genetic data trace humanity's origin to a single woman and man, evolutionary biologists assert that mitochondrial Eve and Y-chromosomal Adam were not the first humans. Rather, according to these scientists, many "Eves" and "Adams" existed. In their scenario mitochondrial Eve and Y-chromosomal Adam were the lucky ones whose genetic material survived. The genetic lines of the other first humans were lost over time.

This explanation may be in the realm of possibility, but it seems highly contrived and unlikely. It could work *if* only a few of the first humans reproduced or were allowed to reproduce. On the other hand, the RTB model evaluates the data at face value and provides the simpler explanation.

Evolutionary biologists propose various ideas to explain away the implications of the human population genetic data. However, these explanations lack support from other areas of science. At times they even seem to contradict the data. The explanations, though entrenched in naturalism, are not necessarily superior to the straightforward interpretation of the data—an interpretation in complete agreement with the biblical account.

In addition to this genetic data, the study of skeletal remains (paleontology) and old rocks (archeology) can help evaluate other key predictions for humanity's beginnings, as the next chapter shows.

Chapter 5

Bones and Stones

But music for the time doth
Change his nature.
The man that hath no music in himself,
Nor is not moved with concord of sweet
Sounds, is fit for treasons, stratagems
And spoils; The motions of his
Spirit are dull as night, and his
Affections dark as Erebus:
Let no such man be trusted.
Mark the music.
                    —*The Merchant of Venice* Act 5, scene 1

In 2001, John and Sarah Howard received a letter that dramatically changed their lives.[1] The startling news arrived shortly after this British couple moved into their dream home. Situated on beautiful grounds with a natural waterfall in the French countryside of Dordogne, their seventeenth-century home seemed to offer the peaceful refuge they'd anticipated for their retirement years.

The letter came from Mark Delluc, a stranger, who explained to the Howards that he'd been caving near their property. A French army cook who liked to spend his weekends spelunking, Delluc had crawled through a rather dangerous tunnel that led to a previously unknown cave beneath the Howards' garden. To his astonishment, he discovered more than 100 carvings of women, horses, rhinoceroses, mammoths, and animal hybrids—some 12 feet high—covering about 1,000 yards of the cave's walls. These carvings ultimately dated to about 30,000 years ago.

The cave houses not only important artifacts but also the remnants of ancient human artisans. An archeological and paleontological treasure trove, the cave's contents turned the Howards' tranquil haven into a site bustling with scientists and excavating equipment. The find will undoubtedly provide scientific insight into the behavior of some of the earliest people.

In recent years archeologists have made similar finds in other parts of France as well as in Spain, Germany, and other parts of the world. These discoveries yield important clues about human history.

New findings from the archeological and fossil records provide the means to assess several key Reasons to Believe (RTB) model predictions about the timing and emergence of behavior that reflects God's image (see "What Is the Image of God?" on page 83). Artifacts co-deposited with fossils provide clues into the behavior and cognitive ability of hominids and humans. The fossil record supplies the context for the archeological record and helps establish the timing for humanity's appearance.

What tune do the bones and stones sing about humanity's origin? Do they support an evolutionary framework? Or are they better understood through RTB's creation model for humanity's origin?

A Silent Song

The fossil record and archeological data clearly show that by 40,000 years ago people were present in Africa, Eurasia, and even Australia.[2] Anthropologists, however, currently lack consensus on the exact timing of humanity's appearance in the fossil record. Between about 40,000 and 80,000 years ago, humans are largely nonexistent in the fossil record, though controversial archeological evidence suggests they might have lived during this era.[3]

Evolutionary biologists interpret this absence to indicate a population loss that almost led to humanity's extinction. As discussed in the previous chapter, this explanation is used to account for the limited genetic diversity observed among modern-day human population groups. Such a population loss would have forced humanity through a genetic bottleneck.[4] Then, according to evolutionary biologists, at about 40,000 years ago humanity not only recovered from near extinction but also quickly flourished and expanded to fill the earth.

As discussed in chapter 4, problems abound with any model that appeals to population collapse and a genetic bottleneck. Studies conducted by conservation biologists suggest that such a collapse almost certainly leads to extinction. Alternatively, the features of the fossil record between 80,000 and 40,000 years ago could just as easily be considered as evidence that humans first came on the scene about 40,000 years ago. In other words, the fossil record broadly harmonizes with the view that humanity appeared explosively about 40,000 years ago—a theory consistent with the RTB creation model's predictions.

What Is the Image of God?

Genesis 1:26–27 (and Genesis 5:1–2) says that male and female humans were made in God's image. This declaration implies that humans bear a similarity to God, at least in some ways. From a biblical perspective, the image of God designates humanity's distinction from all other created beings.

Scripture doesn't explicitly state what the image of God is. Over the centuries, theologians have discussed and debated this concept. Some take the image of God to describe humanity's spiritual resemblance to God. Others take it to refer to humanity's relational capacity, while some theologians think the image of God allows humans to function as God's representatives or viceroys on Earth.[5] A consensus of these three approaches identifies four characteristics:[6]

1. Human beings possess a moral component. They inherently understand right and wrong and have a strong innate sense of justice.
2. Humans are spiritual beings who recognize a reality beyond this universe and physical life. Mankind intuitively acknowledges God's existence and has a propensity toward worship and prayer.
3. Humans relate to God, themselves, and other people and creatures. There is a relational aspect to God's image.
4. Humanity's mental capacity reflects God's image. Human beings possess the ability to reason and think logically. They can engage in symbolic thought. People express themselves with complex, abstract language. They are aware of the past, present, and future. Human beings display intense creativity through art, music, literature, science, and technological inventions.

Much of human behavior ultimately stems from God's image. Because the archeological record is the product of behavior and activity, it supplies the means to test for His image. Artifacts that result from reason, symbolic thought, technological inventiveness, and artistic, musical, and religious expression will reflect God's image. Because the RTB model views the hominids as animals, it predicts that such image-of-God artifacts will make their first and only appearance in the archeological record alongside human remains.

While artifacts are found with hominids that precede human beings in the fossil record, the RTB model maintains that they will differ fundamentally from those associated with the first true humans. The archeological remains that coincide with hominids should indicate an absence of image-of-God behavior.

Cave Cacophony

Some paleoanthropologists suggest that humans first appeared in the fossil record between 100,000 and 130,000 years ago.[7] The Skhūl cave and Qafzeh caves of Israel contained 100,000-year-old fossils that these scientists interpret as modern human remains. In Ethiopia two partial crania that date between 100,000 and 130,000 years ago also have been categorized as modern human. (A recent radiometric measurement dates the Ethiopian fossils between 198,000 and 104,000 years in age.)[8] So have forehead and cranial fragments from the Klaises River Mouth Cave in South Africa. The latter fossils date between 70,000 and 120,000 years old.

Scientists used the notoriously inaccurate luminescence dating method to determine the timing for all these fossils. Thus the dates derived from this technique might be best viewed as upper limits (see "Luminescence Dating Methods" on page 85). The designation "modern human" is also in question.[9] Although the fossils possess some features in common with modern human anatomy, they also display features not typically seen in people. The skull walls of these specimens are thicker than those observed for human beings. Their faces are broader and the areas above the eye sockets are much thicker. Based on anatomy alone, these hominids appear to be distinct from modern humans and could be thought of as nonhuman, bipedal primates that predated humankind.

The archeological record supports this categorization. Artifacts associated with the fossils recovered in Israel, eastern Africa, and southern Africa indicate distinctly nonhuman behavior. These animals used unsophisticated tools and engaged in crude hunting and gathering. They didn't paint pictures or play music or display any other signs of creativity. (See chapters 2, 11, and 12 for a more detailed discussion of the archeological record and its correlation with the hominid fossil record.) For now, the first unequivocal appearance of human beings in the fossil record occurred around 40,000 years ago.

Though imperfect, the fit between the fossil record and the predictions made by the RTB model seems adequate. The fossil record indicates a recent origin for humanity in a time frame that harmonizes with the biblical account. Evidence for an earlier appearance of humankind is based on fragmentary and inconclusive fossil specimens.

Buried Alive

"The reports of my death have been greatly exaggerated," quipped Mark Twain when he learned that his obituary had been published in the *New York*

Luminescence Dating Methods

Luminescence dating methods measure the amount of light emitted from mineral grains when they are heated in a controlled manner or stimulated by light.[10] The emitted light is used to estimate the age of bones or artifacts sandwiched between the rock layers that house the mineral grains.

The emitted light comes from free electrons trapped within the matrix of the mineral grains. Heat or light releases the electrons from the mineral matrix. When this release happens, the electrons move through the matrix to find positively charged holes. As the electrons fall into these holes, they release energy in the form of light. In other words, they luminesce.

The free electrons become part of the mineral matrix when radioactive uranium, thorium, and potassium decay. The energy liberated from radioactive decay excites electrons in the mineral matrix. Once excited, they travel through the matrix, leaving behind positively charged holes. Impurities in the mineral, however, can trap the free electrons in a high-energy state before they can find a previously vacated electron hole. With time, more and more trapped electrons accumulate in the mineral matrix. In this way the number of trapped electrons (and their luminescence when heated or optically stimulated) reflects age.

When minerals are exposed to sunlight or heat from the environment, the trapped electrons return to a lower-energy state. In this way luminescence techniques measure the time that has transpired since a mineral grain was exposed to sunlight or heat.

While the principles behind luminescence techniques seem straightforward, practical application difficulties limit their accuracy. For example, different mineral matrices trap free electrons with different efficiencies, depending on the types and levels of impurities. If the sample matrix is less efficient at trapping electrons than the calibration standard, the sample seems younger than it actually is. If the sample matrix traps electrons more efficiently, then the sample appears older than it actually is. The quantity of radioactive isotopes in the sample can also skew its age artificially, making it appear older or younger. In other words, calibration methods suffer from some level of uncertainty due to various matrix effects.

A sample's history also affects luminescence dating. For the most accurate dates possible, the mineral grains must be exposed to sufficient sunlight or heat. This exposure returns all trapped electrons to low-energy states. When this return occurs, the luminescence clock is set to zero. If this event does not occur before the mineral grain is buried, then the clock overestimates the sample's age. If the mineral grain is exposed to heat (or sunlight) after burial, trapped electrons are prematurely released, making the sample appear artificially young.[11]

Journal. The RTB model was presented with its own "obituary" on the day when *Nature* published reports of new hominid (bipedal primate) finds in Ethiopia.[12] A young-earth creation organization misconstrued the data, describing the fossils and their geological and archeological contexts as beyond the scope of RTB's framework. This misunderstanding led to the erroneous conclusion (reported on the Internet) that these newly discovered hominids dealt "a severe blow" to the RTB model.[13]

In brief, an assertion was made that the Ethiopian finds were modern humans and therefore invalidated RTB's biblical account of humanity's origin and spread. But was this really the case? How does RTB's creation model fare in light of these Ethiopian finds?

Brain activity continues

The Ethiopian finds, unearthed and described by a team headed by UC Berkeley paleoanthropologist Tim White, consisted primarily of three fossilized crania—two adult and one juvenile. Through the use of a radiometric technique (argon-argon dating), the research team dated the fossil specimens between 160,000 and 154,000 years in age. The team interpreted the anatomy of the three crania to consist of a mosaic blend of "archaic" and "modern" features.

The age and anatomical characteristics led the researchers to assign the Ethiopian specimens to an intermediate position between the ancient *Homo rhodesiensis* and *Homo sapiens sapiens* (human beings). Scientists classified these fossils as a new subspecies, *Homo sapiens idaltu*.[14] But these paleoanthropologists were quite clear—*H. sapiens idaltu* was anatomically distinct from modern humans. Two recent studies by independent teams of paleoanthropologists affirmed this conclusion. Both studies demonstrated that the so-called archaic *Homo sapiens* (hominids) existing between about 500,000 and 100,000 years ago were morphologically (anatomically) distinct from modern humans, just as *H. sapiens idaltu* was.[15]

The researchers also recovered stone artifacts from the geological layers where the fossilized crania were found. These tools lacked the sophistication of implements used by anatomically and behaviorally modern humans. Instead, these objects reflected the crude and primitive technology of *Homo erectus* and Neanderthals. Large mammal remains were also discovered nearby. Inspection of these mammal fossils indicated that they were hunted and butchered, presumably by *H. sapiens idaltu*. While hunting reflects some level of intelligence, it is not behavior exclusive to humans. Modifications to the fossilized *H. sapiens idaltu* crania suggested that they were purposely defleshed by their own kind after death—evidence of cannibalistic behavior.[16] While some forms of cannibalism are ritualistic, the defleshing of *H. sapiens idaltu* skulls could equally reflect a natural response to hunger.

The heart still beats

Rather than forcing RTB into "some very torturous positions regarding 'fossil men,'"[17] *H. sapiens idaltu* finds ready accommodation within RTB's human origins framework and in ways the model predicts. *H. sapiens idaltu* (like *H. erectus*, Neanderthals, and other archaic *H. sapiens*) were simply primates—animals that walked upright, possessed limited intelligence, and had some type of culture, but animals nonetheless. All the data support this interpretation. *H. sapiens idaltu* stands as anatomically and behaviorally distinct from humankind (*H. sapiens sapiens*) and dates older than Neanderthal.

The combination of "archaic" and "modern" features possessed by *H. sapiens idaltu* poses no problem for RTB's model. In some sense, all hominids (including *H. sapiens idaltu*) have features that resemble humans. While White's team interpreted the mosaic nature of these hominids to be an indicator of their transitional status, other explanations remain equally plausible.

Human designers often combine two or more distinct designs in creating objects and devices. If people were created in God's image, wouldn't their Creator be expected to do the same? Evolutionists don't always interpret mosaic organisms as transitional intermediates. The duck-billed platypus illustrates the point. This creature possesses a combination of mammalian and avian (birdlike) features. Yet evolutionists don't propose that mammals evolved from birds, with the duck-billed platypus representing a transitional form between these two groups.

The discovery of *H. sapiens idaltu* leaves RTB's model alive and well. Any reports of it succumbing under the weight of this find have been greatly exaggerated.

"Mark the Music"

Without question, hominids living as long ago as 2 million years used tools and possessed a "culture" of sorts. Still, their crude technology and simple lifestyle remained static for hundreds of thousands of years. When new modes of technology and culture appear in the archeological record, the advances represent relatively small steps upward, followed by long periods of stasis. (See chapters 2, 12, and 13 for descriptions of the technology used by the various hominids found in the fossil record.) Even as recently as 100,000 years ago, the hominids used remarkably unsophisticated technology. But at 40,000 years ago, something quite amazing happened. Until then, according to paleoanthropologist Christopher Stringer, hominids had simply marked (cultural) time:

> For millennia upon millennia, we [hominids] had been churning out the same forms of stone utensils, for example. But about 40,000 years ago, a perceptible shift in our handiwork took place. Throughout the Old World, tool kits leapt in sophistication with the appearance of Upper Paleolithic style implements. Signs of use of ropes, bone spear points, fishhooks and harpoons emerge, along with sudden manifestations of sculptures, paintings, and musical instruments....We also find evidence of the first long-distance exchange of stones and beads. Objects made of mammal bones and ivory, antlers, marine and freshwater shells, fossil coral, limestone, schist, steatite, jet, lignite, hematite and pyrite were manufactured. Materials were chosen with extraordinary care: some originated hundreds of miles from their point of manufacture....It is an extraordinary catalogue of achievements that seem to have come about virtually from nowhere—though obviously they did have a source. The question is: What was it?[18]

Though Stringer sees an evolutionary connection between modern humans and the hominids that predate them in the fossil record (see "What Do Anthropologists Mean by 'Human'?" on page 34), the archeological record displays something other than a gradual evolutionary emergence of human culture. Rather, the record's defining characteristic is a veritable explosion of civilization. This eruption is considered anthropology's "big bang."

Instead of detailing all these archeological finds (a task that lies beyond this book's scope), a survey of the archeological evidence follows. Even this brief sampling reveals the dramatic and sudden appearance of human behavior and its sharp contrast with the behavior displayed by hominids.

From crude man to craftsman

The so-called archaic *H. sapiens* found in the fossil record between 250,000 and 100,000 years ago used tools categorized as Middle Stone Age, Mode III, Middle Paleolithic, or Mousterian, depending on the archeological site's geographical location. The tools and associated technology were more advanced than those used by *H. erectus* (*H. erectus* used Mode II or Acheulean technology). Still, they were relatively unsophisticated.[19]

The primary method used by hominids to manufacture crude tools consisted of flaking stone fragments from a rock core with a hammer stone. This Middle Stone Age technology varied little through time (from 250,000 to 40,000 years ago) and across geography.

Between 50,000 and 40,000 years ago, a quantum leap occurred in tool inventories, manufacturing techniques, and usages.[20] This new technology (called Late Stone Age, Mode IV, or Late Paleolithic) includes a wide range of sophisticated implements made by complex manufacturing techniques. In addition to employing stone, the first humans used ivory, bone, and wood. They transported the raw materials used for tool production significant distances.

Stone tools became smaller in size and were made with more precision than those recovered from Middle Stone Age and other comparable ancient sites. Often these later stone implements were intentionally dulled at one end and attached to wooden handles and shafts. Other tools were cut from bone and ivory, then carefully carved and polished. The first humans made projectile points, awls, punches, fishhooks, harpoons, and needles with eyes. They lived in solidly built dwellings and made fireplaces and hearths bordered with stones for heat retention. Compared to the earlier hominids, the first humans behaved in sophisticated ways that reflected superior cognitive abilities and technical inventiveness.

Closing in for the kill

The hunting practices of the first humans also showed greater sophistication than those of Middle Stone Age hominids (as seen at sites in southern Africa).[21] First, the animal remains from these Late Stone Age sites are much more diverse than those collected from Middle Stone Age locales. Late Stone Age sites contain many more fish and fowl skeletons. Fish gorges and net sinkers also have been found in Late Stone Age digs. The design, manufacture, and use of these implements required sophisticated cognitive capacity.

Late Stone Age sites contain a preponderance of buffalo and wild boar remains. These animals are challenging to hunt and require well-crafted projectiles to kill. Without adequate weapons, hunters could easily have become injured. In contrast, the Middle Stone Age hunters appear to have limited themselves to relatively easy-to-kill game that would not put up much of a fight when hunted.

The first humans apparently gathered and trapped both tortoises and shellfish, as did some Middle Stone Age hominids. However, the remains found at Late Stone Age sites tend to be more abundant and smaller. Larger tortoises and shellfish are easier to collect than smaller ones. The fact that the remains are smaller in Late Stone Age sites suggests that the first humans must have intentionally sought these animals for food and used relatively sophisticated gathering techniques.

Taking care of their own

The diverse and sophisticated tool kits and superior hunting practices employed by the first humans provided a benefit hominids did not enjoy. The earliest human clans included a much greater proportion of older individuals to younger than did groups of australopithecines, *H. erectus*, and Neanderthals. Researchers from the University of Michigan (UM) and the University of California, Riverside (UCR), demonstrated this difference in longevity by comparing the third molars (M3) from human fossil remains (dated at 30,000 years ago) with those from older hominid specimens.[22]

In all primates, the third molar erupts at the time of reproductive maturity. This developmental milestone allowed the researchers to assess the proportion of younger and older adults in the hominid and early human fossil record by examining the wear of M3 teeth: little wear signifies a younger adult; significant wear indicates an older adult.

From M3 wear patterns, the UM and UCR researchers estimated the older-to-younger-adults (OY) ratio to be 0.12 for australopithecines, 0.24 for *H. erectus*, 0.39 for Neanderthals, and 2.08 for humans.

Before the first humans appeared, few hominids lived much beyond reproductive maturity. With humanity's arrival, however, longevity in the population dramatically increased. While identifying the causes of longevity is difficult, an extended life span likely reflects the benefits associated with more sophisticated technology and superior hunting practices. Longer life spans also allow for greater social cohesion and more complex social structures. With a greater proportion of older individuals in their populations, the first humans had an increased opportunity for learning and transferring of knowledge. For older individuals to persist in the population, the younger adults had to care and provide for them. In return, however, the older adults could help care for the clan's children.

The difference in longevity between the first humans and the hominids indirectly indicates that the earliest human beings possessed superior cognitive ability. They also lived within a complex social structure that provided the platform for the preservation of knowledge and the care of less productive members of the clan (young children and older adults).

A girl's best friend

Unlike the hominids that predate them in the fossil record, the first humans invested time and energy in making jewelry and other items of personal adornment.[23] They used teeth, bone, antlers, amber, ivory, marine shells, polished stones, and ostrich eggshells to make beads, rings, and pendants.

Until recently, paleoanthropologists thought the use of such body ornaments appeared first in Africa and then later in Europe and Asia. The oldest sites known to contain jewelry had been Enkapune Ya Muto in Kenya, Mumba Cave in Tanzania, and Border Cave in South Africa. These sites yielded body ornaments, mostly beads produced from ostrich eggshells. Fragments of eggshells that appear to be discards from failed attempts to make beads[24] date to about 40,000 years in age.[25]

Then, in 2001, an international research team discovered marine-shell beads in Turkish and Lebanese caves.[26] The finds from these sites date to between 39,000 and 43,000 years in age. Ancient jewelers in these regions chose marine shells for bead manufacture apparently on the basis of aesthetics. Instead of using mollusk shells left over from meals, they selected shells of unusual appearance—exceptionally white shells or ones brightly colored with intricate patterns. These shells came from creatures too small to contain food value. As at the African sites, these ornamental shells far outnumber those that remained after food consumption. Based on these finds, research collaborators concluded that body ornamentation emerged simultaneously in Africa, Europe, and Asia at a time that closely coincides with humanity's origin.

Personal adornment offers no immediate advantage for survival. Rather, this behavior reflects advanced cognitive capacity and artistic expression. Designing, assembling, and weaving body ornaments also marks the use of symbolic language. Such decorations communicate group membership, social identity, and gender.

Cave museums

Paleoanthropologists have discovered several sites around the world that contain evidence for artistic expression, but none has been studied as much as the European ones.[27] For many, the cave art found in France and Spain symbolizes prehistoric art and illustrates the dramatic behavioral differences between humans and the hominids.

Archeologists have discovered about 150 caves containing paintings and carvings. Perhaps the two most spectacular caches of cave art come from the Lascaux and Chauvet caves of France. These two sites date to 17,000 and 32,400 years in age, respectively.[28] The artwork found in them consists of human images and depictions of large mammals, such as deer, bison, horses, and mammoths. The Chauvet Cave uniquely depicts predators such as hyenas and leopards.[29] The cave paintings were made with pigments prepared from charcoal, iron oxide and manganese oxide, minerals, and plant oils.

Archeologists and paleoanthropologists debate the purpose of cave paintings and carvings.[30] Some think the work was generated for the sake of art itself, while others see the creativity as being based on superstitions. Human artists might have depicted predators and prey with the hope of increasing their hunting bounty. Some scientists maintain that the cave art held religious significance and illustrated sacred beliefs. These scholars assert that the paintings represent the visions of entranced shaman priests. In some cases, the drawings are located in difficult-to-reach cave chambers and might have adorned the walls of a primitive sanctuary.

In addition to creating cave art, the first humans engraved images on portable objects. They also sculpted animal and human figurines and "Venus" statuettes. The best known and most extensively studied were found in France, Spain, and Germany. They date to between 20,000 and 28,000 years in age. In 2003, archeologist Nicholas Conrad announced the discovery of the oldest known sculptures, recovered from caves in Germany. These figurines date to between 32,000 and 34,000 years in age.

One publicized piece from this cache depicts a human-lion hybrid known as the "lion man," or *Lowenmensch*.[31] In the same cave, Conrad discovered miniature sculptures made of ivory that include horses and birds.[32] He also found a large deposit of ivory and bone shavings. The cave artifacts appear to have come from an artist's studio.

As with the cave art, archeologists and anthropologists ponder the significance of the figurative art made by the earliest humans. Clearly the creativity reflects humanity's unique capacity for symbolic thought and the use of complex artistic tools. It also indicates that the first people had some concept of an imaginary world. These figurines might have represented characteristics possessed by animals that humans either admired or desired. The statuettes also might have been religious objects, or (given their size) they might even have been toys.

The music man

In addition to expressing themselves through visual art, ancient humans made music. Archeologists have found musical instruments in sites located in northern Africa, Europe, and Asia—places occupied by some of the earliest known men and women.[33] Typically, these instruments were created from the long bones of birds and functioned as whistles and flutes. In some cases, percussion instruments have also been recovered.

Recently, a team of German archeologists reported the discovery of one of the world's oldest musical instruments in Geissenklösterle, a cave near Ulm in southern Germany.[34] The team unearthed an ivory flute, dated to between 30,000 and 37,000 years of age, that was manufactured and played by some of the first humans in Europe. This discovery is notable for two reasons. First, the flute was made out of the best material available to the first humans. Constructing a flute from hollow bird bones would have been far simpler than carving a flute from solid ivory. The artisans had to carefully hollow out the ivory, then precisely align, bind, and glue together the two halves. Second, this ivory flute, about one and a half feet in length, has three finger holes, giving it the capacity to play complex melodies and rich harmonic tones. A deep appreciation for music evidently gave the first humans motivation to produce musical instruments of the highest quality.

Artistic and musical expression was not part of the earlier hominids' life. This behavior is unique to humans and coincides exclusively with human remains. Perhaps one of the most important advances in prehistoric archeology in recent years is the recognition that artistic (including musical) expression didn't emerge gradually but rather exploded onto the scene simultaneously with humanity's appearance about 40,000 years ago.[35] Archeologists and anthropologists refer to this surge of human culture as "the big bang of art."

A significant pattern—with respect to human origins—was recently observed when archeologists compared the art of the Chauvet Cave with that of Altamira and Lascaux.[36] Though the Chauvet Cave art dates to 30,000 years in age, its sophistication is no different from that of Altamira and Lascaux artwork, which dates to between 12,000 and 17,000 years in age. The quality of the cave art does not display a progression from simple representations to complex. The representations are complex from the outset. Anthropologist Anthony Sinclair noted:

> We imagine that the first artists worked with a small range of materials and techniques, and produced a limited range of representations of the world around them. As new materials and new techniques were developed, we should see this pattern of evolution in the archeological record. Yet for many outlets of artistic expression—cave paintings, textiles, ceramics, and musical instruments—the evidence

increasingly refuses to fit. Instead of a gradual evolution of skills, the first modern humans in Europe were in fact astonishingly precocious artists.[37]

Dressed for success

Clothing use also appears to be a practice associated exclusively with humans. Archeologists lack direct evidence for clothes, because skins and furs don't survive long. The recovery of ivory needles (with eyes) from sites that date to around 40,000 years ago, however, can be considered indirect evidence of sewing because these devices were needed to manufacture wearing apparel.

As mentioned in the last chapter (see pages 76–77), the origin of human body lice provides an indirect proxy for the first garments. Body lice are obligatory ectoparasites that require human attire to survive. The origin of body lice coincides with the origin of clothes. Based on the genetic variation of a global sample of such lice, it appears that these lice originated around 72,000 years ago (± 42,000 years).[38] This result indicates that clothes came into use as soon as humanity began. It also implies that hominids never got dressed. If they did, body lice would predate humanity.

On bended knee

Archeologists struggle to identify religious expression in the archeological record. Speculation characterizes this endeavor and any conclusions about it must be considered tentative. Archeologists frequently search for evidence of ritual behavior in the archeological record as an indicator of religious belief, because rituals signify belief in action.

The earliest humans might have had at least some religious motivations when they produced cave and figurative art. If so, spiritual expression dates to at least 30,000 years ago. Of course, this interpretation of cave art and figurines in the archeological record might not be valid.

Frequently, archeologists examine grave sites looking for evidence of burial practices as signs of ritual behavior. Some findings suggest that Neanderthals (see chapter 12 for more details) and other hominids might have buried their dead. But these burial practices appear nonritualistic and relatively simple.[39] The Neanderthals dug shallow graves that contained few if any artifacts. Human burial practices contrast sharply.[40] Often multiple burial plots are found together. Occasionally they appear to comprise a graveyard or cemetery. Large rocks covered some graves. Such stones may reflect ritual behavior and also a desire to protect and preserve the human body.

Early burials involved a profusion of grave goods (special items and body ornaments), providing strong evidence for ritualistic beliefs. These articles suggest that humanity had a sense of an afterlife.

A grave site in Russia provides one of the most striking examples of ritualistic burials.[41] Dug into permafrost, the Sungir grave site dates to about 22,000 years ago. Though older grave sites are known in France, the elaborate nature of the burial at the Sungir site makes it notable. Excavation revealed two skeletons of children—one male and one female. The male was covered with 4,903 beads, while the female was covered with 5,374. Placement of the beads suggests that they were originally attached to clothing long since disintegrated. The male wore a belt made of 250 arctic fox teeth. Several ivory lances and other artifacts were also buried with the children. Estimates indicate that thousands of hours were required to manufacture all these items. Other equally elaborate graves are located near the Sungir site.

Currently, archeologists lack a rigorous date for the onset of religious expression. This human behavior is much more difficult to identify and interpret than is art, music, or jewelry use. However, it is safe to say that spiritual activity dates to at least 28,000 years ago. Ritual burials and possible religious expression (through art) appear unique to human beings.

Who Knew?

The RTB model predicts that evidence for behavior reflecting God's image should appear abruptly in the archeological record and should correlate exclusively with the appearance of humankind. The archeological and fossil records reveal this exact pattern.

Anthropologists and archeologists can readily distinguish between humans and hominids in the fossil record based not only on morphology but also on behavior. Hominids possessed some low level of culture and technology, but these were relatively simplistic and remained stagnant for long periods of time. Then, around 40,000 years ago (about the time humanity appears throughout the fossil record), advanced human culture exploded onto the scene.

The culture and technology displayed by the earliest human beings indicate that they possessed: (1) advanced cognitive ability; (2) the capacity for symbolic thought; (3) a powerful imagination; (4) superior craftsmanship; (5) inventiveness and superior adaptability; (6) a driving desire for artistic and musical expression; and (7) ritual behaviors and religious activity. Theologians generally consider all these characteristics as defining features of God's image in humans. None of the hominids that precede humans in the fossil record displayed these unique behaviors. Nor did they live in complex societies with tight social cohesion. These first human societies promoted the care of more vulnerable older members, who in turn cared for the children and became the source of knowledge for the next generation.

In short, the patterns found in the fossil and archeological records are precisely those that should be seen if David's perspective was correct—a Creator made them male and female in His image recently and by divine intervention. The RTB model reasonably explains the archeological and fossil records. By comparison, how does Darwin's view fare? Can evolutionary models account for the big bang of advanced human culture?

A Lucky Happenstance?

Evolutionary biologists and anthropologists (for the most part) agree that a sharp difference exists between the culture and technology of humankind and those observed for hominids existing between 250,000 and 50,000 years ago. Frequently, scientists refer to this quantum change in behavior as the "dawn of human culture," the "human revolution," a "creative explosion," the "great leap forward," or the "sociocultural big bang."[42]

While most scholars recognize the sudden burst of advanced human culture and technology in the archeological record, they struggle to make sense of it. Some anthropologists have argued that the social structure of modern humans was much different from the one displayed by earlier hominids. According to this view, the newer social structure required recording and communicating complex ideas—*need* led to the creative explosion seen in the archeological record. Others assert that the invention of new technology catalyzed a cascade of advances that produced the sociocultural big bang.[43]

As anthropologist Richard Klein points out, these explanations don't account for the biological advances contemporaneous with humanity's great leap forward.[44] Social changes and technological advances couldn't bring about the fundamental changes that led to inherently human behavior. Rather, it must have worked the other way around. Fundamental biological changes must have preceded social and technological progress.

Klein argues that a biological explanation best accounts for the human revolution.[45] He maintains that a "fortuitous mutation" led to the modern human brain. This supposed mutation produced the brain structures that support and provide for humanity's language capacity.[46] Once language capacity was established, human culture rapidly advanced. In other words, Klein's model relies on a "just-right" mutation. This mutation altered the brain's development in the just-right way to generate the complex brain structures and motor control of the tongue and facial muscles that suddenly allowed people to speak and to process spoken language.

This scenario seems to stretch the bounds of credulity, especially given the typically deleterious nature of mutations, the complexity of the brain's structures, and the extensive integration of its components at macroscopic, microscopic, and molecular levels. In reality, hundreds of simultaneous just-right mutations would be required to transform the archaic hominid brain into a human one.[47] (Chapter 13 discusses additional problems with Klein's scenario in light of the recently discovered language gene.)

Recently a team of molecular biologists attempted to understand the emergence of the human brain from an evolutionary perspective by comparing nervous system genes of humans, chimpanzees, macaque, rodents, and mice. These investigators demonstrated that 214 genes, which play a role in the development of the nervous system (and also determine brain size), are significantly different in humans. From an evolutionary standpoint, it appears as if these genes have undergone a hyperevolutionary transformation that is categorically different from the way that the scientific community envisions the evolutionary process to proceed. It almost appears as if an intelligent agent intervened to orchestrate the substantial genetic changes needed to produce the human brain.

In a sense, overlap exists between the RTB model and Klein's explanation for the sociocultural explosion. The RTB model maintains that human behavior in the archeological record results from God's direct creative work when He made human beings in His image. Klein's model essentially appeals to multiple simultaneous "miraculous" genetic changes to account for modern humans' behavior.

Or Maybe It's Really Nothing

Instead of trying to explain the dramatic appearance of human behavior in the archeological record, a few anthropologists attempt to dismiss it. They claim that the behavioral differences between humans and earlier hominids have been overstated. Though evidence for the human revolution pervades the archeological record, detractors point to two lines of evidence to support the view that modern human behavior emerged gradually, not suddenly. One line of reasoning argues that Neanderthals (which appear in the fossil record between 150,000 and 30,000 years ago in Europe, western Asia, and the Middle East) behaved much the same way as modern humans do. The other implies that the behavior associated with modern man had already emerged by the time human beings appear in the fossil record.

The Neanderthal fossil and archeological evidence, when considered in its entirety, falls short of supporting this claim. And a majority of paleoanthropologists disagree with this minority view. (The differences in the behavior of Neanderthals and humans are discussed in greater detail in chapter 12.) But what about other hominids' humanlike behavior?

The Katanda riverside site in the Democratic Republic of the Congo and the Blombos Cave in South Africa suggest to some paleoanthropologists that modern human behavior emerged earlier than 40,000 to 50,000 years ago. At the Katanda site, luminescence dating of sand that surrounds artifacts and animal and fish bones dates them at 90,000 to 150,000 years in age. These items consist of tools that could be assigned to either the Middle or Late Stone Age. Because the articles could belong to the Late Stone Age, a few anthropologists take this as evidence that modern human behavior appeared over 100,000 years ago.[48]

Likewise the Blombos Cave contains classic Middle Stone Age artifacts mixed in with mammal bones, fish bones, and shellfish dated as older than 70,000 years based on luminescence dating.[49] Again, because the animal remains are reminiscent of those at Late Stone Age sites, archeologists take this data as evidence for the beginning of modern human behavior prior to 40,000 or 50,000 years ago. More recently, a team of anthropologists working in the Blombos Cave discovered bone tools similar to those produced by modern humans at sites that routinely date between 35,000 and 40,000 years old. This research team also dated their Blombos find at greater than 70,000 years old using a luminescence dating method.[50] In addition, the anthropologists recovered red ocher with engravings and jewelry beads made of marine shells that date by a luminescence technique to 77,000 years ago.

The case for an early appearance of modern human behavior, based on the Katanda riverside site and the Blombos Cave artifacts, is not as ironclad as it might seem. If the evidence from these sites is taken at face value, it creates a disjointed archeological record. Archeologists would have to explain why modern human behavior is localized to these few sites for tens of thousands of years before artifacts that reflect modern human behavior appear in other Late Stone Age sites.

The most reasonable explanation for the Katanda riverside and Blombos Cave sites is that artifacts were deposited at different times and became mixed into the same layer. It's clear that both humans and hominids repeatedly occupied the Blombos Cave site. Recent work supports such a view.[51] This recent study surveyed artifacts and animal remains recovered from two layers of a coastal South African cave (Ysterfontein) that date at about 34,000 years in age and between 51,000 and 71,000 years in age, respectively. (The upper layer corresponds to the Late Stone Age and the lower layer to the Middle Stone Age.) Analysis of these two layers clearly portrays marked differences in the hunting and foraging practices of humans and hominids. Humans who occupied this site 34,000 years ago showed much more advanced and sophisticated behavior than did the Middle Stone Age hominids that occupied the site 20,000 to 35,000 years earlier.

Further, it's both possible and likely that the dates measured at the Katanda riverside and Blombos Cave sites represent an overestimate. Luminescence dating methods were used. Because these techniques often yield exaggerated ages (see "Luminescence Dating Methods" on page 85), both sites may actually be examples of Late Stone Age sites, not Middle Stone Age deposits.

Though some anthropologists challenge the idea that a cultural big bang occurred, this challenge rests on tentative grounds. The same evidence can be interpreted as providing additional support for the explosive appearance of human behavior. When all the data is considered, human behavior consistent with God's image appears suddenly. Its timing coincides with the appearance of humanity in the fossil record, just as the RTB model and the biblical creation account require.

Genetic and archeological evidence indicates that humans appeared on Earth recently, perhaps as recently as 40,000 years ago. The next chapter examines another line of research that shows how humanity's origin coincides with several astronomical and geological time windows. Did explicit timing make Earth and its planetary and galactic environs a place perfectly suited for humanity's needs, or could this timing have been an accident?

Chapter 6

The Best Possible Time

There are more things in heaven
And earth, Horatio,
Than are dreamt of in your philosophy.
—*Hamlet* Act 1, scene 5

Night after night, as David gazed up at the glistening stars and glowing moon, he saw a message of man's significance. He recognized the power of a magnificent Creator at work in the heavens and even in his own existence. Today many people think David was wrong. But was he? Could a lucky fluke—or millions of flukes combined—make human life appear? Or does the precise fine-tuning of Earth, the solar system, and even the entire universe at perfect points in time display the intent and involvement of a divine hand?

Naturalistic scenarios don't predict a specific timing for humanity to appear. In addition to the unlikelihood of human life occurring at all (see "What Are the Chances?" on page 157), the evolutionary model indicates that the origin of humans could have happened earlier or (more likely) later. On the other hand, the Reasons to Believe (RTB) biblical creation model predicts the timing of humanity at a special moment in Earth's history—one ideal for people to enjoy the best possible physical conditions, not only for their survival but also to accommodate a large population, global occupation, civilization, and high-technology transportation and communication systems.[1] Both human origins models can be tested by determining whether the necessary physical conditions could possibly coincide as random events or if the various time windows are so narrow that their simultaneous alignment reflects foresight and planning.

Until the last decade, scientists lacked the data and theoretical sophistication to offer more than a cursory reply to the question of humanity's time frame. Fortunately, new scientific discoveries—from the largest space-time scales to the smallest—now permit scientists to address the issues.

On a Large Scale

Human survival and technological civilization demand precise conditions. Advanced life depends on a planet with a rich array of "heavy" (as in heavier than helium) elements. Nuclear furnaces inside stars forged these elements. When the nuclear burning periods came to explosive ends in supernovae, the first supergiant stars spewed heavy elements into space (more specifically, into the interstellar medium). As new stars formed in regions enriched by these elements, the second generation of stars produced even greater concentrations of heavy elements. Likewise, third-generation stars—still richer. At least 9 billion years of star formation, star burning, and star death contributed to the making of a planet as heavy-element rich as Earth.

But after Earth formed, huge asteroids and comets pelted the planet for three-quarters of a billion years, turning the planet at times into a molten mass.[2] X-ray radiation and large, random changes in the Sun's brightness also prevented the survival of *any* life during Earth's first 550 million years[3] Once the first life-forms did appear, these simple organisms needed nearly another 4 billion years to process and redistribute Earth's heavy elements into forms essential to human survival—and to the possibility of human civilization (see "Why Only Simple Life for So Long?" on page 103).[4]

In other words, human civilization could not have arrived, survived, and thrived on Earth any earlier than it did. However, conditions in the Milky Way Galaxy (MWG) dictated that civilization couldn't have come much later, either.

A Goldilocks Galaxy

For human life to survive, dozens of cosmic conditions must be just right.[5] For example, advanced life requires a not-too-large and not-too-small spiral galaxy with a just-right-sized central bulge, a just-right set of neighboring galaxies, and a just-right position and velocity relative to those galaxies and to other groups of galaxies in the universe.[6] Though the MWG meets these just-right requirements, it can't maintain them indefinitely. With age, a spiral galaxy's primary spiral structure tends to develop substructures such as branches, spurs, and feathers. Various phenomena within and between the spiral arms (ultraharmonic resonances, nonlinear dredging, and local transient gravitational instabilities) increasingly generate these disruptive features.[7] As the branches, spurs, and feathers develop and multiply, they subtly disturb the movement of planetary systems in their orbits around the center of the galaxy.

Why Only Simple Life for So Long?

The ashes of previous generations of stars enriched Earth with enough long-lived radiometric elements to drive life-critical plate tectonics for billions of years. The concentrations of these radiometric elements and the chemical forms of nearly all other metals would have been deadly for advanced life. Elements such as arsenic, boron, chlorine, chromium, cobalt, copper, fluorine, iodine, iron, manganese, molybdenum, nickel, phosphorous, potassium, selenium, sulfur, tin, vanadium, and zinc are poisons, but they are also life essential.[8] Advanced life requires that certain minimum abundances of each must be present in the environment in soluble forms. Too much, however, proves deadly.

Over a few billion years, specific sulfate-reducing bacteria stripped Earth's waters of low (but still deadly) concentrations of particular poisonous elements. Some of these bacteria consumed water-soluble zinc and turned it into zinc precipitates of pure sphalerite. Sphalerite is insoluble and, therefore, safe for advanced life. Moreover, once the bacteria formed sufficiently large and enduring populations, they produced sphalerite[9] ore deposits, which future humans could easily exploit to make pure zinc metal.

Researchers now recognize that sulfate-reducing bacteria produced most, if not all, of the concentrated (thus economic to mine) ore deposits of iron, magnesium, zinc, and lead. Ores of trace metals such as silver, arsenic, selenium, and other life-essential (but potentially deadly) poisons may similarly owe their concentrations—and accessibility—to sulfate-reducing bacteria. In addition, these bacteria play a critical role in Earth's sulfur and carbon cycles, both of which are necessary for maintaining life.[10]

Other simple life-forms helped prepare the way for advanced life on Earth's landmasses. Detailed analyses of cryptogamic crusts (soils composed of clay, sand, fungi, mosses, and photosynthetic or oxygen-producing bacteria, existing symbiotically) demonstrate that these microbial soils dramatically transformed both the temperature and the chemistry of Earth's early landmasses. This transformation prepared the way for more advanced vegetation.[11] These findings solve a long-held mystery—why the lack of evidence for advanced land vegetation prior to about a half billion years ago?

Even a tiny disturbance in the solar system's orbit around the MWG's nucleus would eventually expose all the planets (including Earth) to deadly radiation and destructive gas and dust clouds. This susceptibility requires Earth's galaxy to be old enough to provide the necessary resources (heavy elements) to sustain human civilization but not so old as to have generated significant spiral substructures.

Astronomers see these substructures developing in the MWG. And many other spiral galaxies in its neighborhood already manifest substructures at levels that would pose grave dangers for a civilized, intelligent species.

The MWG's primary spiral structure opens only a narrow time window for human existence. Ongoing star formation maintains the structure, while certain gases and dust make the stars. However, the older a spiral galaxy is (the MWG is considered middle-aged), the emptier its gas reservoirs become.[12] For human life to exist, a galaxy must sustain its primary spiral structure long enough for a planet with the required endowment of resources to form. These resources must develop in the required location relative to the spiral structure. But the galaxy must be young enough that its primary spiral structure has not yet begun to collapse nor its spiral substructure begun to grow to ominous proportions.

Galaxy models demonstrate that once star formation ceases, the primary spiral structure collapses in only two to five galactic rotations (about 500 million to 2 billion years). Astronomers have noted a decline in the number of spiral galaxies in the total cosmic population over the past 5 billion years—from 30 percent to just 6 percent. And the number continues to drop. So humanity's galactic moment is brief. In fact, many more cosmic moments must be carefully aligned to permit the possibility of human civilization.

Safe Supernova Moment

Like all spiral galaxies, the MWG has endured massive stellar explosions (supernovae) throughout its history. Astronomers estimate that over the past 13 billion years one supernova has occurred somewhere in the galaxy every 50 years, on average.[13] Throughout the past billion years, these supernova events took place mostly in the spiral arms. Because Earth's solar system resides between two of the MWG's spiral arms, the probability for a close supernova encounter has been high and remains high.

Astronomers see evidence of some recent massive stellar explosions relatively close to our solar system. The remnants of these supernovae were created by the explosions' shock waves, which formed "shells" and "bubbles" of hot gas filled with charged particles. These remnants range in age from 2 to 50 million years.[14] In particular, astronomers determined that supergiant stars in the Scorpius-Centaurus OB association (a grouping of very bright young stars located in the constellations Scorpius and Centaurus) have experienced about 20 supernova explosions in the past 11 million years.[15] Astrometric data show that 5 to 7 million years ago the solar system was located much closer to the Scorpius-Centaurus OB association than it is today.[16] In fact, some of the supernovae probably occurred as close to Earth as 130 light-years.[17] At that distance they would have shone about a hundred times brighter than a full moon.

These intensely bright events emitted deadly x-rays, gamma rays, and ozone-destroying ultraviolet radiation. The radiation from more recent and nearby supernovae would have either destroyed or (at the very least) seriously disrupted human civilization—if it had existed then. The same supernovae may account for the extinction of several hominid species that lived before the human era (see chapter 2). Furthermore, geologists have found an excess of iron-60 (the marker of a close supernova encounter) in deep ocean crust samples. These findings indicate that the Pliocene-Pleistocene mass extinction of life (about 2 million years ago) was caused by, or was at least initiated by, one of the Scorpius-Centaurus supernovae.[18]

The solar system has experienced even more frequent life-disturbing encounters as a result of core-collapse supernovae, also known as hypernovae. A team of German and Brazilian astronomers discovered that very high-energy cosmic rays arriving from the center of the MWG are the remnants of events called gamma-ray bursts that occurred near the galactic core about a million years ago.[19] They also determined that gamma-ray bursts occur about once every million years in the MWG. Since gamma-ray bursts anywhere in the galaxy are deadly for human life, the timing of humanity's arrival and the maturation of human civilization must be precisely selected to avoid such events.

Encounters with OB associations and their supernova swarms have impacted the solar system throughout its history. Humanity currently enjoys a respite between such encounters. Furthermore, the rate of isolated supernova events has been unusually low throughout the epoch of human civilization. Since the beginning of serious astronomical study (about 2,500 years ago), only eight have been observed, and none of these occurred close enough to be deadly.[20] Supernova remnants (the traces of past supernova eruptions) inform astronomers that at least four, and possibly as many as 11, more supernova events have occurred in the human era—again, none nearby.[21] Supernova conditions in all contexts have remained just right for human civilization.

Favorable Molecular Cloud Moment

As the solar system revolves around the center of the MWG, it encounters a giant molecular cloud about every 100 million years. About once every billion years, the solar system encounters an especially dense molecular cloud.[22] Earth's atmosphere picks up a considerable amount of interstellar dust during these encounters. This additional dust absorbs and scatters so much sunlight that for a time Earth's surface temperature drops precipitously.

At its worst, this dramatic cooling causes a snowball event, the glaciation of 80 percent or more of Earth's surface. During such an event, lower temperatures produce more ice and keep snow from melting. The high reflectivity of snow and ice permits less of the Sun's heat to be absorbed and the temperature drops even further. This colder condition generates more snow and ice, triggering runaway glaciation. The last such snowball event took place just before the Cambrian explosion, 543 million years ago.

Average-density (and some less-than-average-density) molecular clouds have caused more moderate, but still severe, ice ages every few tens of millions of years. The origin of humanity and the development of global civilization happened to occur between these fateful events. The timing in regard to molecular cloud encounters has been just right.

Ideal Solar Moment

The Sun rises and the Sun sets. Nothing in human experience seems more dependable. The Sun consistently bathes the planet with life-sustaining levels of heat and light. Yet it was not always so, nor will it be so forever.

Every year the Sun burns a little more brightly. The nuclear furnace at the Sun's core fuses more and more hydrogen into helium. This extra helium acts as a catalyst to stimulate more efficient hydrogen burning.[23] Consequently, the Sun grows more luminous with age. However, the Sun's luminosity is also affected by its mass, and every year the solar wind carries away a tiny amount of that mass. Even this small loss can significantly decrease the Sun's brightness.[24]

When the Sun began fusing hydrogen into helium, its mass was 4 to 7 percent greater than its current mass.[25] But this youthful Sun lost mass at such a high rate (a thousand times the present rate) that its luminosity initially declined in spite of the increasing helium abundance at its core. Thus, for the first 1.0 billion to 1.5 billion years of Earth's history, the Sun's luminosity declined. It bottomed out at about 14 to 16 percent of its current level.

Life could survive on Earth as early as 3.8 billion years ago (when the Sun was so much dimmer) only because higher quantities of carbon dioxide and water vapor and possibly methane in Earth's atmosphere provided just enough of a warm blanket to compensate for that early loss of brightness.[26] These greenhouse gases trapped far more of the early Sun's heat. However, both atmospheric and solar radiation conditions were so harsh and changeable back then that only primitive life-forms (such as bacteria) could survive even with the help of this blanket.

Human life, and especially global civilization, requires an exceptionally stable Sun with just-right luminosity. Such stability is lacking in solar-type stars younger than the Sun. A recently completed survey of stellar flares shows how unstable and erratic such stars can be. In particular, they exhibit significantly stronger and more frequent flaring.[27]

The composition of grains found in meteorites and lunar samples reveals that during the Sun's first billion years its flare activity and wind flux were about a thousand times greater than they are today.[28] These radiation levels made life impossible for advanced plants and animals. For the next 3 billion years, solar flaring activity and wind flux averaged about 10 times their current levels.[29] Global civilization could not have survived such conditions. Thus solar activity alone ruled out the possibility of human civilization any time prior to a half billion years ago.

Studies of stars slightly older than the Sun, but of similar mass, indicate that solar flare activity may eventually pick up again. Alpha Centauri, aged 5 billion years (Sun's age = 4.56 billion years), already manifests double the wind flux and flaring activity of the Sun.[30] In addition, 10 of 17 nearby slightly older solar-type stars show significant year-to-year brightness changes.[31]

The Sun's slow but continual brightening already threatens humanity's survival. For the past 3.8 billion years, a carefully timed introduction of the just-right life-forms in just-right abundances and diversities removed just enough of the greenhouse gases from Earth's atmosphere to compensate perfectly. (Meanwhile, life-forms, plate tectonics, and water erosion converted water, silicates, and carbon dioxide into oil, coal, sand, limestone, carbonates, kerogens, and natural gas—each with great usefulness for human civilization and technology.)[32]

However, after 3.8 billion years of this balancing act, the greenhouse gases have been seriously depleted. They now measure just above the minimum level required for the survival of plants. Life on Earth, therefore, faces a catch-22 crisis. The Sun's increasing brightness will either scorch life to death or else the necessary loss of carbon dioxide and water vapor in the atmosphere to avoid scorching will starve plant life, destroying the base of the food chain. Within 5 to 20 million years, a serious drop in plant productivity will occur. This lack of vegetation will drive most, if not all, large advanced animal species to extinction. Within 100 to 200 million years, all but certain extremophile microbes (unicellular life-forms that tolerate extremely harsh conditions) living in exotic refuges will vanish. Within 500 million years, no conceivable life-form will be able to survive anywhere upon Earth.

Global civilization (in contrast to a regionally restricted stone-age existence) requires globally benign and relatively stable climatic conditions. Such conditions require an exceptionally stable Sun. And that is what humanity currently enjoys. Variations in the Sun's diameter are tiny (less than five milliarcseconds, or 0.0003 percent).[33] A recent measurement of the Sun's neutrino flux (including all three flavors of neutrinos) shows that the Sun's light and heat output has remained exceptionally steady over the past 50,000 years and will continue to hold steady for the next 50,000.[34] This steadiness coincides with humanity's origin (as described in chapters 4 and 5)—at the just-right solar time.

Best Lunar Moment

Earth's rotation rate places another constraint on the planet's suitability for humans. At life's first appearance, Earth was spinning four to six times faster than it does today. Such rapid rotation produced wind velocities up to a few thousand miles per hour. A six-foot-tall creature would have experienced wind velocities a thousand miles per hour faster at head height than at foot level. No wonder large land animals (including birds, mammals, reptiles, dinosaurs, and amphibians) lived only during the past 15 percent (the last 543 million years) of life's history.

The Moon makes the biggest impact on slowing Earth's rotation rate. Since the gravitational tug is a little stronger on the side of Earth facing the Moon than on the side facing away, the difference in the two forces produces ocean tides. The tidal torques exerted by the Moon (and to a lesser degree by the Sun) operate as a set of brakes, slowing Earth's rotation.[35]

This slowing can be observed indirectly in the fossil record of certain corals. According to dendrochronologists (scientists who use organisms, both living and dead, as dating tools), corals that date older than 400 million years show much more than 400 daily growth rings in each yearly band. These rings indicate that Earth not so long ago had a rotation rate between 20 and 21 hours per day.[36]

According to the best calculations, Earth's rotation rate was 23 hours per day just over 100 million years ago, and a little more than 100 million years from now it will be 25 hours per day. This longer (or shorter) day could seem like a dream come true, but the realities would be a nightmare.

At 23 hours per day, Earth's rotation caused stronger winds on a global scale. In particular, tornadoes and hurricanes were much more frequent, more devastating, and longer lasting. Jet stream patterns yielded wider variations in rainfall; so parts of Earth were much wetter, while other parts were much drier.

During a 25-hour day, temperature variations from day to night will be extreme enough to cause widespread death. The jet stream patterns will weaken, bringing less rainfall to land. Parts of the planet will require complex and costly technological intervention to remain habitable and Earth's capacity to produce food will become severely challenged.

Humans indeed arrived at the ideal moment in the tidal history of the Sun-Earth-Moon system. From all angles, the 24-hour rotation period appears just right for human civilization and technological advance.

Perfect Eclipse Moment
The visual wonders of solar eclipses may be less essential for human existence than air, food, and water, but they do play a significant role in the development of civilized society. Solar eclipses are also essential to humanity's ability to discover and comprehend the nature of the universe. Remarkably, human existence coincides with the era of "perfect" solar eclipses.

Because the Moon and the Sun cover up exactly the same angle in the sky, people can sometimes see the Moon perfectly block out the Sun with a disk neither bigger nor smaller than the Sun. These perfect solar eclipses have enabled both ancient and modern astronomers to measure the sizes of, and distances to, the Sun and the Moon.[37] Such measurements helped the ancients establish the scale of the solar system and nearby stars, which proved fundamental to launching the disciplines of astronomy, mathematics, and physics. Perfect solar eclipses also allowed scientists to discover and study the Sun's corona.

Once ancient astronomers discovered that solar eclipses occur in highly reliable and repetitive cycles, they began using the data to devise accurate calendars.[38] Thus perfect solar eclipses provided early people with a "clock" for planning and patterning their existence as societies and for making an accurate record of their history.

Just three years after Albert Einstein proposed his theory of general relativity, a perfect solar eclipse advanced science by providing critical confirmation of the theory.[39] This particular eclipse allowed astronomers to see stars close enough to the solar disk that they could determine whether the Sun's gravity bends starlight, just as general relativity predicts.

The Sun-Earth-Moon system is the only three-body arrangement known to astronomers that permits observers to see frequent perfect solar eclipses. But the solar system is not static. So the window of viewing opportunity has limits. Today about half of all solar eclipses are "annular." (Because the Moon's orbit is not perfectly circular, at times when the Moon's distance from Earth is great enough at the instant of a solar eclipse, the Moon's disk appears smaller than the Sun's. During an annular eclipse, a ring of sunlight appears all around the Moon's disk and blazes so brightly that observation of the solar corona and adjacent stars proves impossible.)

Every year the Moon spirals away from Earth by about four centimeters.[40] This outward movement means that in about 20 million years *all* solar eclipses will be annular.[41] However, roughly 20 million years ago, all solar eclipses remained total for so long that the solar corona couldn't have been noticed even if an astronomer had been alive in that era to observe it.

The length of the Moon's shadow at which a precisely perfect solar eclipse can be observed is 238,100 miles. Today, the average distance of the Moon from Earth is 238,500 miles.[42] The fact that this average distance is so close to the perfect distance indicates that humans appeared on Earth at the just-right time to witness the maximum number of perfect solar eclipses.

Beneficial Tectonic Moment

Earth's plate tectonic activity plays a critical role in compensating for the gradual increase in the Sun's luminosity. It also helps provide, prepare, and maintain the continental landmasses for human habitation. Mountain building, the growth and transformation of continental landmasses, and the nourishment of plant life (foundational to the food chain) all depend crucially on plate tectonics. This activity also fulfills one of the most crucial roles in maintaining the life-essential carbonate-silicate cycle.[43]

Heat released from the decay of radiometric elements in Earth's core and mantle drives tectonic activity. Because radiometric decay declines exponentially, the heat release today is about five times less than when life first appeared on Earth 3.8 billion years ago. Thus human beings (since their first appearance less than 100,000 years ago) experience only a tiny fraction of the tectonic activity that Earth's first life-forms did.

Less tectonic activity means fewer earthquakes and volcanic eruptions, which means less human death and destruction. Nevertheless, a certain minimum level of tectonic processes is necessary to compensate for the Sun's increasing luminosity. This activity is also necessary to sustain adequate nutrient supplies for plants and sufficient continental landmass growth.

Tectonic activity causes not only continental growth but also continental drift. The current positions, sizes, and shapes of Earth's continents can be attributed to a few billion years of plate movement. The result of this tectonic history is a set of time-sensitive geologic features that prove significantly beneficial to human life and civilization:

- With almost all of the continental landmass located in the northern hemisphere and so little in the southern latitudes (and even less at large southern latitudes), Earth's present orbit keeps most people closest to the Sun in the winter months. Northern latitude winters are warmer and its summers are cooler, so most of humanity avoids uncomfortable and even dangerous climatic extremes.
- The continents, though separated by large oceans, have points of close contact with one another. These points once facilitated rapid early human migration from the region of human origin to all the continents, making global civilization possible.
- Continents are oriented in such a way as to provide long north-south boundaries for the oceans. These boundaries help break up the jet streams so that rainfall gets more evenly distributed. Continent orientation also enhances tidal delivery of nutrients to (and removal of waste products from) the biomass-rich continental shelves.
- The continents make up 29 percent of Earth's total surface area. Such a ratio of continents to oceans helps provide humanity with maximal biological resources.

Each of these tectonic features foster just-right conditions for humanity and for human civilization.

Optimal Petroleum Moment

Both sedimentation and plate tectonics tend to bury organic material. Heat, pressure, and time transform the buried organic matter into kerogen (high-molecular-weight tars). With yet more time and heat, a significant portion of kerogen is converted into petroleum.[44] Still more time and microbial activity lead to the degradation of petroleum into methane (natural gas).[45]

Certain kinds of organisms are much more likely (upon death and burial) to be transformed into kerogen than others. Among the most efficient kerogen producers were the swarms of small animals that inhabited large shallow seas after the Cambrian explosion. Therefore, for accumulation of the richest possible reserves of fossil hydrocarbons, a fixed period of time had to transpire between the epoch when efficient kerogen producers were dominant on Earth and the appearance of human beings.

There is more to the production of fossil hydrocarbon reserves than just the burial of certain organisms and their progressive conversion into kerogen, petroleum, and methane. Certain sedimentation processes are needed to lay down porous reservoir rocks. Later, these stones must be overlaid with fine-grained rocks with low permeability (sealer rocks). Finally, certain tectonic forces are required to form appropriate caps under which fossil hydrocarbons can collect.[46]

While specific sedimentary and tectonic processes take a long time to produce appropriate reservoir structures for collecting and storing fossil hydrocarbons, too much time will lead to destruction of the reservoirs. Other tectonic and erosion processes eventually cause the reservoirs to leak. If too much time transpires, the fossil hydrocarbon reservoirs empty out.

Both methane and kerogen play significant roles in sustaining modern civilization and technology. Both play a backseat role, however, compared to petroleum. It appears that human beings indeed arrived at the just-right fossil hydrocarbon moment.

A Classic Climatic Moment

At first glance, the time frame for Earth's favorable climate may seem unremarkable, but new evidence from Ellesmere Island (Canada's northernmost large island) suggests differently.[47] Paleontologists discovered 4-million-year-old fossils of plants, insects, and mammals there that required significantly warmer climates. According to calculations, temperatures on the island were once warmer by 27°F in the winter and by 18°F in the summer. Such warm temperatures at this high latitude mean that sea levels were higher during that era, rainfall distribution was different, and the tropics were unbearably hot.

Deep ice cores in adjacent Greenland reveal that, a few tens of thousands of years ago, annual temperature averages sometimes shifted by as much as 12°F in less than a 50-year period.[48] Such rapid and dramatic temperature shifts may help explain why hominids never developed large populations or broad habitats. Another study shows that the Indian monsoons became stronger during and immediately after the last ice age.[49] These findings may help explain why human civilization and urbanization did not effectively spread worldwide until roughly 10,000 years ago (see chapter 8).

Apparently, the ideal climate for global civilization exists only for a limited time. For optimal comfort and long-term stability, the timing of humanity is just right.

Other Just-Right Necessities

Global human civilization and its technology requirements must somehow fit into many other narrow time windows. Additional risks exist. If even one of the MWG's 200 billion stars (or numerous pieces of "fluff") were to pass too close to the solar system, human civilization would suffer severe damage if not wholesale destruction. Likewise, a gamma-ray burst (lasting a couple of minutes or less) within the MWG, or in a neighboring one, could devastate at least half the planet.

Earth today resides in a safe zone with respect to asteroids and comets. No major collisions have occurred in the past million years and astronomers see no likelihood of one in at least the next thousand years. The solar system currently enjoys freedom from destructive resonances among its planetary orbits. These periodic gravitational disturbances arise when one planet's orbital period is either an exact multiple (for example, one, two, three, or four times) or a simple fraction (such as one-third, two-thirds, two-fifths, or three-quarters) of another planet's orbital period. As the Sun orbits the galactic center, it currently manifests only minimal movement above or below the galactic plane. Thus advanced life is protected from the deadly radiation that emanates from the galactic core.

Several dozen more terrestrial time windows could be added to those described in this chapter.[50] Even more amazing than the length of the list is the fact that so many independent time requirements coincide. What could explain their simultaneous occurrence? The fact that human beings arrived at all—and arrived at the best imaginable time in cosmic, climatic, galactic, geologic, and solar system history to facilitate rapid development of global civilization— whispers (or perhaps shouts) of careful planning and purposeful preparation.

All the necessary windows for human life and human civilization opened at the just-right time and all at once. Human life appeared, as predicted in the RTB creation model, at the perfect moment in Earth's history. Such purposeful design might also include specific parameters for each individual life span. The next chapter explores how long a human being's own unique time window can remain open.

Chapter 7

How the Fountain of Youth Ran Dry

Out, out brief candle!
Life's but a walking shadow, a poor player,
That struts and frets his hour upon the stage,
And then is heard no more.
                    —*Macbeth* Act 5, scene 5

Good nutrition, excellent health care, biomedical advance—even with tremendous effort and expense, science can't yet extend human lives much beyond 80 or 90 years. Over the last century, life expectancy might have doubled, but living to 100 still rates a newspaper write-up. Trying to imagine early humans living for over 900 years seems impossible. But that's what the Bible says happened. So how could the long life spans described in Genesis 5 and 11 be possible?

Genesis 6:3 may present additional scientific challenges. According to one interpretation, this passage indicates that God shortened maximum human life to about 120 years. Such life spans fit more closely with modern-day experience. Still, one can't help but wonder how people could have lived so long. And if they did, what cut their lives so short?

Some people suggest that the biblical years of life were measured by other markers, such as the Moon. (Twelve lunar years equal about one solar year.) However, such explanations cause other concerns.[1] Biblically, Adam was 930 years old when he died. Translating lunar "years" into solar would make Adam just over 77 at the time of his death. But this calculation would also make Adam only 10½ years old when Seth was born. Likewise, Mahalalel (the father of Jared) would have been 5½ years old when his son was born. So what did happen?

According to the Reasons to Believe (RTB) model, the literal meaning of "years" for the Genesis account of early human life spans is accurate. This interpretation leads to an inescapable prediction—the first humans' life spans were several hundred years and became progressively shorter early in human history. Interestingly, the Bible is not alone in claiming that the first humans (before the flood) lived much longer than people do today. In Mesopotamia, the Weld-Blundell prism (dating to the third millennium BC) and the Nippur tablets list eight pre-flood kings who lived thousands of years each.[2]

Are the problems associated with this feature of the RTB model intractable? As previous chapters attest, the model receives strong support from genetic studies and the fossil and archeological records. Still, for the biblical model to have legitimacy, the long lives in Genesis must be accounted for. The RTB model must accept the burden of proof by demonstrating that the long life spans recorded in Genesis are scientifically plausible.

The latest breakthroughs in the biochemistry of senescence (aging) and new understanding of recent changes in radiation exposure provide important insights on the matter. Taking into account new discoveries about the aging process and death, biochemists are now rethinking the maximum possible human life expectancy.[3] These key advances can be used to evaluate an important prediction made by the RTB model.

Staying Young
Biochemists still lack complete understanding of aging and death. Significant progress, though, has been made in the past decade. Scientists have identified a number of distinct biochemical mechanisms—reactive oxygen species, caloric restriction, heat shock proteins, and telomere loss—that impact the aging process and the duration of human life. In most cases, when researchers subtly manipulate these processes, they can dramatically increase the life expectancy of laboratory organisms, such as mice, yeast, fruit flies, and nematodes. Genetic mutations and radiation also play an important role.

Restrict reactive oxygen species
The free-radical theory of aging is one of the leading explanations for senescence.[4] Reactive oxygen species (ROS)—derivatives of molecular oxygen, such as superoxide, hydroxy free radicals, and hydrogen peroxide—are some of the most important free radicals found inside the cell (see "Free Radicals" on page 117). The cell's machinery routinely produces ROS during the normal course of metabolism.[5]

The free-radical theory of aging postulates that ROS react randomly and indiscriminately inside the cell to damage important cell components. ROS,

Free Radicals

In chemical compounds, electrons find stability by forming pairs. Free radicals are chemical entities that possess one or more unshared electrons as part of their molecular makeup. A free radical's unshared electron(s) makes it highly reactive and chemically destructive. When a molecule possesses an unshared electron(s), it reacts vigorously with other compounds because the unshared electron aggressively "seeks out" another electron with which to pair.

for example, attack proteins, DNA, and lipids (the molecules that make up the cell's membrane).[6] This damage to cellular components is cumulative and over time mars cell function. As a result, researchers theorize, long-term oxidative stress contributes to aging.

Fortunately, the cell has mechanisms in place to buffer against the harmful effects of ROS. For example, some enzymes convert these free radicals into harmless compounds.[7] Other antioxidant defenses, such as vitamin C, vitamin E, and glutathione, can also be found inside the cell.[8] However, the level of activity of these protective systems is insufficient to prevent all the damage caused by ROS over the cell's lifetime.

A team of pharmacologists recently demonstrated that augmenting the cell's native antioxidant defenses subverts the aging effects of ROS.[9] They found that administering synthetic compounds (superoxide dismutase/catalase enzyme mimetics)[10] to nematodes extends the organism's average life span by 44 percent.[11] These researchers think the human life span may be prolonged by the same type of "pharmacological intervention."[12] This suggestion appears to have merit. Researchers have observed that age-related learning loss and memory loss in mice caused by ROS could be reversed with the use of superoxide dismutase/catalase enzyme mimetics.[13]

Researchers also have extended the life spans of fruit flies by as much as 40 percent by manipulating catalase and superoxide dismutase genes.[14] Further indication that catalase and superoxide dismutase levels influence life spans comes from work by researchers at the University of Texas in Houston. These scientists developed data indicating that disrupting superoxide dismutase activity might be a viable therapy to selectively kill cancer cells.[15] In addition, investigators have observed that the life span of the nematode dramatically *decreases* when one of its genes that codes for catalase becomes mutated.[16]

Researchers have also observed life span changes associated with the altered function of enzymes that repair oxidative damage to the cell's components. For example, the amino acid methionine is unusually susceptible to oxidative damage. However, the enzyme methionine sulfoxide reductase reverses oxidative damage for both free and protein-bound forms of methionine. Researchers from the National Institutes of Health have shown that the increased expression of the gene that encodes methionine sulfoxide reductase increases the life span of human T cells.[17] This team of investigators also demonstrated that mice without the methionine sulfoxide reductase gene have dramatically shortened lives.[18]

Recent work on catalase, superoxide dismutase, and methionine sulfoxide reductase does more than help define the role of ROS in the aging process. The revelations also suggest a scientifically plausible way God could have designed humans with 900-year life spans—and how man's life expectancy might have grown progressively shorter around the time of the flood. Modulating the activity of these enzymes in the cell can lengthen or shorten life. As researchers continue to demonstrate their ability to alter the life spans of model organisms by directly manipulating cellular antioxidant defense systems, it becomes increasingly reasonable to believe that God might have been the first to do so.

Cut calories

Scientists have also discovered that caloric restriction extends life span.[19] Reducing food intake by 30 to 70 percent can extend life expectancy by up to 40 percent for a wide range of organisms from yeast to mammals—assuming a nutritious diet. In humans, long-term calorie restriction reduces the risk of atherosclerosis.[20]

For some time, researchers have thought that taking in fewer calories lengthened life span by decreasing metabolic activity. In turn, this reduction limited the amount of ROS produced by the cell and hence the degree of oxidative damage.[21] Recent studies, however, indicate that increases in longevity via caloric restriction occur through a mechanism distinct from the free-radical theory of aging.

Biochemists now recognize that caloric restriction increases the activity of sirtuin (or Sir2). This enzyme plays a key role in extending life spans.[22] Sirtuins occur in a wide range of organisms, including humans.[23] Sir2 becomes active inside the cell when the levels of nicotinamide adenine dinucleotide (NAD^+) increase. The amount of this compound in the cell varies in response to the cell's energy status. In a cell's energy-rich state, NAD^+ levels fall off. In a cell's energy-poor state, NAD^+ levels rise. Caloric restriction brings the cell down to an energy-poor state and thus increases the NAD$^+$ level and Sir2 activity.[24]

Sir2 functions as a histone deacetylase.[25] In other words, Sir2 removes an acetyl chemical group (deacetylates) from the lysine amino acid components of histone proteins. Histones associate with DNA in the cell's nucleus. Removing the acetyl groups from histones exposes positive charges. Because of the attraction between positive and negative charges, this exposure causes the histones to tightly associate with DNA, which carries a negative charge.

When histones and DNA strongly interact, genes "turn off," or become silenced, and the organism's genome is stabilized.[26] This stability presumably limits the normal wear and tear on DNA that occurs during metabolism and so delays the aging process. Researchers note that when they inhibit Sir2 activity, the cell displays a biochemical profile that resembles the changes that take place during aging.[27]

Sir2 activity might also exert its life-extending benefits in other ways. Recent work indicates that increased activity of this enzyme prevents the neurodegeneration associated with diseases like Parkinson's and Alzheimer's. In mammals, activation of Sir1 (which corresponds to Sir2 in yeast) prevents axons from degenerating.[28] Sir1 also acts on key enzymes that inaugurate the process of programmed cell death (apoptosis).[29] This process occurs when cells suffer damage. Unfortunately, apoptosis will destroy irreplaceable cells, like those found in nerves and muscles. This type of cell loss contributes to the aging process.

Scientists have begun to manipulate sirtuin activity in an attempt to lengthen the life expectancy of laboratory organisms. For example, researchers observe that when they add an additional gene for Sir2 to yeast and nematodes, their life spans increase.[30] Recently, a team of pharmacologists discovered a number of compounds that activate Sir2 in yeast and mimic the benefits of caloric restriction.[31] One of the most potent, resveratrol, is found in red wine. When administered to yeast, this compound increases life expectancy by 70 percent! Researchers think this breakthrough may one day lead to pharmaceutical agents that can delay aging.

As with catalase, superoxide dismutase, and methionine sulfoxide reductase, increased Sir2 activity translates into longer life spans. It represents another way God could have designed human biochemistry to allow people to live several hundred years. And with a subtle adjustment, life spans could have been shortened to no more than 120 years.

Produce heat shock proteins

Biochemists also recognize heat shock proteins as important determinants of life span. The cell produces these proteins when under stress. Traumatic conditions can cause proteins to unfold and lose their native structure. Not only do these unfolded proteins lose their three-dimensional shape, they also interact abnormally with other proteins to form massive aggregates. These aggregates disrupt cellular function and take part in the etiology (causation) of several neurodegenerative diseases, such as Alzheimer's and Huntington's disease.

Researchers have observed that the life spans of model organisms (including nematodes and fruit flies) decrease when the genes that code heat shock proteins become disabled. Conversely, when these genes are overexpressed, life spans increase by as much as 45 percent.[32] In nematodes, heat shock proteins delay the formation of protein aggregates that characteristically form when these worms age.

Once again, the first humans could have been created to have significantly higher heat shock protein activity than is observed in contemporary people. Likewise, God might have lowered the level of heat shock protein gene expression at the time of the flood to begin the process of restricting human life spans to 120 years.

Target the telomeres

Altering telomerase activity can also impact human longevity. Telomerase is an enzyme complex that maintains the length of telomeres—the terminal ends of chromosomes.[33] Housed in the cell's nucleus, DNA is packaged with proteins to form chromosomes (see "Chromosomes" on page 208). Prior to cell division, each chromosome duplicates. Upon cell division, the parent and daughter chromosomes separate from one another and become equally distributed between the two daughter cells.

Telomeres—noncoding repetitive DNA sequences at the terminal ends of chromosomes—maintain chromosome stability. During DNA replication, telomerase maintains telomere length. Without sufficient activity, telomeres become successively shorter with each round of cell division. If telomeres disappear, chromosome stability is lost and cell division ceases. Loss of telomerase activity and the disappearance of telomeric DNA are associated with aging.[34]

Telomere length indicates the health (or lack thereof) for cloned animals.[35] Researchers have been able to extend life by introducing telomerase into cultured human cells lacking this function.[36] Cancer cells (considered to be essentially immortal) manifest elevated telomerase activity.[37] Because of this association, some potential anticancer therapies target telomerase.[38]

Recent research suggests that the relationship between telomere length and longevity is more complicated than previously thought.[39] For example, in an environment where cancer is possible, higher telomerase activity might actually shorten rather than lengthen life spans. Still, human life expectancy does change with variations in telomerase function.

Researchers are aware of other enzymes (in addition to Sir2, catalase, telomerase, heat shock proteins, and superoxide dismutase) that affect longer life spans when their activity increases. For example, investigators have just discovered that human cells age much more rapidly when their DNA double-strand repair mechanism lacks efficiency, because this inefficiency causes genome instability.[40] However, researchers don't have a clear understanding of how this process, or others like it, relates to aging.

As scientists pursue the biochemical basis for senescence, additional insights on regulating human life spans will emerge—insights that might explain how the Creator increased or decreased life spans as described in Genesis.

Manipulate genetic mutations

Biochemists studying the aging process have discovered a number of mutations that shorten life spans. For example, mutations to the *WRN* gene cause Werner's syndrome,[41] one among other "progeria" disorders that result in premature aging. Biochemists still do not have a clear picture of the relationship between these mutations and the early onset of senescence.

Additionally, a team of investigators recently discovered that mice with deficient expression of the so-called klotho gene age rapidly.[42] Scientists are still working to discover what this gene does and how its loss impacts the aging process. As researchers investigate these mutations, new discoveries hold the promise of providing valuable insight into senescence.

In some respects, it's not surprising that gene mutations cause premature aging. Such defects generally disrupt the cell's normal operation. When this occurs, disease invariably follows, and some disorders just happen to involve premature aging. However, a series of surprising discoveries indicates that some gene mutations actually lead to dramatic *increases* in life expectancy. In other words, these mutations promote longevity.

In 1998, researchers reported that a mutation to a single gene (called the methuselah gene) increases fruit fly life spans by 35 percent.[43] Fruit flies that lack a functional methuselah gene resist stress caused by starvation, pesticides, and high temperatures better than their counterparts with an intact gene.

Biochemists don't understand how the methuselah mutation confers extended longevity. They do know, however, that this gene encodes a protein involved in signaling pathways.[44]

Recent work by investigators from the University of Connecticut identified another single gene mutation that extends life span.[45] These researchers discovered a mutation in fruit flies that disables a gene (called the *Indy* gene) that plays a role in metabolism. The loss of this gene's activity makes metabolism less efficient. Inefficiency in metabolism means that the organism can't extract energy from food effectively. This condition mimics caloric restriction. Fruit fly life spans *doubled* as a result of the *Indy* mutation!

The *daf-2* mutation in the nematode *Caenorhabditis elegans* is one of the most thoroughly studied life-extending single gene mutations.[46] The *daf-2* gene codes for a cell-surface receptor protein that resembles insulin-binding proteins. The occurrence of insulin signaling in many different creatures gives the nematode results broad applicability. Researchers have discovered similar genes in fruit flies and mammals. These scientists think *daf-2* gene activity inhibits the activity of *daf-16*, a gene that triggers multiple cell functions (such as resistance to microbial infection, repair of DNA damage, scavenging of free radicals, and production of heat shock proteins) that promote longevity. When *daf-2* mutates, this inhibition no longer takes place and increased longevity results. In fact, it doubles.

Researchers have discovered some nematode strains (*C. elegans* double mutants) that display extreme longevity. For example, mutations in the *daf-2* and *clk-1* genes, or in the *daf-2* and *daf-12* genes, respectively, extend life expectancy by a factor of five.[47] There doesn't yet seem to be any cost associated with extended life span—these *C. elegans* double mutants appear fully healthy.[48]

Researchers so far have not conducted the necessary studies to determine how or if these results for *C. elegans* apply to humans. But given that the biochemistry of *C. elegans* and humans is fundamentally the same, it's easy to imagine that the longevity effects observed for nematodes may be applicable for humans.

Based on these mutation studies, it appears as if mortality has been programmed into the genome of organisms. According to molecular geneticist Cynthia Kenyon, "It's inescapable that aging is regulated deliberately by genes."[49] This insight excites biochemists who study the aging process. They now hypothesize that simply by disrupting the activity of a few genes, they could dramatically extend human longevity.

The long life spans recorded in Genesis 5 and 11 seem plausible in light of the advances in the biochemistry of aging. Subtle differences in biochemistry—whether an increase in the activity and expression of enzymes like superoxide dismutase and Sir2 or the disruption of a few genes, such as the *Indy* or methuselah genes—translate into dramatic increases in longevity. In many cases, the biochemical changes that increase life expectancy appear independent of one another. Their effects might be additive. The research suggests how Adam could have lived to be 930 years old.

Biochemical manipulation is only one method to regulate human longevity. Recent astronomical studies on nearby supernovae point to another mechanism that could have been involved in shortening human life spans.

Reduce radiation risk

One of humanity's biggest killers is cancer. Some of the biochemical adjustments for extending life spans (such as increased telomerase activity) encourage more efficient growth of certain cancers. Thus, for significantly longer human life spans to be possible, cancer risk factors must be lowered. One of the biggest cancer risks for human beings is radiation. The deadliest radiation comes from cosmic rays and the radiometric decay of radioactive isotopes in Earth's crust.

The crustal components that pose the largest risks are igneous rocks, which contain high levels of radioactive material. If humans were to avoid living anywhere near igneous rocks, they could effectively reduce their cancer risk. Given the ubiquitous exploitation of asphalt, concrete, and granite, such avoidance today is nearly impossible. However, according to the Bible, in the days before the Genesis flood, humanity's habitat was limited to an igneous-deficient region (namely the Mesopotamian Plain), and the use of igneous material for building projects had not yet occurred.

Cosmic radiation that affects humans comes predominantly from supernova remnants within the Milky Way Galaxy (MWG). Because supernova eruptions occur at different times and places throughout the galaxy, there might have been epochs in the human era during which exposure to cosmic radiation was lesser (or greater) than at other times. But for the most part, this cosmic radiation bathes Earth rather uniformly in time and place. Two astronomers have discovered a different story, however, for a certain period in human history.

Since 1996, Anatoly Erlykin and Arnold Wolfendale have been studying the high end of the particle energy spectrum (above a quadrillion electron volts per nucleon) of cosmic-ray air showers.[50] They've found two peaks in the spectra (identified with oxygen and iron nuclei) protruding above the background.

This energy profile bears the signature of a single source—a local, recent supernova eruption.[51] In other words, while the thousands of supernova remnants scattered throughout the MWG account for most of the cosmic radiation background, the two peaks are explained by the single, recent, local supernova, which accelerated oxygen and iron nuclei via shocks in the hot interstellar medium.

In 1997, Erlykin and Wolfendale determined that this supernova eruption must have been closer than 3,000 light-years and more recent than 100,000 years ago.[52] These limits made the Vela supernova (distance = 936 light-years;[53] eruption date = 20,000 to 30,000 years ago[54]) a likely candidate. With improved data, Erlykin and Wolfendale concluded that the supernova was so close that the solar system probably resides just inside the shell of its remnant.[55] Because the supernova erupted many thousands of years ago, the remnant itself would occupy up to 40 degrees of the sky, making it very difficult to distinguish from the background.[56]

The local, recent supernova event identified by Erlykin and Wolfendale may help explain the long life spans of the first humans. These earliest humans, living before the supernova eruption event, would have been exposed to much less of this high-energy, heavy-nuclei cosmic radiation. Consequently, they might have faced a lower risk of cell damage and cancer. The people (living before and up to the time of the Genesis flood) had the potential to live much longer lives.

Living Long

Substantial advances in the biochemistry of aging, and associated studies in physics and astronomy, are thrilling to observe. Still, much more remains to be discovered and understood about the complex process of growing old. Recent discoveries clearly indicate that aging results from subtle changes in cellular chemistry. These insights give investigators hope and confidence that in the near future they will be able to interrupt the aging process, at least to some degree. Direct intervention through drug treatment and gene manipulation may alter life spans in the near future.

Biochemists' successes in prolonging the life span of model organisms in the laboratory, along with the encroaching ability to increase human life expectancy through biochemical manipulation, lend scientific plausibility to the long life spans described in Genesis 5 and 11. Human attempts to alter life spans might be a reflection of the Creator's ability to do so.

Changes in Earth's cosmic radiation environment, as well as isolation from igneous rocks, likely joined biochemical manipulation to dramatically impact human longevity. No one knows exactly how God regulated human life spans. However, recent discoveries in astronomy and the biochemistry of aging satisfy an important prediction of the RTB human origins model and continue to build the case for the reliability of Scripture.

The next chapter evaluates the RTB model by examining recent genetic, archeological, and geological studies on the timing and patterns of migrations in early human history.

Chapter 8

People on the Move

Wherein I spoke of most disastrous chances:
Of moving accidents by flood and field,
Of hair-breadth 'scapes i' the
Imminent deadly breach,
Of being taken by the insolent foe
And sold to slavery, of my
Redemption thence and portance in
My travels' history;
Wherein of antres vast and deserts idle,
Rough quarries, rocks, and hills
Whose heads touch heaven,
It was my hint to speak—such was
The process—.
—*Othello* Act 1, scene 3

Nearly everyone in the United States knows something about their family history. They've likely heard about the countries their ancestors came from and perhaps a few other details. Irishmen proudly tell how their grandfathers chose to immigrate to America. An African descendant might raise his voice in grief as he remembers slavery's injustice.

Old World roots reveal significance far beyond individual lives. Each genealogy intertwines with the grand collection of stories that make up a country's history. The shaping influence of immigration (and emigration) is not unique to the United States. Exploration, migration, conquest, and forced relocation (slavery) characterize much of human history. As a result, people groups have moved around the world to the point that humanity occupies almost every imaginable place on Earth.

Historians frequently study the movement and displacement of population groups to gain understanding of their sociocultural and geopolitical impact. Anthropologists also study historical patterns of human migrations. However, rather than focus on more recent travels, these scientists devote their attention to the original distribution of human population groups and their primeval relocations around the world.

Prehistoric distribution of human clans and their early migrations closely relate to humanity's origin. The multiregional hypothesis asserts that, between 1 and 2 million years ago, hominids such as *Homo ergaster* and other archaic *Homo sapiens* migrated from Africa into Europe and Asia. Multiregionalists think that in each of these three regions, early hominids separately evolved into modern humans. In their view, various people groups are indigenous to the regions of the world where they currently reside.

Evolutionary biologists who hold to the out-of-Africa hypothesis, on the other hand, maintain that humanity originated recently (less than 150,000 years ago) in Africa. These proponents claim people moved from East Africa to populate Europe, Asia, Australia, and finally the Americas. In the process, the first humans either displaced the local hominids or migrated to these regions after the hominids living there became extinct.

The Reasons to Believe (RTB) creation model also holds the view that humanity originated recently, from one location somewhere outside the Garden of Eden (presumably in or near the Middle East) and from there spread to the remainder of the world. Many of the predictions made by the RTB human origins model regarding populating the earth overlap those made by the out-of-Africa model (see chapter 3). In contrast, the predictions made by the multiregional hypothesis stand distinct from these two models.

In the past, anthropologists have used fossil, geological, and archeological data to characterize humanity's original distribution and spread. Recently, molecular anthropologists have contributed to the research through the use of mitochondrial DNA (mtDNA) and Y-chromosomal genetic markers. The combined data now yield a better understanding of early human history that discriminates among various origins models. What does the overall picture reveal about the beginnings of African, European, Asian, Australian, and American people groups? Evidence has been gathered from all over the world.

Africa

The fossil, archeological, and genetic evidence (see chapters 4 and 5) indicate a recent origin for human beings. An accumulation of data shows that humanity began less than 100,000 years ago from a small population located in a single region in East Africa, near the Middle East. The relatively high level of genetic diversity observed for African populations indicates that they are the oldest people groups. So does their genetic structure, which encompasses all non-African populations. The genetic fingerprints of all non-African people groups constitute a subset of the African DNA sequences (referred to as haplotypes).[1] From an evolutionary perspective, genetic data strongly support the out-of-Africa hypothesis and indicate that all of humanity arose from one African subpopulation. This evidence also harmonizes with several key predictions made by the RTB creation model (see chapter 4).

Y-chromosomal analysis indicates that Ethiopian and Khoisan populations are the oldest human groups and share a common origin. Three genetic types make up the Ethiopian population. One of these subsets appears to be ancestral to all non-Africans. DNA markers indicate that some of the members of this Ethiopian group migrated from the location of humanity's origin through the Middle East and into Europe and Asia.[2] Another subset consists of genetic fingerprints found outside Africa. This group likely results from "back-migrations" into Africa after humanity spread from its original locale.[3]

Some sub-Saharan populations possess mtDNA and Y-chromosomal DNA fingerprints unique to Africa.[4] These populations appear to represent groups that descended from the Ethiopian-Khoisan ancestral group and migrated south, deeper into Africa from humanity's original location. Some genetic markers in sub-Saharan populations come from outside Africa and likely result from back-migrations as well.[5]

Europe

Where did the first Europeans come from? For years, questions about the origin of human population groups in Europe have been part of the larger debate that takes place between proponents of the multiregional and out-of-Africa hypotheses. Multiregionalists maintain that the first Europeans evolved from Neanderthals, whereas proponents of the out-of-Africa hypothesis think the first Europeans migrated there only recently, replacing Neanderthals. The RTB model, likewise, views Neanderthals as distinct from humans. It predicts that the peopling of Europe occurred during humanity's relatively recent spread from the Middle East to the rest of the world.

Fossil evidence

The human fossil record in Europe is sparse (as is the case for all regions of the world). The first undisputed human remains there date no older than 36,000 to 40,000 years in age.[6] The scanty fossil record tentatively attests that the first humans appeared on the European continent about that time.

Archeological evidence

The much more abundant archeological record generally agrees with the fossil record. The first archeological sites attributed to humans (assigned to the Aurignacian culture) date back no more than 40,000 years in age.[7] By association, this date implies the likelihood that the first humans did not appear in Europe until then.

Genetic evidence

The morphological differences between humans and Neanderthals (discerned from the fossil record), and the dramatic differences between Neanderthal and human behavior (inferred from archeological remains), suggest that humans did *not* evolve from these hominids. (Chapters 5 and 12 discuss this evidence in detail.) But, for some researchers, this data by itself lacks conclusiveness. It has been inadequate to settle the controversy between multiregionalists and out-of-Africa proponents. However, recent genetic studies provide fresh clues about the origin of the first Europeans that may help resolve the conflict.

Molecular anthropologists can now use both mtDNA and Y-chromosomal DNA analyses to characterize European origins. So far, all genetic markers found among European people groups trace back to recent eastern African (Ethiopian) populations, located near the Middle East.[8]

As mentioned previously, the mtDNA fingerprint of people currently living outside Africa is a subset of African mtDNA sequences (haplotypes). All non-African haplotypes appear to descend from two, designated as M and N. The M haplotypes are typically found in Asia. N haplotypes occur primarily in western Asia and Europe.[9] Molecular clock analysis places the origin of the M and N lineages at 52,000 years ago ($\pm$ 27,000 years).[10] (The uncertainties associated with dates derived from all molecular clock analysis, and specifically mtDNA analysis, are discussed in chapter 4 on pages 67–69.)

Genetic analysis also connects European Y chromosomes (and all others outside Africa) to a subset of African DNA sequences.[11] The high level of genetic resolution characteristic of Y-chromosomal data affords molecular anthropologists a more detailed description of the possible route the first humans took when they populated Europe. Two of the three dominant Y-chromosomal haplotypes in Europe ($M173$ and $M17$) appear to have originated from the $M45$ haplotype.

The $M45$ haplotype occurs at a high frequency among people groups from central Asia and in turn appears to descend from the $M89$ haplotype found in the Middle East. These characteristics reveal that the first humans took a roundabout journey from the Middle East to Europe through central Asia. Molecular clock analysis places the origin of $M173$ at about 30,000 years ago.[12]

The third most prominent Y-chromosomal haplotype in Europe ($M172$) first appears about 10,000 years ago. This haplotype seems to descend from $M89$ (the Middle East) and most likely represents human migrations that took place when agriculture spread from the Middle East into Europe.[13]

The genetic evidence indirectly indicates that the first Europeans did not arise from Neanderthals. Rather, these people trace their ancestry to the first humans in East Africa. From there, people appear to have migrated through the Middle East into Asia and then into Europe.

In recent years, anthropologists have successfully recovered mitochondrial DNA from Neanderthal remains. In comparing this astonishing piece of evidence with human mitochondrial DNA, scientists acquired direct information about the genetic relationship between Neanderthals and the first humans in Europe. Chapter 12 discusses these studies and further probes the relationship between Neanderthals and humans.

Asia

Among anthropologists, the question of how humanity wound up in Asia has been a contentious one. Those who hold to the multiregional hypothesis believe modern Asians are indigenous to that region. Proponents of this theory maintain that Asian and Oceanic human beings evolved from archaic *H. sapiens*, which in turn arose from *Homo erectus*. People who favor the out-of-Africa hypothesis, however, assert that the first Asian dwellers descended from the first modern humans and only recently (within the last 50,000 to 70,000 years) migrated into that region. They think the hominids that previously lived there made no evolutionary contribution to humanity and went extinct before the first modern humans appeared.

Traditionally, anthropologists have turned to the fossil and archeological records to unravel this controversy—without much success. Recent comparative genetic studies on Asian and African population groups, however, provide the solution to one of anthropology's most intriguing puzzles.

Fossil evidence

Paleoanthropologists have discovered several sites in China that contain human remains. A few of these sites have been dated to 67,000 years ago. Anthropologists widely consider these as controversial estimates. In reality, the sites are likely no older than 30,000 to 40,000 years.[14] The oldest human fossils in Japan date 17,000 years old.[15] Anthropologists Li Jin and Bing Su recently surveyed the hominid fossil record in China and discovered that a 60,000- to 70,000-year gap exists between the last appearance of archaic *H. sapiens* (about 100,000 years ago) and the first appearance of human beings (about 30,000 to 40,000 years ago).[16]

Archeological evidence
Once humans entered Asia, they must have spread quickly. Approximately 20 sites have been discovered in East Asia that date older than 30,000 years in age. None is older than 40,000 years.[17]

One piece of dramatic evidence for rapid movement comes from the Yana archeological site in the Siberian Arctic, at the mouth of the Yana River where it empties into the Laptev Sea. Artifacts from this site indicate that people lived there as far back as 27,000 years ago.[18] Prior to the discovery of the Yana site, anthropologists did not think humans lived in the Siberian Arctic until about 13,000 to 14,000 years ago. The Yana site not only suggests rapid human migration throughout Asia but also indirectly reflects the sophisticated technology and advanced cognitive ability required to survive the harsh conditions of the Siberian Arctic.

Genetic evidence
Molecular anthropologists use both mtDNA and Y-chromosomal DNA analyses to characterize the Asian origin of humanity. To date, all genetic markers found among Asian clans trace back to East African populations, located near the Middle East.[19] The genetic evidence indirectly indicates that modern humans did not arise independently in East Asia from earlier existing hominids.[20]

Mitochondrial-DNA variants (designated as haplotypes *C, D, E,* and *G*) occur widely in population groups with historical connections to South and East Asia as well as the Americas. These haplotypes descended from *M*, one of the mtDNA variants found in East African populations.[21] Mitochondrial-DNA molecular clock analysis has been used to date the origin of the *M* haplotype at between 25,000 and 80,000 years ago.[22]

Y-chromosomal analysis tells a story that closely aligns with the mtDNA data.[23] Two prominent Y-chromosomal haplotypes found in East Asia (*C* and *D*) descend from the *M*168 haplotype. This haplotype originated in East

Africa, near the Middle East. Molecular clock studies variously date the start of *M*168 at 31,000 to 79,000; 56,000 to 81,000; and 36,000 to 109,000 years ago, respectively.[24]

Genetic data also trace the route early humans took on the way to Asia. These migrants appear to have traveled along the southern coast of Asia and turned north. Some continued the coastal migration into Indonesia.[25]

While the fossil and archeological evidence fails to discriminate among the models that attempt to account for the lineage of people in Asia, the genetic data appears to indicate that the multiregional hypothesis cannot be correct. (Chapter 11 discusses the relationship between the hominids of East Asia and the first humans in more detail.) Collectively, the evidence indicates that people populated Asia by rapidly migrating there from a location near the Middle East. Based on the fossil and archeological evidence, Asia's first human inhabitants reached their destination about 30,000 to 40,000 years ago.

Australia

Anthropologists interested in the peopling of Australia are also entrenched in controversy. Scientists are unsure of when this continent became inhabited, how many migrations were necessary to populate it, and the source of the migrants.

Fossil evidence

Paleoanthropologists identify the LM3 remains, recovered at the dried Lake Mungo site, as the oldest human fossils in Australia. The luminescence method dates the LM3 specimens as 62,000 years old.[26] Given the notorious inaccuracy of this technique, the number must be considered as an upper age limit only (see "Luminescence Dating Methods" on page 85). Subsequent re-dating of these remains (again using the luminescence method) variously renders the LM3 fossils to be about 30,000 or 40,000 years in age.[27] The LM1 fossils from the Lake Mungo site date between 17,000 and 26,000 years in age, based on radiocarbon dating.[28] Luminescence dating of these LM1 specimens places their age at around 40,000 years.[29] Given the accuracy of radiocarbon dating, this measurement provides a helpful calibration of the luminescence dates for the LM3 specimens.

At another important fossil site, Kow Swamp, human fossils date about 12,000 years in age.[30] Some anthropologists consider these fossils to be more robust than those from Lake Mungo, which appear gracile (small and slender). Based on physical differences, scientists argue that Australia was populated by two separate migrations reflected in the contrasting makeup of the Kow Swamp and Lake Mungo fossils.[31] Other anthropologists dispute this interpretation. Rather, they insist that Australia was inhabited by a single migrational event.

Archeological evidence

Traditionally, anthropologists have regarded the oldest archeological sites in Australia to be Malakunanja, Nauwalabila, and Jinmium. The first luminescence dating efforts placed the age of these sites at about 60,000 years.[32] (A few luminescence measurements indicated the age of Jinmium as 176,000 years.) For some time, anthropologists have considered these dates controversial. One reason is that the oldest archeological site in New Guinea dates no older than 40,000 years in age.[33] Given its geographical location, this New Guinean area should have been occupied by humans earlier than any of the Australian sites.

Recent studies indicate that the dates for these sites are inaccurate. For example, radiocarbon measurements date charcoal at Jinmium between 1,000 and 3,000 years in age.[34] In fact, no radiocarbon testing of sites in Australia yields dates older than 40,000 years.

Genetic evidence

Genetic studies provide insight into the origin of the first Australians. A recent look at Y-chromosomal DNA from 12,000 individuals shows conclusively that indigenous Australian people (as well as Asian and Oceanic groups) share a genetic connection with African populations. Molecular clock analysis indicates that African, Asian, and Oceanic people diverged from a common ancestor sometime between 35,000 and 89,000 years ago.[35] Mitochondrial-DNA analyses date the origin of native Australians to between 51,000 and 85,000 years ago and date the coalescence of these aboriginal populations with others outside Australia between 60,000 and 119,000 years ago.[36]

Y-chromosomal studies also suggest the route these ancestors took as they migrated from Africa into Australia. An unusual Y-chromosomal variant (designated haplotype *M*130) occurs at a noticeable frequency (over 60 percent) among aboriginal people. The *M*130 haplotype occurs at a 15 percent frequency in New Guinea populations, at a 10 percent frequency among Malaysians, and at a 5 percent frequency among Indian people groups. This haplotype is not found in any other population. The *M*130 haplotype descended from another haplotype (designated *M*168) that traces back to "Y-chromosomal Adam" and has its origin in East Africa, near the Middle East.[37] Based on this pattern, anthropologists think the first Australian inhabitants consisted of a genetically homogeneous group that followed the southern coast of Asia as they traveled to Australia.

Abundant food sources along the coast and moderate temperatures allowed these migrants to travel rapidly. If their society moved an average of just over 10 miles per year, anthropologists estimate that the journey could have been completed in less than 1,000 years. Anthropologist Spencer Wells refers to this migratory route as a "coastal superhighway."[38]

Some mtDNA research confirms this pathway.[39] One study detected a rare mtDNA haplotype among native Australian people. Though nonexistent in the Middle East and Europe, this haplotype occurs at a 20 percent frequency in India and at a 100 percent frequency among the aboriginal people of Australia. This unusual haplotype traces back to "mitochondrial Eve" through another haplotype ($L3$) that originated in East Africa, near the Middle East. Such a pattern of genetic diversity makes sense only if humans made their way along the South Asian coast.

Other mtDNA researchers see a different picture for the habitation of Australia. Their view is that Australia was colonized multiple times by different people groups between 40,000 and 70,000 years ago.[40] Alternatively, this research could indicate that a heterogeneous collection of people migrated into Australia from Asia during one time period.

Geological considerations
During the last ice age, Australia, New Guinea, and Tasmania comprised a large continental landmass called Sahul. In spite of the much lower sea levels at that time, a strait more than 50 miles wide separated Sahul from Asia.[41] The first inhabitants of Australia, New Guinea, and Tasmania must have built seaworthy vessels to migrate to Sahul from Asia. In fact, some anthropologists suggest that the first Australians took eight separate sea voyages from island to island to complete their journey.[42] The ability to build seaworthy vessels and navigate them across a stretch of open ocean provides indirect evidence that the first humans to enter Australia possessed relatively sophisticated technology and advanced cognitive ability.

Anthropologists have a long way to go to develop a consistent picture of the peopling of Australia. Taken collectively, the evidence indicates that humans began to inhabit Australia about 30,000 to 40,000 years ago. Dates for earlier occupation are based on luminescence techniques that typically overestimate the age of fossil specimens and artifacts. The genetic evidence suggests the intriguing possibility that the first human occupants rapidly migrated along the southern coast of Asia from near the Middle East to Australia. The last leg of the journey required them to possess the technological know-how to survive a sea voyage. Genetic evidence, however, leaves open the possibility that the first inhabitants migrated from Asia into Australia at several different times.

The Americas

One of the most intriguing research goals in contemporary anthropology is to decipher how and when humans came to North and South America. Anthropologists generally agree that the first human groups to populate the Americas came from Asia. They likely crossed the Bering Strait into North America.[43] Beyond this agreement, however, controversy swirls around the timing, the number, and the patterns of human migration.

Fossil evidence

The oldest human fossils recovered in North and South America date to between 13,500 and 9,500 years old.[44] Unfortunately, anthropologists have only scarce and fragmentary remains to study. Some of the best-known human fossils include: (1) the "Luzia" find (recovered from Minas Gerais, Brazil), indirectly dated as 13,500 years old; (2) the Buhl woman (found in Buhl, Idaho), which directly dates as 12,900 years in age; (3) the Prince of Wales Island man (discovered near the coast of Prince of Wales Island, Alaska), directly dated as 11,000 years old; and (4) the Spirit Cave man (recovered from a rock shelter in Nevada), directly dated to 10,600 years old.

These and other fossils record that human beings occupied the Americas at least 13,000 years ago. They don't necessarily indicate, however, that the Americas were populated via a single mass migration. Most anthropologists theorize that the colonization of North and South America was a complex undertaking. Some assume Native Americans descended from people who migrated from northeast Asia in one great surge. Others assert that northeast Asian peoples entered the Americas in three migratory waves, with Native Americans collectively representing the descendants of all three immigrations.[45]

A recent anatomical study suggests that the peopling of the Americas was considerably more complicated. Anthropologists from Mexico and Spain analyzed 33 human skulls (recovered from the Baja California peninsula) that date between 2,800 and 300 years old. The anatomical features of these remains show stronger affinity to the ancient human remains recovered in the Americas (Paleoamericans) than to modern Native Americans.[46]

Presumably, these 33 individuals represent descendants of the earliest

Paleoamericans. The scientists' data suggests that Native Americans have no genetic connection to these first inhabitants of the Americas. Based on this study and others, it appears that two separate people groups colonized the Americas. One group likely shared ancestry with the first Australian people. They migrated from the southern Pacific Rim. These people were the Paleo-americans who ultimately left no currently living descendants in the Americas. The second group migrated from northeast Asia and gave rise to modern-day Native Americans.

Mammal fossils also provide information about the timing of human migrations to the Americas. Upon arrival in North America, the first people encountered elk, yaks, bison, lions, mammoths, mastodons, and giant ground sloths. The fossil record indicates that within a thousand-year span from 11,500 to 10,500 years ago, many of these mammals disappeared. The first inhabitants might have hunted them to extinction.[47]

Archeological evidence
Numerous sites throughout North America indicate that humans, specifically the Clovis culture, inhabited the New World by about 13,500 years ago.[48] By about 12,000 years ago, other civilizations (such as the Folsom) began to appear. The Clovis and Folsom societies were confined to North America. In South America, distinct cultures also existed.

Some anthropologists think that the people who produced the Clovis culture were the earliest immigrants to North America.[49] Other scientists claim these people weren't the first. Evidence for pre-Clovis people is still tenuous and highly controversial. Almost all archeological locations historically assigned to pre-Clovis time frames prove younger than the oldest Clovis areas when carefully reevaluated.[50] However, a growing number of recently discovered pre-Clovis sites appear authentic.

These sites (dating at least 1,000 years older than the most ancient Clovis finds) have been discovered in South Carolina, Alaska's Yukon, Brazil, Chile, and Venezuela.[51] The Meadowcroft site in Pennsylvania dates to nearly 22,000 years ago. Another site near Richmond, Virginia, dates to about 18,000 years in age. Controversy still surrounds the dates for these locations, but the collective weight of evidence suggests the possible existence of pre-Clovis people.

Linguistic evidence
Some anthropologists think the languages spoken by Native Americans hold clues to the timing and pattern of their migration into the Americas.[52]

Linguists identify three families of languages spoken by Native Americans: Amerind, Na-Dene, and Eskimo-Aleut. Each is believed to represent a separate migration into the Americas. Using a technique called glottochronology, linguists can estimate the divergence times of different language groups from a common source. According to this approach, Amerind branched off about 11,000 years ago, Na-Dene about 9,000 years ago, and Eskimo-Aleut about 4,000 years ago. Presumably, these divergent times roughly correspond to the time of migrations into the Americas. (Those who hold this position maintain that Native Americans of today are descended from these three migrations.)

Genetic evidence

Molecular anthropologists also study the genetic makeup of Native American peoples in an attempt to characterize their origins. Much controversy surrounds these studies because extensive genetic mixing has occurred among Native Americans. Further, some genetic mixing has occurred between Native Americans and the European and African immigrants to the New World.[53]

However, Native American people display much lower genetic diversity than any other human population group. This conformity suggests that Native American groups are relatively young. They must have experienced a genetic bottleneck when a small population subset migrated from Asia into the Americas.[54]

Early genetic studies relied on classic markers and showed a close connection between Native Americans and Asian people groups. These markers typically yield two clusters that correspond to Arctic people groups and North and South American populations, respectively. These clusters tend to align with linguistic groupings, and their existence supports the idea of three separate migrations into the Americas.[55]

More recent work focuses on mitochondrial DNA. Researchers recognize five mtDNA variants (haplotypes A, B, C, D, and X) among Native Americans. Three of these haplotypes trace to Siberia and East Asia; one traces to southeastern Asia; and one haplotype (X), which occurs at an extremely low frequency (less than 3 percent), originates in Europe.[56] Mitochondrial-DNA molecular clock estimates for the divergence time of Native American populations (from their most recent common ancestor) range from 37,000 years ago to 12,000 years ago. This timing depends on the specifics of the analysis and the particular haplotype studied.[57]

Scientists vigorously debate the proper interpretation of these mtDNA findings. Some molecular anthropologists argue that the Amerind groups entered North America in two separate waves between 34,000 and 26,000 years ago, and between 15,000 and 12,000 years ago, respectively. These scientists also think the Na-Dene people were the last of the original migrants to the Americas (between 10,000 and 7,000 years ago).[58] Challengers to this interpretation maintain that the mtDNA data reveals a single migration into the Americas followed by differentiation into separate population groups.[59]

Molecular anthropologists are also focusing attention on the variation of Y-chromosomal DNA in an attempt to understand the peopling of the Americas. Several Y-chromosomal haplotypes (unique to Native American populations) have been discovered. These haplotypes trace to people with a historical connection to the eastern and southern regions of Siberia.[60]

The Y-chromosomal DNA data can be interpreted two ways. To some researchers, studies suggest that only a single migration into the Americas happened sometime between 20,000 and 10,000 years ago.[61] To others, the Y chromosomes of Native Americans reveal a second movement into the Americas that took place after the initial migration.[62]

Geological considerations

Between 75,000 and 10,000 years ago, Earth experienced an ice age that locked up large quantities of water at the polar caps and in massive continental ice sheets. During this same era, the Bering Land Bridge connected Asia to North America.[63] For most of this time, conditions on the Bering Land Bridge were likely too harsh for human habitation and migration. However, between 14,000 and 11,000 years ago, the temperatures apparently warmed enough to permit human passage.[64]

Scientists debate the route taken by the first human inhabitants of the New World *after* they crossed the Bering Land Bridge. Until recently, most anthropologists agreed that the first migrants worked their way through an ice-free corridor linking the Alaskan and Canadian Yukon with the rest of North America. During this time, massive ice sheets buried much of what are now Canada and the northern United States. Periodically, however, an ice-free corridor is thought to have opened between the Cordilleran and Laurentide Ice Sheets.[65]

Some anthropologists now dispute this model. They think the first humans in the Americas migrated southward along the Pacific coastline. This route would explain the rapid habitation of South America, once people reached the New World.[66]

When did the first humans inhabit the Americas? Where did they come from? These questions still have no clear-cut answers, and much work needs to be done before they finally come. Yet, when considered in its entirety, the evidence seems to favor the view that the first Americans came from both northeast and southern Asia roughly 15,000 to 12,000 years ago. They arrived in two, or possibly three, migrational waves. Once in the New World, the first inhabitants quickly spread to occupy all of the Americas.

An Emerging Model

Collectively, the fossil, genetic, geological, and archeological evidence indicates that people groups with historical connections to different regions of the world just recently (within the last 40,000 to 30,000 years) arrived in these locations. Their ultimate origin traces to contemporary East African populations, with the Middle East as the likely starting point of migrations that took early humans to Europe, Asia, Australia, and the Americas. (Recent work on human parasite genetics confirms this conclusion—see "Parasites Track Human Migrations" on page 141.) Within the evolutionary context, this description of early human history squares with the out-of-Africa model and leaves the traditional multiregional hypothesis with little, if any, evidential basis. Chapters 11 and 12 discuss additional challenges that confront the multiregional hypothesis.

While the scientific evidence makes the out-of-Africa hypothesis compelling, it fits awkwardly within the traditional human evolutionary framework. (The uncomfortable fit is discussed in chapter 4.) Acceptance of the out-of-Africa hypothesis requires rejection of the multiregional hypothesis, long regarded as the best evolutionary explanation for humanity's origin. Instead of evolving over 2 million years, humans originated recently. The multiregional hypothesis readily accommodates the hominids of Africa, Europe, and Asia as part of the human evolutionary framework. However, the out-of-Africa model finds no place for them. Instead of Africans, Europeans, and Asians evolving from hominids indigenous to these regions, the out-of-Africa model has no place for the archaic *H. sapiens* of Europe and Asia (see chapter 2).

"Such Was the Process"

The pattern and the timing of early human migrations fully harmonize with the RTB creation model and its prediction that humanity spread around the world from (or from near) the Middle East. The migratory pathways of the first humans, though still somewhat vague, fit well within the biblical account of human origins and dispersion.

Migrations occurred with astonishing rapidity. Between 40,000 and 30,000 years ago, humans moved simultaneously from near the Middle East into

Parasites Track Human Migrations

Molecular anthropologists gain insight into early human history from examining the genetic variation of human parasites. An intimate association with humans allows these pests to serve as genetic stand-ins for studying human population groups. Researchers believe the timing and location of origin, as well as the spread of these parasites around the world, mirror the timing, location, and spread of humanity. Molecular anthropologists use worldwide genetic variation of these infectious agents in the same way as they use human genetic variation to understand early human biogeography.

Genetic studies on worldwide populations of the malaria parasite (*Plasmodium falciparum*), the bacterium that causes ulcers (*Helicobacter pylori*), the JC polyomavirus, and body lice (*Pediculus humanus*) all indicate a relatively recent origin of humanity (no more than 100,000 years ago) in a single location in Africa, near the Middle East (see pages 74–77). These parasite studies also indicate that humanity migrated from the Middle East into Europe and Asia, and from Asia into the Americas in a pattern consistent with the predictions made by the RTB model.[67]

Europe, Asia, and even Australia. This quick spread of humankind has no compelling explanation within the evolutionary framework. On the other hand, the RTB creation model anticipates and explains the rapid movement of humanity around the world. Genesis 11:9 says that "the Lord scattered [human beings] over the face of the whole earth." This passage states that humanity spread from the Middle East in a hurry, motivated by a divine impetus.

Looking back over highlights in the ongoing quest for an understanding of human origins, an increasingly plausible fit can be seen. According to both the scientific data and the biblical account, humanity had a recent origin (less than 100,000 years ago) in a single location (which corresponds to the Garden of Eden) from a small original population. Humanity's genetic fingerprint traces back to a single man and a single woman. At around 40,000 years ago, the archeological record reveals a sociocultural explosion. This "big bang" of human culture consists of new behaviors that can be taken to reflect God's image. As discussed in this chapter, the people groups scattered around the world trace their ultimate origin to one time and place, one human pair. People came only recently (within the last 40,000 to 30,000 years) to Europe, Asia, and Australia—still more recently to the Americas.

The timing of humanity's appearance precisely coincides with several astronomical and geological time windows that render Earth's environment particularly suitable for human civilization. Furthermore, advances in the biochemistry of aging, along with astronomical discoveries regarding recent supernova events, lend credence to the long life spans mentioned in Genesis.

These findings also resonate with the out-of-Africa hypothesis. Though an awkward fit in the evolutionary framework, the out-of-Africa hypothesis does provide a general accounting for the data. The big question is which model *best* explains humanity's origin?

One way to discriminate between the RTB and out-of-Africa models is to assess the validity of human evolution. If abundant evidence for human evolution exists, then the out-of-Africa hypothesis gains support. However, if scientific testing renders human evolution untenable, the RTB model becomes the preferred explanation. The following six chapters critically evaluate the evidence for human evolution. The next chapter begins this process by asking, is human evolution a fact?

Chapter 9

Is Human Evolution a Fact?

O, there be players that I
Have seen play—and heard others praise, and that
Highly—not to speak it profanely,
That neither having th'
Accent of Christians nor the
Gait of Christian, pagan, nor
Man, have so strutted
And bellow'd that I have
Thought some of Nature's journeymen
Had made men, and not made
Them well, they imitated humanity
So abominably.
—*Hamlet* Act 3, scene 2

The morning bell rings and high school students jostle their way into Ms. Henderson's classroom. The biology teacher greets them as they settle into their seats and then announces that today the class will begin a new unit on evolution.

A collective groan rises from the students as they take out their notebooks and pick up their pens. Ms. Henderson instructs the class to open their textbooks. Even before she begins to lecture, several students start to murmur. Michael blurts out the question on their minds, "Isn't evolution just a theory?"

Michael hopes to cast doubt on the details to be discussed in the coming weeks. He knows many biologists present the theory of evolution as a well-established fact. Michael also knows that common usage of the word "theory" indicates speculation based on a hypothetical set of circumstances.

Biology teachers and evolutionary biologists are frequently confronted with this objection to evolution. Paleontologist Niles Eldredge responds to the challenge by pointing out that,

> The common expression "evolutionary theory" actually refers to two
> rather different sets of ideas: (1) the notion that absolutely all organ-
> isms living on the face of the Earth right now are descended from
> a single common ancestor, and (2) ideas of *how* the evolutionary
> process works.... Creationists love to gloss over this rather clear-cut,
> simple distinction between the idea that (1) life has evolved, and the
> sets of ideas on (2) how the evolutionary process actually works.[1]

In other words, Eldredge and other evolutionary biologists maintain that
the idea of evolution is both a fact and a theory. *That* it occurred is the fact.
How it occurred is the theory. These biologists actively debate evolution's
mechanism, but they insist the debate doesn't mean that the fact of evolution
is uncertain.

Evolutionary biologists base their claim on two main lines of evidence:
shared anatomical features and the fossil record. Common features permit organisms to be grouped into nested clusters or hierarchies. Evolutionists take
this pattern to indicate that life descended with modification from a common
ancestor—in other words, life evolved. The fossil record shows that different
life-forms existed on Earth at different times in history and reveals a progression from simple to complex organisms.[2]

But does this evidence necessarily compel the conclusion that evolution
just naturally happened? From the day-age creationist perspective (associated
with the Reasons to Believe [RTB] model), the nested clusters could just as
easily reflect the handiwork of a Creator who chose to employ a common blue-
print and reuse many of the same design elements.

The fossil record also finds ready explanation from a day-age vantage
point. As indicated in the Genesis 1 and Psalm 104 creation accounts, the Creator transformed the planet and brought life into existence in a purposefully
progressive fashion. This act includes the creation of different life-forms at different eras in Earth's history.

If even one other model can logically account for the patterns observed
among living organisms and for the data from the fossil record, why does the
scientific community continue to defend evolution as a fact instead of a theory?

Phillip Johnson, one of the leaders of the intelligent design movement,
argues that the contemporary scientific enterprise is inextricably intertwined
with the philosophical position called naturalism.[3] According to this system of
thought, reality consists only of the physical, material universe. Nothing ex-

ists beyond the universe. In other words, naturalism rejects the possibility of the supernatural and miracles. This idea requires that science must explain the universe and all phenomena within it exclusively through a naturalistic framework.

This restrictive realm of natural cause-and-effect processes insists that the fossil record (which shows different life-forms at different eras) must be interpreted within the context of naturalism—life being transformed from one form into another. The philosophical assumptions of contemporary science *force* the fact of evolution. The evidence is irrelevant. The idea of natural-process evolution must be true because the philosophy of naturalism, by definition, excludes supernatural explanations. No other choices are permitted for philosophical reasons.

Alternate perspectives, however, allow for the possibility of evolution but also keep open the idea that supernatural involvement may account for the features of life and aspects of its natural history. For scientists to establish evolution as a certainty within this broader context, the theory must withstand the rigors of testing. Within a framework that allows for supernatural causes, the idea that evolution occurred remains (like all scientific ideas) provisional. It must be evaluated with each new discovery and in juxtaposition to alternative theories.

"Not to Speak It Profanely"

The hominid fossil record provides the chief means to determine whether or not humans evolved. In one sense, the debate among scientists about evolution's mechanism is immaterial. To establish evolution's validity, workable mechanisms that could bring about the biological transformations required by the theory must be identified. However, it's not necessary to identify and evaluate the plausibility of each mechanism. The tenets of human evolution can be evaluated in a strictly empirical fashion from the fossil record alone. The hominid fossil record acts as a proxy for the natural history of these primates. If indeed humanity evolved from an apelike ancestor, the fossil record must display telltale patterns and features.

To uphold the theory, the hominid fossil record should be rooted in a single knuckle-walking apelike primate that existed between 6 and 5 million years ago. Over time, a variety of hominids should appear in a branching, treelike pattern from this ancestral form, and a clear evolutionary pathway from this supposed ancestor to modern humans should be evident.

Hominid fossils should also document the gradual emergence of the

A Presumed Connection

For human evolution to be declared a fact transitional forms that link the apelike ancestor to modern humans should be found in the fossil record. Do the hominids represent these necessary transitional intermediates? To answer this question, one must first understand what evolutionists mean when they use the term "transitional intermediate."

Most people understand this term to refer to a progression of organisms that represent the evolutionary transition of one species (or higher biological groups) into another. That is, transitional intermediates should progressively link one organism to another.

Sometimes evolutionary biologists refer to the entire collection of organisms between two time points in the fossil record as transitional intermediates. Implicit in this reference is the assumption that evolution must be true. When evolutionary biologists have no real understanding of the precise evolutionary pathway that connects two organisms, they remain convinced that one must exist and that it will be uncovered in the organisms that intervene between two time points. Hence, they deem all the organisms that exist between two time points in the fossil record as transitional forms, whether or not these organisms actually define the progressive transition from one organism into another.

When paleoanthropologists refer to various hominids as "transitional intermediates," they use this term in the latter sense, not the former. In other words, paleoanthropologists have no real knowledge of evolution's path from an apelike ancestor to modern humans. They assume, though, that one must exist among the hominids in the fossil record. The hominids don't necessarily link an apelike ancestor to modern humans in a progressive transformation, but rather they exist as organisms between the two time points—roughly 6 to 5 million years ago and the current era.

anatomical and behavioral traits that define humanity, such as large brain size, advanced culture, and the ability to walk erect. Furthermore, transitional forms that connect australopithecines to primitive *Homo* specimens, and then connect these to modern humans, should be readily discerned in the fossil record (see chapter 2 and "A Presumed Connection"). If these broad requirements cannot be met, then human evolution *cannot* be declared a fact. Other human origin models should be entertained.

The RTB model also yields predictions about the features of the hominid fossil record. This model views the hominids in the fossil record as animals, created by God, that later went extinct. If this concept is correct, then it reasonably follows that hominids should appear suddenly on Earth (and consequently in the fossil record). Once created, these animals should have experienced little if any evolutionary change, and the fossil record should show evidence of such stasis.

This chapter describes the efforts of paleoanthropologists to locate the common ancestor of the hominid and great ape lineages and the attempts to define the evolutionary pathways that purportedly led from this ancestral form to modern humans. Chapter 10 examines what the hominid fossil record reveals about the origin of two of humanity's defining characteristics: the ability to walk erect and large brain size. Chapters 11 and 12 discuss the current evolutionary status of *Homo erectus* and Neanderthals, key transitional forms in many evolutionary scenarios. Before moving into these discussions, however, it's important to understand the features of the hominid fossil record and how they impact paleoanthropologists' ability to establish the "fact" of human evolution.

"They Imitated Humanity So Abominably"
The same adage that applies to computers also applies to science: garbage in, garbage out. No matter how powerful the computer or how sophisticated the software questionable input leads to suspect output. In the same way, scientific conclusions are only as sound as the quality of information used to derive them. If researchers have poor-quality data, then any conclusion drawn from them will be speculative at best.

When most people think of hominid fossils, they picture nearly complete skeletal remains. Popular presentations almost always feature the "Turkana boy" specimen (more than 90 percent complete) or "Lucy" (a nearly 40 percent complete postcranial skeleton). Yet these specimens are highly unusual. Most hominid fossil discoveries consist of partial crania, partial jaws, isolated teeth, and occasionally isolated limb fragments.[4] Paleoanthropologists rarely find a complete cranium, let alone an entire skeleton. Moreover, very few hominid species have extensive representation in the fossil record. In most cases, a limited number of fragmentary fossil finds and a handful of specimens define a species.

Without a large number of specimens, paleoanthropologists can't accurately decipher the range of morphological variation that occurs within a population or across geography and time. Without this knowledge, it's uncertain whether hominids with morphological differences from two time periods in the geological column represent two distinct species with an evolutionary connection or the range of variation within a particular species.

Highly publicized work by Kent State University (KSU) scientists illustrates how the failure to account for a species' biological variation can mislead. This KSU study examined the sexual dimorphism of *Australopithecus afarensis*. ("Sexual dimorphism" describes size differences between the males and females of a species.) Anthropologists find this characteristic interesting because it provides insight into hominid reproductive behavior and social structure.[5]

Traditionally, paleoanthropologists reported *A. afarensis* as displaying significant sexual dimorphism.[6] This declaration was based, however, on body mass estimates from only a few specimens. According to the KSU paleoanthropologists, the dimorphism claim (taken by many as orthodoxy) remained unproven since it had not "adequately compensated for the effects of temporal and geographic variation as opposed to normative population-level dimorphism."[7]

The KSU scientists reexamined the sexual dimorphism in *A. afarensis* from a site dated at 3.2 million years old. This find consisted of several *A. afarensis* individuals that suffered simultaneous death and burial. While less than ideal, the site provided a truer indication of the biological variation within this species. The results showed that the sexual dimorphism for *A. afarensis* was no greater than that in modern humans.[8]

While this high-profile study focused on *A. afarensis* biology rather than evolutionary status, the results emphasize how crucial it is for paleoanthropologists to understand the extent of biological variation within each hominid species. Lack of understanding or misperceptions along these lines can lead to wildly incorrect conclusions.

Not only do paleoanthropologists have a limited number of fossil specimens to study, often the hominid remains were crushed or shattered prior to fossilization and further deformed by geological processes. These limitations make proper analysis of the hominid fossil record difficult.

The discovery of the hominid *Kenyanthropus platyops*, along with attempts to place it in hominid evolutionary trees, illustrates the potential pitfalls caused by deformed fossils. In the spring of 2001, paleoanthropologist Meave Leakey and her associates reported finding a 3.5-million-year-old cranium in the Lake Turkana region of Kenya. This hominid fossil displayed an unusually flat face compared to the faces of australopithecines.[9] Given its unusual features, Leakey placed the hominid in a new genus, *Kenyanthropus*, and this particular creature was classified as *K. platyops*. The hominid *Homo rudolfensis* was reclassified as

K. rudolfensis as a result.

Because hominids with facial features similar to *K. platyops* don't appear in the fossil record until about 2 million years ago, Leakey argued that they represent a previously unrecognized branch in the hominid evolutionary tree. Even more importantly, Leakey maintains that, because of its flat face, *Kenyanthropus* (not the australopithecines) more likely gave rise to the *Homo* genus.[10] This find may overturn seemingly well-established ideas about human evolution. According to Leakey, the australopithecines—long regarded as the evolutionary predecessors to the *Homo* genus and ultimately to modern humans—may actually be an evolutionary side branch and dead end.

In the midst of this excitement, paleoanthropologist Tim White has asserted that *Kenyanthropus* is an illegitimate genus. He argues that *K. platyops* represents an *A. afarensis* specimen. According to White, *Kenyanthropus*' flat face is a distortion caused by geological processes. White thinks that fine-grained rock entered into cracks in the skull, distorting facial features.[11]

Other paleoanthropologists disagree. They maintain that *Kenyanthropus* is a true genus and that its flat face is a real biological feature.[12]

Controversy will likely surround *Kenyanthropus*' status for some time. The important point is that distortions and deformations of hominid fossils obscure paleoanthropologists' ability to construct accurate evolutionary trees. Implications are enormous for human evolutionary scenarios. (See chapter 10 for further discussion on the effects of distorted fossil features on hominid brain-size measurements.)

Lump Them Together or Split the Difference?

The limited number of fossils, pervasive problems of damaged and distorted and incomplete features, and paleoanthropologists' lack of understanding about hominids' intraspecies biological variation cause another problem. It's impossible to know how many hominid species actually existed. While this kind of challenge confronts all paleontologists, it's particularly acute for those studying the hominid fossil record. Without a solid understanding of the number of hominid species, it's impossible to define evolutionary relationships among them and map out the pathway that led to modern humans with any level of confidence.

A long-standing philosophical debate among paleoanthropologists further exacerbates the problem of determining the number of hominid species. This controversy is called the "lumpers" versus "splitters" debate. The issues center on whether subtle morphological differences displayed by the various hominid fossils indicate biological variation within a species (*intra*specific) or variation between species (*inter*specific).[13] Lumpers tend to regard morphological differences as insignificant. Splitters use even the smallest anatomical differences as the basis to classify hominid fossils as distinct species.

In the 1950s, most paleoanthropologists were splitters. This approach changed during the 1960s and 1970s, when the lumper perspective became dominant. The pendulum now swings back toward the splitter position.[14] As a result, the number of hominid species in the fossil record can artificially expand or contract, depending on the paradigm of the day or a particular paleoanthropologist's viewpoint. When a splitter reports on a new fossil find, he or she likely classifies it as a new species or even a new genus. If a lumper makes the same discovery, the fossil is likely assigned to an already existing taxon (a biological group, such as species or genus).

The controversies at the cutting edge of paleoanthropology are often philosophical and methodological rather than scientific. The lumper-splitter debate ultimately undermines confidence in the evolutionary scenarios advanced to explain human origins. When philosophical issues define a controversy, additional research usually can't bring resolution.

The lumper-splitter debate has now extended to the genus level. Over the last several years, hominids that date to between 7 and 3.5 million years of age have been discovered and assigned to new genera: *Ardipithecus, Kenyanthropus, Orrorin,* and *Sahelanthropus.* These four categories add to the two well-established genera, *Australopithecus* and *Homo,* and the sometimes-disputed genus *Paranthropus.* Evolutionary biologist Francisco Ayala recently argued that the creation of these four new genera is not justified. He proposed a novel classification scheme for the hominids.[15]

Ayala replaces the current seven genera with four others: (1) *Preanthropus,* which includes *Orrorin tugenensis, Australopithecus anamensis, A. bahrelghazali, A. garhi,* and *A. afarensis;* (2) *Ardipithecus,* which includes *A. ramidus;* (3) *Australopithecus,* which includes *A. africanus, A. aethiopicus, A. robustus,* and *A. boisei;* and (4) *Homo,* which includes *K. platyops.* Currently Ayala holds *Sahelanthropus* in reserve (as a fifth genus) until more work can be done.

To arrive at this new scheme, Ayala dropped the genera *Kenyanthropus, Orrorin,* and *Paranthropus* and redefined the membership of the traditional genera *Homo* and *Australopithecus.* Ayala also proposed a novel evolutionary tree rooted in *Preanthropus.* The new *Ardipithecus* and *Australopithecus* genera are evolutionary side branches and dead ends. According to Ayala, *Homo* emerged just before *Preanthropus* terminated.

How paleoanthropologists will respond to this new proposal remains unclear. But one thing is certain—extensive confusion surrounds hominid classification at both the species and the genus levels. This chaos renders any proposed hominid evolutionary tree as speculative.

In science, ongoing research often clears up uncertainty and helps resolve
controversy. The reverse seems to be happening in paleoanthropology. New
hominid discoveries and data analysis only ratchet up the chaos and dispute.
The number and classification of hominid species are particularly problematic.
Recent work on *Homo habilis* further illustrates this difficulty.

Traditionally, paleoanthropologists have regarded *H. habilis*, which appears
in the fossil record at about 2.5 to 2.4 million years ago, as the first member of
the *Homo* genus and as the transitional form that links the australopithecines
to *H. erectus*.[16] Paleoanthropologists now recognize another hominid, *H. rudolfensis*, as a contemporary of *H. habilis*, one that possesses a broader, flatter
face and a slightly larger cranium.

In 1999, paleoanthropologists Bernard Wood and Mark Collard challenged
the placement of *H. habilis* and *H. rudolfensis* in the genus *Homo*. They argued
that based on body mass, body proportions, teeth, and jaw structure, these two
hominids should be classified as australopithecines.[17] This new classification
weakens *H. habilis'* status as a transitional species between the australopithecines and *H. erectus*. Instead of providing a gradual transition between these
two hominid groups, Wood and Collard's reassignment of *H. habilis* and *H.
rudolfensis* creates a discontinuity.

The classification of *H. rudolfensis* has become even more complicated.
As mentioned previously, Leakey reclassified *H. rudolfensis* (in 2001) as *K.
rudolfensis*, based on the affinity she perceived between this hominid and *K.
platyops*.[18] Given this status, within the span of less than two years, paleoanthropologists have placed *H. rudolfensis* in three different genera!

In 2003, an international team of paleoanthropologists reported on the
discovery of a hominid jaw and lower face (that date between 1.84 and 1.79
million years old) in the Olduvai Gorge region of Tanzania. The scientists classified this specimen as *H. habilis* and argued that its morphological features
form a bridge between *H. habilis* and *H. rudolfensis*.[19] This designation invalidates *H. rudolfensis* as a species. In other words, the differences between these
two hominids may fall within *H. habilis'* normal range of morphological variation.

Who is right? Is *rudolfensis* a *H. habilis* or an *A. habilis*? Is *rudolfensis* an *A. rudolfensis* or a *K. rudolfensis*? Or did *H. rudolfensis* even exist?

Paleoanthropologists' inability to determine the number of hominid species and properly classify them creates real problems that prevent scientists from establishing the evolutionary pathway to humans. This complication is particularly poignant when it comes to *H. habilis*. Many evolutionary scenarios place this hominid as a key transitional form rooting the *Homo* genus. Yet, if its status as a species can't be settled, how much confidence can be placed in hominid evolutionary trees?

Out on a Limb

Given all the difficulties associated with the hominid fossil record, it's not surprising that paleoanthropologists radically disagree on the evolutionary relationships among the hominids, specifically on the progression pathway that led to modern humans. Examination of any textbook or treatise on human evolution attests to this conflict.[20]

Until a few years ago, paleoanthropologists primarily debated whether *A. africanus* or *A. afarensis* morphed into *Homo*. These scientists also engaged in a minor dispute over the genus *Paranthropus*. Some argued that *A. aethiopicus*, *A. boisei*, and *A. robustus* (known as robust australopithecines) should be recategorized as a new genus, *Paranthropus*. Others maintained that this taxon is illegitimate and that these three hominids properly belong in *Australopithecus*. Still, nearly all paleoanthropologists agreed that these three hominids were an evolutionary side branch and dead end.

This debate became more complex in 1999 when an international team of scientists reported on the discovery of a new hominid species, *Australopithecus garhi*, dated at about 2.5 million years ago.[21] Because *A. garhi* might have used tools to butcher animal carcasses, some researchers have proposed that this australopithecine gave rise to *Homo*. Others dispute this interpretation and consider *A. garhi* an evolutionary dead end.

These minor controversies pale in comparison, however, to those recently inaugurated with the discoveries of *K. platyops* and *Sahelanthropus tchadensis*. Instead of these new hominid discoveries bringing clarification and resolution, they throw the entire field into even greater chaos. If *Kenyanthropus* is indeed a legitimate hominid taxon, then neither *A. africanus* nor *A. afarensis* led to humanity—*Kenyanthropus* did. This reclassification renders the australopithecines as nothing more than an evolutionary side branch leading nowhere. The discovery of *Kenyanthropus* potentially invalidates all traditional hominid evolutionary trees found in textbooks.

During the summer of 2002, French paleoanthropologist Michel Brunet reported on the recovery and characterization of a complete hominid skull, plus a partial jaw and teeth, from the Sahel region of Chad. These finds date to about 7 million years in age and were assigned to *S. tchadensis*—a new genus and species.[22] Although *S. tchadensis* dates at 7 million years in age, its facial anatomy appears as advanced as *H. habilis*, which dates at 2.5 million years. The australopithecine facial features are much more primitive than those of *Sahelanthropus*. This realization has prompted some anthropologists to speculate that *Sahelanthropus'* lineage might have been the one that led to *Homo*. And again, the australopithecines are rendered an evolutionary side branch and dead end.

In the midst of these controversies, additional work published by Collard and Wood raises serious and fundamental questions about the capability of paleoanthropologists to ever establish evolutionary relationships among hominids.[23] In their view, any evolutionary tree paleoanthropologists construct for hominids will always be hopelessly uncertain.

Paleoanthropologists typically use comparisons of hominid cranial and dental (anatomical) features to build evolutionary trees, since these fossils supply the chief data available. However, as Collard and Wood point out, the use of hominid craniodental features to discern evolutionary relationships has never been validated. To make their point, these two paleoanthropologists compared evolutionary trees constructed from craniodental data with those built from DNA and protein sequences for two currently existing groups of primates. One group included humans, chimpanzees, and gorillas. The other consists of baboons, macaques, and mangabeys. For both sets of primates, the evolutionary trees built from DNA and protein sequences differed significantly from those constructed from craniodental data.

Evolutionary biologists now consider evolutionary trees produced with molecular data inherently more robust than those derived from anatomical features. This development has forced paleoanthropologists to conclude that "little confidence can be placed in phylogenies [evolutionary trees] generated solely from higher primate craniodental evidence. The corollary of this is that existing phylogenetic hypotheses about human evolution are unlikely to be reliable."[24]

In light of these results, "that human evolution occurred" becomes a scientifically untenable statement. In order to demonstrate that humanity originated through biological evolution, robust evolutionary trees must be established. Collard and Wood have shown that such determinations may never be possible for hominids so long as craniodental data is all they have to work with. In fact, more recent work indicates that this problem extends beyond the hominid fossil record. Evolutionary biologists from the University of Helsinki (Finland) question the reliability of *any* evolutionary tree generated from dental data.[25]

These scientists are not the only paleoanthropologists to demonstrate problems with hominid evolutionary trees. Others have rigorously detailed additional difficulties with the methods and data used to build the trees.[26] Any evolutionary relationships set forth are highly tentative, little more than sheer speculation. It's no wonder that each new hominid discovery throws the field of paleoanthropology into chaos and forces researchers to redraw the trees.

A Tree or a Lawn?

To declare human evolution a scientific fact, paleoanthropologists must do much more than reliably define evolutionary relationships among the hominids in the fossil record. They must also establish an evolutionary pathway that compels widespread acceptance among biologists. In addition, this lineage must readily accommodate new hominid fossil discoveries. Paleoanthropologists must also demonstrate that hominids in the fossil record descended from a single apelike species in a branching, treelike manner rooted 6 to 5 million years ago.

The hominid fossil record as yet fails to display this expected pattern. Instead of an evolutionary tree, hominid discoveries form a bush or lawn. Throughout the hominid fossil record, paleoanthropologists observe a menagerie of species that coexisted. For example, *Australopithecus* (or *Paranthropus*) *robustus* and *Australopithecus* (*Paranthropus*) *boisei* with *Homo* (*Australopithecus*) *habilis*, *Homo erectus*, *Homo antecessor*, *Homo heidelbergensis*, *Homo helmi*, *Homo rhodesiensis*, *Homo sapiens idaltu*, and *Homo neanderthalensis* all existed between 2.5 million and 100,000 years ago (see figure 2.1). Between roughly 3 million and 1.5 million years ago, *Australopithecus* (*Paranthropus*) *robustus*, *Australopithecus* (*Paranthropus*) *aethiopicus*, *Homo* (*Australopithecus*) *habilis*, *Homo* (*Australopithecus/Kenyanthropus*) *rudolfensis*, *Australopithecus garhi*, and *Australopithecus africanus* all lived simultaneously. Between 4.5 and 3 million years ago, *Kenyanthropus platyops*, *Australopithecus bahrelghazali*, *Australopithecus afarensis*, and *Australopithecus anamensis* coexisted.

Recently, the hominid fossil record in the 4-million-year time regime became even bushier with the recognition that hominid remains recovered from caves at Sterkfontein, South Africa, properly date to that era, not to 3 or 2 million years ago, as previously thought.[27] The revised date indicates that these Sterkfontein hominids were not contemporaries of *A. afarensis* but of *A. anamensis*.

Paleoanthropologists have also recently recovered two more australopith-ecine species from the nearby Jacovec caverns in South Africa that date at 4 million years. These new hominids are currently unassigned, but they are mor-phologically distinct from *A. anamensis*. The difference is significant because, prior to this work, paleoanthropologists thought that *A. anamensis* was the sole existing hominid of its epoch. According to some evolutionary scenarios, *A. anamensis* rooted the human evolutionary tree. Instead, the hominid fossil record forces the tree to become bushier at its base. And humanity's supposed ancestor hides among the many branches.

This broadening trend continues all the way back to 7 million years ago, with the recent discoveries of *Ardipithecus ramidus* (as old as 5.8 million years), *O. tugenensis* (dated between 6.1 and 5.8 million years in age), and *S. tchadensis* (7 to 6 million years in age). The discovery of *S. tchadensis* in central Africa, a region traditionally thought to fall outside the hominids' geographical range, shocked paleoanthropologists. They quickly recognized that other hominids, which wait to be discovered, likely existed in this time frame. When science writer John Whitfield wrote that the *S. tchadensis* discovery was just "the tip of [the] iceberg—one that could sink current ideas about human evolution,"[28] his reaction typified the response of the paleoanthropological community.

Instead of finding a single species that gave birth to two evolutionary branches (apes and hominids), paleoanthropologists now acknowledge a pleth-ora of hominids that existed 7 to 6 million years ago. Wood likens the structure of the hominid fossil record at its base to the Cambrian explosion. Wood states, "The fauna of the Burgess Shale in Canada, which samples a bewildering ar-ray of invertebrate groups some 500 million years ago, is a famous example of diversity at the base of an adaptive radiation. Does *S. tchadensis* belong to the African equivalent of the Burgess Shale?"[29] In other words, when hominids first appear in the fossil record, they make an explosive, not a gradual, entrance.

The geographical distribution of these first hominids was also quite ex-tensive (Chad, Kenya, and Ethiopia). This range is also unexpected from an evolutionary standpoint, since evolutionary radiations should emanate from the same locale.

The recent discovery and analysis of hominid teeth (dated at 5.6 mil-lion years in age) adds further credence to the view that an explosive diversity of hominids arose suddenly in the hominid evolutionary tree.[30] These teeth come from an *Ardipithecus* specimen. However, their dental characteristics are distinct from those assigned to 4-million-year-old *A. ramidus* specimens. This work indicates that older specimens of *A. ramidus* represent a distinct species, named *Ardipithicus kadabba*. With this discovery, hominid diversity (at the time when these primates first appear in the fossil record) expands to include at least four different species that grouped into three distinct genera.

The discovery of explosive hominid diversity creates another problem for human evolutionary models. Most evolutionary anthropologists place the time when hominid and ape lineages diverged at 6 to 5 million years ago. Yet *S. tchadensis* appears in the fossil record nearly a million years prior to that divide. The time when the first hominids appear in the fossil record simply doesn't match the predictions of human evolutionary models.

An Unavoidable Conclusion

The data available to paleoanthropologists and ultimately to teachers remain insufficient to formally demonstrate human evolution to be a fact. These scientists have limited understanding of the number of hominid species that existed, their geographical distribution, and the range of their biological variation. Without greater understanding, it's impossible to determine hominid evolutionary relationships and the pathway that might have led to modern humans. Paleoanthropologists struggle with a sparse record and with fossils that are damaged, deformed, and incomplete. The craniodental features of the fossils (the primary morphological traits available for study) are biologically inadequate to construct reliable evolutionary trees.

The hominid fossil record's defining feature further exacerbates this problem. Instead of hominids emerging from a single species and diversifying in a treelike fashion, an explosive diversity of hominids occurred at the time of their first appearance in the fossil record. This explosion of coexisting species persists throughout their history. The pattern and timing of the hominids' first appearance directly contradicts evolution's scenarios for their origins. Moreover, calculations made by astrophysicists indicate the high improbability that evolutionary processes could ever produce modern humans from bacterial life in the brief time available in Earth's history. (See "What Are the Chances?" on page 157 for an astrophysics perspective on human evolution.)

Paleoanthropologists are dedicated and talented scientists who must not be disparaged because their discipline lacks robust data. However, given that these scientists cannot reasonably map out the naturalistic route that produced modern humans, to consider human evolution anything more than a theory seems unwarranted. *That* human evolution occurred is as much a theory as *how* it occurred.

What Are the Chances?

While paleoanthropologists struggle to discern evolutionary connections among the hominids in the fossil record, astrophysicists (attempting to quantify the likelihood that intelligent life exists in the universe beyond Earth) have identified another series of problems for human evolution. According to various calculations based on physical conditions, it is extremely improbable that modern humans evolved from bacteria through natural means, given the brief time window of Earth's habitability.

In one study, astrophysicists John Barrow, Brandon Carter, and Frank Tipler comment on the surprisingly large number of highly improbable steps in the supposed natural evolution of an intelligent species on Earth.[31] Moreover, the number of such steps merely represents a lower limit; evolutionary biology has not yet advanced sufficiently to determine their actual number. Restricting the count to just the known problem steps (which are statistically independent) in the evolution of *Homo sapiens sapiens*, the trio produced a probability figure for the emergence of humans from a suite of bacterial species in 10 billion years or less: $10^{-24,000,000}$. (In other words, a decimal point 24 million places to the left of the 1.)[32]

An independent calculation done by evolutionary biologist Francisco Ayala places the probability for humans arising from single-celled organisms at $10^{-1,000,000}$. As Ayala and others pointed out, animals on ancient Earth did not know they were supposed to evolve in such a way that human beings could later appear. Natural selection operates only during an animal's lifetime. It cannot select a portion of a genome with the intent of using that genome portion 1, 2, or 3 billion years later.

To put the calculated probabilities for humans arising from single-celled organisms into perspective, if every proton and neutron in the universe were a planet, and if each of these planets contained as many single-celled organisms as Earth does today (a trillion quadrillion single-celled organisms), the probability that humans could have arisen once in the universe would be $10^{-999,921}$, according to Ayala's calculation. According to Barrow, Carter, and Tipler's calculation the number would be $10^{-23,999,921}$.[33]

Such incredibly tiny probabilities warrant the conclusion that, from a naturalistic perspective, no physical intelligent life should exist at all—anywhere in the universe.

The pattern of the hominid fossil records can, however, be readily explained within the framework of RTB's human origins model. It regards the hominids as animals created by God. The explosive initial diversity of hominids in the fossil record and their persistent diversity for the past 7 million years is the very feature expected in the fossil record if the hominids were formed by the Creator's hand.

How do other aspects of the hominid fossil record fare within the evolutionary framework and RTB's biblical model? The next chapter examines two additional features of human origins—the emergence of bipedalism and the increase in brain size.

Chapter 10

Bipedalism and Brain Size

If a man's brains were in's
Heels, weren't not in danger of
Kibes?
                    —*King Lear* Act 1, scene 5

Most human beings can walk and chew gum at the same time. As they hurry along, people often contemplate their destinations—work, home, or maybe a meeting with old friends. People usually have something specific on their minds. They think, remember, and move in ways that animals do not.

However, anthropologists don't hesitate to classify human beings as mammals belonging to the order *Primates*. The features that distinguish people from other primates include (1) bipedalism—the ability to walk erect; (2) a large brain; (3) a large ratio of brain size to body mass; (4) unique skull features— a short face, characteristic jaw robustness, distinguishing anterior and cheek teeth anatomy, and tooth eruption patterns; (5) characteristic body proportions, including relatively long legs and short arms; (6) limited sexual dimorphism—little size difference between females and males; (7) extensive manual dexterity; and (8) an advanced culture.[1]

Evolutionary biologists consider bipedalism and brain size to be humanity's two most significant anatomical features. For these scientists, understanding the emergence and development of bipedalism and brain size equates to knowledge about the origin of humankind. Recent advances in paleoanthropology and paleoecology (the study of ancient ecologies) shed new light on the emergence of these characteristics. The new discoveries provide an important opportunity to evaluate key aspects of both the evolutionary paradigm and Reasons to Believe's (RTB) model.

Standing on Their Own Two Feet

Evolutionists postulate that an apelike ancestor gave rise to the great ape and human lineages; therefore, bipedal primates must have evolved from knuckle-walking quadrupeds. Chimpanzees and gorillas knuckle-walk. They use a special type of terrestrial quadrupedalism (ground-based locomotion employing all four limbs). Their hands don't rest on their palms or fingers but on their knuckles. This design allows chimpanzees and gorillas to walk using all fours while sparing their long, curved fingers for climbing and moving through trees.[2]

Paleoanthropologists have proposed myriad hypotheses to explain how bipedalism could result from natural-process evolution. One early explanation (later abandoned) suggested that bipedalism emerged to free hands for tool use. Evolutionary biologists rejected this idea because the fossil record contradicts it. Fossils clearly demonstrate the existence of bipedalism at least 2 million years before tool use appeared in the archeological record.[3]

Home, Home on the Range

Traditionally, most hypotheses that try to account for bipedalism's emergence depend on East Africa's transformation from a woodland and forest environment to an arid and open grassland.[4] Under these conditions, terrestrial quadrupeds faced (1) reduced food supplies because of the fragmentation of continuous forested land; (2) increased risk from predators due to the lack of camouflage found in an arboreal environment; and (3) the inability to avoid direct sunlight.[5]

Bipedalism offers a way to meet all these challenges. Walking erect—an efficient means of locomotion at slow speeds—conserves energy and allows for efficient long-distance running.[6] This method of travel allowed bipedal primates to traverse long distances while foraging for food. After finding their food, these hominids could carry the foraged items long distances as they returned home to provide for their young.[7] Standing erect also permitted bipedal primates to detect predators sooner and from a greater distance in an open savanna than if they walked on all fours.

In addition, bipedalism offers a thermoregulatory advantage.[8] An upright bipedal primate absorbs 60 percent less heat than an ape walking on all four limbs. A quadrupedal stance exposes the entire back to direct sunlight, whereas standing erect exposes only the head and shoulders.

Evolutionary biologists have yet to reach consensus on the selective pressures that might have produced bipedalism in primates, nor have they demonstrated the evolutionary mechanism that brought about these anatomical and physiological characteristics. To date, the most commonly cited evolutionary pressure to explain this transformation remains the loss of a woodland habitat throughout East Africa.

What a Difference!

Any transition from a quadruped to a biped would involve extensive anatomical changes (see figure 10.1).[9] These changes include the following:

Relocating the foramen magnum
The foramen magnum (the opening in the base of the skull that receives the spinal column) must be relocated from the posterior to the center of the skull base. This position eliminates the need for powerful neck muscles, because the vertebral column effectively balances the head.

Restructuring of the inner ear bones
The inner ear bones, which play a role in balance, must be altered to support bipedalism.

Introducing spinal curvature
The lower and upper vertebral column must possess forward curvature to maintain bipedalism. This curvature, coupled with the backward arc in the middle of the spinal column, allows the backbone to function as a spring.

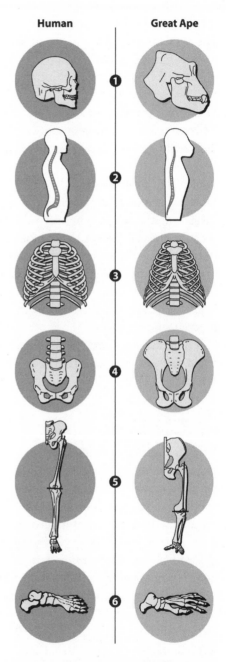

Figure 10.1: Anatomical Differences between Knuckle-Walkers and Bipeds

Restructuring of the rib cage
The apes' inverted funnel-shaped rib cage accommodates the use of their arms for locomotion. The bipeds' barrel-shaped rib cage allows for effective use of the arms for nonlocomotor function.

Reshaping the pelvis
To accommodate changes to the hip joints and muscles needed for bipedalism, the pelvis of a biped must be lower and broader than in knuckle-walking apes.

Altering the lower limbs
Bipedal primates not only have longer lower limbs than quadrupeds, but the valgus angle (the angle between the femur and the midline of the body) also must be altered. Longer lower limbs shift the center of mass toward the lower body. Angling the femurs inward moves the center of mass closer to the midline of the body. The altered center of mass allows for stability in bipedal locomotion.

Enlarging joint surfaces
Not only must the knee be restructured to accommodate the changed valgus angle, but joint surfaces must also be enlarged. This larger contact area helps the knee and other joints withstand the stresses of standing and walking upright.

Restructuring the foot
Even the feet require an altered structure to support bipedalism. The transformation includes a platform foot with arches for better shock absorption. The big toe (*hallux*) must also be relocated, elongated, and aligned with the other toes. This structure allows the toe to make the last point of contact with the ground as the leg swings forward during a bipedal stride.

Reorganizing the body's musculature
Given the global skeletal changes that must take place to transition from quadruped to biped, much of the musculature of the biped must also be altered, not only to accommodate the skeletal differences, but also to support bipedal locomotion.

Predictions
Dramatic anatomical changes must occur in a coordinated fashion to trans-

form quadrupeds into bipedal primates. If bipedalism emerged through natu-ral-process biological evolution, the aforementioned alterations should occur gradually, well after the time apes and humans supposedly diverged. Moreover, the first form of bipedalism should be crude and inefficient. Once appearing, early forms should gradually transition to the more efficient obligatory biped-alism of modern humans. And, there must be significant evolutionary pressure to force knuckle-walking apes, perfectly suited for their environment and life-style, to give way to upright walking primates.

The predictions that follow from RTB's model (which views bipedal pri-mates as coming into existence through God's direct creative activity) are markedly different from those that stem from the evolutionary paradigm. If this design feature resulted from God's command, then bipedalism would:

1.   appear suddenly in the fossil record;
2.   remain essentially unaltered; and
3.   be optimal as soon as it appears.

Footloose
Several recent discoveries from the fossil and geological records are radically transforming paleoanthropologists' view of the origin and natural history of bipedalism.

And suddenly—but when?
In 1995, a team of paleoanthropologists described the fossil remains of a new australopithecine species named *Australopithecus anamensis*. This hominid, uncovered in Kenya (originally dated between 4.2 and 3.9 million years in age),[10] has been confirmed as 4.07 million years old.[11] At that time, an analysis of an *A. anamensis* tibia clearly and surprisingly established bipedal capacity, pushing back the appearance of bipedalism by nearly a quarter of a million years. Prior to this find, the oldest primate with bipedal capabilities of a *Aus-tralopithecus* was believed to be *A. afarensis* (about 3.9 million years ago). *A. anamensis'* bipedalism placed the first appearance of upright walking closer to the time when the ape and human lineages would have split (6 to 5 million years ago). Paleoanthropologists took this unexpected finding to mean that the forces of natural selection had much less time to generate bipedalism (given the extensive anatomical changes needed) than seems reasonable to anticipate.

A series of discoveries has pushed bipedalism's emergence to the brink of the alleged human-ape divergence. In 1994, another team of paleoanthropologists uncovered the remains of a hominid in Ethiopia dated at 4.4 million years in age. This specimen, originally named *Australopithecus ramidus*, was later reassigned to a new genus, *Ardipithecus*.[12] At the time of its discovery, scientists were not certain if *Ardipithecus ramidus* had bipedal capacity.

Some thought this hominid might have stood upright, based on the location of its foramen magnum. Their uncertainty was laid to rest in 2001 when members of the team reported on more *A. ramidus* remains recovered in Ethiopia, dated at 5.8 and 5.2 million years in age.[13] The analysis of these new fossils unequivocally indicated that this hominid walked erect. (The specimens were later reassigned to a new species, *Ardipithecus kadabba*.) This dramatic discovery not only pushed the hominid fossil record back by a million years but also placed the appearance of bipedalism as concurrent with the first appearance of hominids.

Two more finds continue the trend started with *A. anamensis* and *A. ramidus*. In 2001, a team of French paleoanthropologists reported on fossils from Kenya that date between 6.1 and 5.8 million years in age. The French scientists assigned these specimens to a new hominid species dubbed *Orrorin tugenensis*. Studying a femur, the French fossil hunters concluded that this newly discovered hominid walked erect.[14]

In 2002, another team (headed by French paleoanthropologist Michel Brunet) recovered and characterized a remarkably complete hominid skull, along with a partial jawbone and teeth, from the Sahel region of Chad. These fossils dated about 7 to 6 million years in age.[15] Brunet's team assigned them to a new genus (*Sahelanthropus tchadensis*), nicknamed "Toumai," which means "hope of life" in the local language.

Skull features indicate that Toumai man possessed the ability to walk erect, as did *O. tugenensis* and *A. ramidus* (*kadabba*). Collectively, the fossil record shows that bipedalism did not emerge gradually, as expected in an evolutionary framework. Rather, this defining trait for humanity appeared suddenly and concurrently with the hominids' first appearance, as RTB's human origins model predicts.

At home—where?

Recent work designed to characterize the environment in which the oldest bipedal primates lived has also yielded unexpected results. *S. tchadensis*, *O. tugenensis*, *A. ramidus*, and *A. anamensis* did not live in an open savanna. They lived in woodlands and forests.[16]

Further studies now indicate that *A. afarensis* lived in a mix of woodland

and open savanna environments.[17] An australopithecine species (*A. bahrelghazali*) recovered in Chad and dated between 3.5 and 3.0 million years in age also lived in a mixed habitat.[18] Another hominid specimen (*Kenyanthropus platyops*), dated at 3.5 million years in age, likewise lived in a predominantly woodland and forest environment that included open grasslands.[19] As one researcher commented, these discoveries "challenge some long-cherished ideas about the mode and timing of hominid evolution."[20]

Anthropologist and science writer Roger Lewin echoes this concern. "The popular notion of our forebears striding out of dense forest onto grassland savanna is likely to be more fiction than fact."[21] This new recognition creates difficulty for the evolutionary paradigm because it eliminates the driving force traditionally thought to have produced bipedalism.

A recent geological study investigating the aridification of East Africa (the transformation of its woodlands into an open range) further stymies the notion that the loss of a woodland environment drove the emergence of bipedalism. This study shows that the Indonesian seaway closure 4 to 3 million years ago eventually led to reduced rainfall in East Africa, gradually changing the woodlands into grasslands.[22] The dating of this transformation, however, places it no earlier than 4 to 3 million years ago. So bipedalism had already appeared by the time East Africa became arid.

Reaching higher

The problems associated with the traditional evolutionary accounts for bipedalism's emergence have prompted primatologist Craig Stanford to propose an alternative explanation.[23] Stanford posits that the first step toward bipedalism occurred when a forest-dwelling, apelike proto-human began to stand erect in order to reach fruit on branches that otherwise would be inaccessible. Stanford points to the behavior of chimpanzees in the wild, which occasionally stand erect while feeding, as support for his idea. Presumably this behavior, improving survivability and reproductive success, gradually led to the ability to walk erect. As the forests of East Africa gave way to open grasslands, bipedalism offered further advantages. According to Stanford, bipedalism allowed the first hominids to cover greater distances to scavenge calorie-rich meat from animal remains.

While this model accounts for bipedalism's emergence in a woodland environment, it doesn't explain bipedalism's sudden appearance in the fossil record. Stanford's hypothesis has bipedalism emerging slowly and gradually, at least initially. Yet this is not what the fossil record shows.

A changing gait—how?
A recent statistical analysis of over 200 pelvic bones from apes, extinct hominids, and modern humans reveals a historical pattern that amplifies the challenge facing the evolutionary explanation of bipedalism's natural history.[24] Instead of gradually changing over time, bipedalism endured through two long
periods without change. The first period lasted roughly 5 million years—the
second, 2 million. The fossil record indicates that transition from one form of
locomotion to another took place rapidly.

Australopithecines manifested facultative (optional) bipedalism. The
Homo genus has always possessed obligatory bipedalism. Though australopithecines existed for nearly 3 million years, their facultative bipedalism did not
gradually change into an obligatory form. Rather, it remained static throughout the duration of the australopithecines' existence. With the appearance
of the *Homo* genus, a distinct new form of bipedalism (obligatory) suddenly
showed up in the fossil record.

From an evolutionary perspective, this change would require a rapid transition in a narrow time window. And since obligatory bipedalism first appeared
in the *Homo* genus, it too has remained static for nearly 2 million years. Interestingly, *Homo erectus* and Neanderthals possessed an identical form of obligatory bipedalism, but distinct from that seen in human beings. Again, with the
arrival of humanity, a new form of bipedalism suddenly emerged.

While the pattern of stasis punctuated by sudden change—as exemplified
by bipedalism in the fossil record—runs counter to evolutionary expectations,
it seems to be a fingerprint of divine creative activity. If God created the australopithecines (and other closely related genera), as well as the *Homo* bipedal
primates, scientists could expect that the bipedalism expressed by each hominid should be optimal within the context of its particular environment and
lifestyle. Once created, natural selection would keep each type of bipedalism
static because any change would result in a nonoptimal form that would compromise survivability.[25] Moreover, given the differences between the australopithecines and the *Homo* primates in lifestyle and environment, the creation
model anticipates that God would create each of the two with different forms
of bipedalism. This divine intervention would be manifested by the sudden appearance of a new form of bipedalism in the fossil record.

Recent scientific advances in the natural history of bipedalism provide a
useful collection of observations. They allow for comparative evaluation of the
evolutionary and biblical scenarios for the origin of humanity. The sudden and
early appearance in the hominid fossil record favors the creation model. That

record shows insufficient time for bipedalism to emerge through natural-process biological evolution. The extensive and coordinated changes to the skeletal and muscular anatomy of knuckle-walking quadrupeds simply could not have occurred that quickly.

Bipedalism's sudden appearance among the first hominids is even more surprising within the evolutionary paradigm, especially given the absence of any significant environmental pressure to force this change. The fossil record also fails to reveal a pattern of gradual evolutionary transformation of crude, inefficient bipedalism into a more sophisticated, efficient form. Rather, two periods of stasis interspersed with rapid change define bipedalism's history.

Sudden appearance and stasis in the fossil record stand as hallmark features of special creation. According to RTB's biblical creation model, God created large primates with optional bipedal capabilities. This model predicts the sudden appearance of various bipedal animals in the fossil record. Moreover, long periods of stasis are also predicted because God would be expected to design a perfect form of bipedalism intentionally suited for the environmental, predatory, and competitive challenges of the given era.

Recent scientific advances offer direct evidence that one of the most important defining features of humanity—obligatory bipedalism—came about through God's direct creative activity. But what does the hominid fossil record say about brain size?

The Bigger the Better
It is not surprising that paleoanthropologists focus significant attention on evolutionary descriptions of brain size. A large brain supports humanity's intelligence and unique ability to develop and use symbolic communication, speech, and tools—all of which are foundational for establishing and maintaining human cultures and civilizations. More importantly, the human brain is structured to support consciousness and self-awareness. As with bipedalism, recent advances yield unexpected patterns that provide another opportunity to compare the RTB and evolutionary scenarios for humanity's origin.

A predictable pattern
Anatomical and physiological complexity and the integrated functioning of the brain's components dictate that for exclusively natural processes to be responsible for humanity's large brain size (and the brain-size to body-mass ratio), evolutionary changes must take place gradually over time. This expectation of gradualism holds true for the line of hominids that putatively led to modern

humans—both within such species and from species to species.

However, if hominids represent God's creative handiwork, the fossil record should reveal a step-wise pattern for brain-size change between species. As new species appear, RTB's model predicts that changes in brain size and architecture (beyond the within-species variation) should be discontinuous—abruptly changing over a narrow window of time.

Continuous or created

Many people believe that the hominid fossil record shows a gradual increase in brain size over time, particularly for those species considered part of the evolutionary pathway leading to modern humans. However, surveys of hominid brain-size measurements show a different pattern.[26] For each hominid species, brain size remains relatively constant throughout the time it existed. The range of variation observed for all biological traits within a population readily explains any intraspecies difference in brain size.

The discontinuous jumps in brain size occur as new hominid species successively appear in the fossil record. For example, the brain size of the australopithecines, which existed from about 5.0 to 1.5 million years ago, was about 400 cm³. Brain size for those specimens assigned to *Homo habilis*, existing between 2.5 and 1.8 million years ago, jumped to between 650 and 800 cm³ in volume. *H. erectus/ergaster* (about 1.8 million to 500,000 years ago) had a brain size that was larger still, ranging between 850 and 1,000 cm³. Neanderthal's brain size was 1,100 to 1,400 cm³. By comparison, modern human brains range between about 1,000 and 1,500 cm³. These numbers show the general pattern of discontinuous leaps in brain size, not gradual increases (see figure 10.2).

Taking body mass into account, the expansion of brain size (referred to as the encephalization quotient, which is brain size divided by body mass) between *H. erectus/ergaster* and modern humans appears even more dramatic (see figure 10.2). For example, the encephalization quotient for *A. afarensis* was 2.5; for *H. habilis*, it was 3.1; for *H. erectus/ergaster*, it was 3.3; and for human beings, it is 5.8.

In addition to brain-size measurements, paleoanthropologists also gain information about brain structure from making endocasts of hominid skull interiors.[27] These endocasts show that brain architecture, like brain size, also remains essentially unchanged through time for each hominid species. Yet, when new hominids appear in the fossil record, they come with significant restructuring of the brain.[28]

As with bipedalism, hominid brain size and architecture remain static

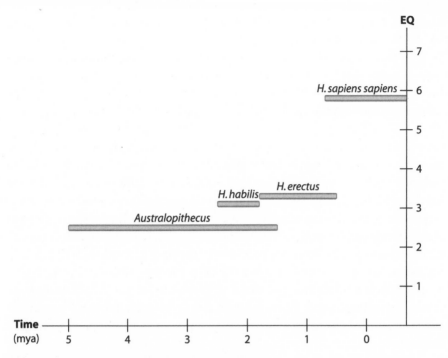

Figure 10.2: Hominid Encephalization Quotients
This plot shows changes in the encephalization quotient (EQ) through time in the fossil record for representative hominids.

through time for a given hominid species. Discontinuous changes in brain size and structure punctuate the stasis. This pattern matches what's predicted by the RTB model. In contrast, no known evolutionary processes can produce this cadence of change.

Difficulties disclosed
Given the importance brain-size variation plays in establishing human evolutionary theory, it seems only fair to note that paleoanthropologists encounter serious difficulties in their attempts to measure brain size from fossil specimens. One of two different methods is applied. The preferred approach involves measuring endocranial volume (a proxy for brain size) by making endocasts of the fossil skull's interior using latex or plaster. However, many available fossil skulls are damaged and deformed. Some are incomplete. The measurement of endocranial volume becomes possible only after researchers correct any damage and reconstruct the skull to include any missing parts.[29] As careful

as a researcher might be, errors in making these reconstructions can happen and mislead as to the true brain size.

The presence of stone within fossilized skulls further complicates hominid brain-size determinations. Stone deposits hamper the preparation of endocasts.[30] The mineralized matrix cannot be removed without damaging the internal features of these skull samples. For such specimens, paleoanthropologists calculate brain size based on measurements of external skull features. Error is a concern because researchers must make assumptions about how external features relate to brain volume. Inaccuracies also result from attempting to make high-precision measurements on deformed or damaged skulls. Thus the reported values of hominid brain size must be regarded as estimates.

The magnitude and impact of these problems recently came to light when a team of paleoanthropologists developed and validated a new methodology to accurately and precisely measure the cranial capacity of fossil skulls. They used 3D computed tomography imaging (CTI) technology and rapid-prototyping stereolithography techniques to make their measurements.[31] The results were highly reproducible and more accurate than any corresponding handmade measurements, with an error bar of just 2 percent when applied to human skulls.

CTI methodology was then applied by the research team to determine the brain size of an *A. africanus* specimen (Stw 505) discovered in Sterkfontein, South Africa, dated at 2.8 to 2.6 million years old.[32] Earlier brain-size estimates for this specimen surpassed 600 cm³, which would make it the largest *A. africanus* brain known, larger than many early *Homo* species brains. CTI methodology, however, showed the brain size of Stw 505 to be about 515 cm³—approximately 15 percent smaller than initial estimates.

This result has not gone unchallenged. Some scientists assert that the paleoanthropologists who made the CTI measurements didn't adequately take into account damage and deformation.[33] This oversight would lead to low-biased results. In response to these protests, the measuring team demonstrated that their conclusion was sound. Their results were derived by careful consideration and correction of any postmortem damage and deformation. Little doubt remains that the Stw 505 specimen is not an extraordinary fossil find but rather represents a typical *A. africanus* skull.

The implications of these CTI measurements extend beyond the importance of the Stw 505 sample. This study's authors reported, "The recognition that no australopithecine has an endocranial capacity approaching, let alone exceeding, 600 cm³, and that several key early hominid endocranial estimates may be inflated, suggests that current views of the tempo and mode of early hominid brain evolution may need reevaluation."[34]

Dean Falk of Florida State University, echoed such concerns. She noted that several endocasts in her collection appear to be considerably smaller than initially measured using calipers.[35] Falk has confidently held to this view even in the face of a direct protest from paleoanthropologist Tim White of University of California, Berkeley.[36]

The bias in past brain-size measurements will likely be extended to include other specimens as the CTI technique is more broadly applied. And the CTI study is not the first to suggest that hominid endocranial volumes reported in the paleoanthropological literature are skewed high. Ralph Holloway of Columbia University pointed out that as early as the 1970s he recognized several reported endocranial volume measurements as inflated.[37] Holloway published endocranial volumes for the Sts 71 specimen of 428 cm^3 and for the Taung child of 404 cm^3, compared to previously reported values at the time of 480 to 520 cm^3 and 525 to 562 cm^3, respectively.

Holloway also measured an endocranial volume of 480 cm^3 for the Sts 5 specimen, which Conroy and his fellow researchers confirmed using CTI.[38] At the 1999 annual meeting of the American Association for Physical Anthropology (in Columbus, Ohio), Falk reported that the cranial capacity of several *A. africanus* specimens was remeasured to be about 450 cm^3, compared to the previous values recorded at near 500 cm^3.[39]

The approaches used by paleontologists to measure the brain size of extinct hominids appear to have yielded results about 15 to 20 percent higher than the actual value. Acknowledging this high bias widens the gap in brain size between extinct hominids and modern humans. From an evolutionary perspective, this difference would push natural selection to transform the brain even more rapidly than previously imagined.

RTB's creation model asserts that God created the various hominids in the fossil record. The natural history of their bipedalism, brain size, and brain structure align with this view. In contrast, the evolutionary paradigm offers no feasible explanation for these features of the fossil record. The next two chapters continue to evaluate the ability of the RTB model to make sense of the hominid fossil record, with the focus now on *H. erectus* and the Neanderthals.

Chapter 11

Who Was Turkana Boy?

> If you prick us, do we not bleed?
> If you tickle us, do we not laugh?
> If you poison us, do we not die?
> And if you wrong us, shall we not revenge?
> If we are like you in the rest, we
> Will resemble you in that.
> —*The Merchant of Venice* Act 3, scene 1

Turkana boy lived about nine years and then died—about 1.6 million years ago. Discovered in 1984 at Nariokotome, on the west side of Lake Turkana in East Africa, the remains of Turkana boy are considered a rare find.

The well-preserved postcranial bone structure of this young hominid offers insight into the physical features of the erectines (hominids that closely resemble *Homo erectus*).[1] Turkana boy possessed a slender pelvis and walked fully erect. Like others of its kind, this biped likely stood just over five feet tall, with an average brain size slightly under 1,000 cm³. These creatures had a brain-size to body-mass ratio about 60 percent that of a modern human being. The question arises: Who were they? Could the erectines have been transitional intermediates?[2]

According to paleoanthropologists, Turkana boy was one of the first unequivocal members of the *Homo* genus. (Though some scientists consider *H. habilis* and *H. rudolfensis* as the first *Homo* species, others consider them to be australopithecines—see pages 151–152). Many evolutionary biologists think Turkana boy and other erectines evolved from *H. habilis/rudolfensis*. How do Turkana boy and other erectines fit into the various human origins scenarios, if at all?

Erectine remains have been found in numerous places throughout Africa, the Middle East, and Eastern Europe. The so-called Peking man specimens recovered in China and other parts of Asia are among the best-known erectine finds.

The textbook view places the first appearance of *H. erectus* in Africa about 2 million years ago. According to this interpretation, after about a million years, the first erectines migrated from Africa into Asia. Then, about 100,000 years ago, these hominids disappeared from the fossil record.

Recent fossil discoveries and dating studies, however, indicate a far more complicated and controversial natural history than portrayed in textbooks. Most paleoanthropologists now reserve the *H. erectus* label for fossils recovered in Asia and Eastern Europe. The African specimens are classified as *Homo ergaster*. Paleoanthropologists generally propose that *H. ergaster* emerged from *H. habilis* and evolved into *H. erectus* after migrating from Africa. Still, *H. erectus* and *H. ergaster* possessed highly similar anatomical features.

In 2002, a team of American and Ethiopian paleontologists challenged the designation of early African and Asian specimens as separate species.[3] They insist that *H. erectus* and *H. ergaster* are a single species—one that displays greater biological variation than originally thought. In support of this revised view, the paleontologists point to the newly discovered *H. erectus/ergaster* fossils in Ethiopia that date to about 1 million years in age with morphology that seems to unify the African and Asian specimens.

A more recent find in Kenya affirms this unity. Researchers uncovered a fossilized skull dated to between 970,000 and 900,000 years in age.[4] This specimen was associated with artifacts assigned to the Acheulean technology, which was used by the erectines (see chapter 2). While the fossil skull possesses features observed for most *H. erectus* specimens, it also displays some unique traits. For one, this specimen owns the distinction of being the smallest *H. erectus* skull (less than 800 cm^3) known to have existed between 1.7 and 0.5 million years ago. The research team that discovered and analyzed this find concluded that the biological variation of *H. erectus* is much more extensive than previously thought. Others disagree and maintain that *H. erectus* is best understood as multiple species, not a single one with widely varying traits.[5]

Even in light of this new skull, many scientists still consider the subtle anatomical differences between *H. erectus* and *H. ergaster* as significant. These paleontologists continue to regard the two hominids as separate species.

So, Which Is It?

The oldest *H. ergaster* finds from Olduvai Gorge and Lake Turkana in East Africa date to around 1.8 million years ago. Given this dating, Turkana boy has now been designated as an *H. ergaster* specimen. Remarkably, though, *H. erectus* remains that date to about 1.8 to 1.6 million years old have been recovered in Asia. (More recent studies dispute these dates and place the *H. erectus* remains from these sites at closer to 1 million years in age.) The date of this *H. erectus* find indicates the possibility of a rapid migration from Africa into Asia.

Paleoanthropologists have also recovered *H. erectus* remains in the Caucasus region of Georgia (the nation) that date at 1.7 million years in age. (Some paleoanthropologists consider these specimens to be a separate species, *Homo georgicus*.) Again, this discovery seems to suggest a rapid spread of *H. erectus/ergaster* out of Africa. There is some indication from the fossil record for a back-migration of *H. erectus* into Africa about 1 million years ago.[6] Given these new dates and *H. erectus/ergaster*'s biogeography, some paleoanthropologists offer alternative views for this hominid's natural history. For example, some assert that *H. erectus* first appeared in Asia, then migrated into Africa. Others propose independent appearances of *H. erectus* in Asia and *H. ergaster* in Africa.[7]

These complications in natural history make *H. erectus/ergaster*'s status in the human evolutionary framework less certain. The out-of-Africa model places *H. ergaster* at the base of the *Homo* evolutionary tree. In that case *H. erectus* would have evolved from *H. ergaster* after migration from Africa. This hominid would thus represent an evolutionary side branch and dead end, becoming extinct about 100,000 years ago.

The out-of-Africa view links *H. ergaster* to the archaic hominids in Africa and eventually to modern humans. The multiregional model suggests a separate role for both *H. ergaster* and *H. erectus* in human origins. Multiregionalists think that *H. ergaster* yielded Africa's modern humans and that *H. erectus* evolved into Asian and Oceanic people groups.[8]

Continuity Controversies

Recent genetic and morphological studies help clarify the relationship between *H. erectus/ergaster* and human beings. Paleoanthropologists who hold to the multiregional hypothesis interpret the hominid fossil record of East Asia and Australasia as displaying anatomical continuity from *H. erectus* to modern Asian and Oceanic people, though significant gaps exist in the fossil record.[9]

A study published in 2001 by University of Michigan researchers illustrates how paleoanthropologists use morphological evidence to support multiregionalism. This study involved a rigorous statistical comparison of a suite of anatomical features found in 25 ancient and 3 recent skulls. The analysis revealed two clusters of features that placed the recent skulls from Australia with ancient ones from Asia. Recent skulls from Europe were grouped with ancient ones recovered in that same area, exactly as expected for the multiregional hypothesis.[10] The weakness of this study, as other paleoanthropologists point out, is that its results rest upon the specific fossils included in the study's sample set.[11]

This particular controversy and the larger question about H. erectus/ergaster's relationship to humans could be resolved if genetic data for H. erectus were available to researchers. Unfortunately, there's no real hope of recovering DNA from H. erectus specimens, because DNA degrades quickly. And no H. erectus specimens exist with undisputed dates more recent than 100,000 years ago.

"If We Are Like You in the Rest"
Genetic studies on current human populations provide an indirect way to test for a genetic connection between H. erectus and Asian and Oceanic peoples. As discussed in chapter 8, mitochondrial- and Y-chromosomal-DNA studies link Asian, Australian, and Oceanic peoples to East African populations (thought to be the first humans).[12] In the most compelling study along these lines, molecular anthropologists analyzed Y-chromosomal DNA sequences taken from over 12,000 males comprising 163 population groups. This work indicated a deep genetic connection and shared ancestry among African, Asian, and Oceanic peoples. According to the data analysis, Asian and Oceanic peoples migrated from Africa between 89,000 and 35,000 years ago.[13] Because the shared origin of these people groups is so recent, Asian and Oceanic people could not have evolved from H. erectus.

Another genetic study further challenges the role that H. erectus played in human origins. In this work (reported in 2001), the investigators started with the assumption that the multiregional hypothesis correctly accounts for humanity's origin. With this perspective in place, the researchers used genetic data from modern human population groups to estimate the genetic contributions and sizes of the ancestral European, Asian, and African populations. They concluded that over 90 percent of the human genetic makeup must have come from Africa.

Specifically, they determined that the African population must have been small and that the populations in Europe and Asia must have been even smaller. With such small founding populations, interbreeding could not have occurred, as required by the multiregional hypothesis. The geographical distances separating the populations were too vast. This contradiction implies that the starting assumption, the multiregional hypothesis, must be incorrect.[14] This conclusion leaves no place for *H. erectus* in humanity's origin.

The Great Divide

Though some hominid fossils seem to display anatomical continuity with human beings, other features speak of discontinuity. The gap is most clearly evident between *H. erectus* and the first humans in Asia. Anthropologists Li Jin and Bing Su recently surveyed the Asian fossil record and discovered that a significant divide (60,000 to 70,000 years wide) exists between the last occurrence of archaic hominids (about 100,000 years ago) and the first appearance of human beings (40,000 to 30,000 years ago).[15] A gap of this magnitude shows the unlikelihood that *H. erectus* or any of its purported evolutionary descendants evolved into Asian, Australian, and Oceanic peoples. This break in the fossil record comports with the genetic evidence that indirectly severs the genetic (and hence evolutionary) link between *H. erectus* and humans.

H. erectus has now been relegated, by both sets of data, to a side branch and dead end in the evolutionary framework. But what about Turkana boy? As an *H. ergaster*, could that skeleton have once framed an ancient human relative?

With *H. erectus* displaced from human lineage, many paleoanthropologists still consider *H. ergaster* part of the evolutionary pathway that led to modern humans. According to this view, *H. ergaster* gave rise to African archaic *Homo sapiens*, such as *H. heidelbergensis*, which appeared around 500,000 years ago. Presumably, these hominids gave rise to modern humans.

New insights into *H. erectus/ergaster* development help define its relationship to humanity.

The Tale of Two Teeth

In 2001, a study characterizing the developmental pattern of *H. erectus/ergaster* teeth emphasized the distance between these hominids and human beings. One way that paleoanthropologists gain insight into the development of extinct hominids is from dental anatomy, because dental development tightly correlates with other steps in the growth process. For example, apes and humans have distinct patterns of permanent tooth eruption. These patterns not only allow researchers to assess the approximate age of a hominid at the time of death but also help them identify potential evolutionary relationships among the hominids in the fossil record.[16] For paleoanthropologists, hominids with similar developmental patterns are more likely to be closely linked by evolutionary descent.

Based on the tooth eruption pattern of *H. erectus/ergaster*, many scientists have traditionally held that this hominid looks more like a human being than like a chimpanzee. On that basis, *H. erectus/ergaster* has long held its status as a transitional intermediate.[17] Two recent studies, however, strongly challenge that status.

Paleoanthropologists have traditionally used the tooth eruption pattern and growth rates of chimpanzees held in captivity to interpret the developmental timing of hominids in the fossil record. Based on this calibration, it appears as though *H. erectus'* maturation rate fell between that of chimpanzees and modern humans. New findings, however, compel a different conclusion.[18]

Instead of relying on growth rates of captive chimpanzees, researchers from the University of California, Santa Cruz, used data developed from chimpanzees in the wild, where maturation proceeds more slowly. When paleoanthropologists factored this observation into their calibration, it showed that the erectines developed much more like chimpanzees than like human beings. According to one of the researchers involved in the study, "These findings do not support *Homo erectus* developmentally as an intermediate between chimplike ancestors and modern humans."[19]

To gain a more detailed understanding of growth patterns and rates, an international team of paleontologists compared the dental anatomy of 13 hominid fossils. They focused on features of tooth microanatomy that result from daily and weekly enamel deposits.[20] These dental characteristics provided the researchers with a direct record of each day in the early life of these hominids. From the daily and weekly features, the research team determined that *H. habilis* and *H. erectus/ergaster* developed in a way that closely resembles the development of apes and australopithecines. Unlike modern humans, who develop much more slowly, the australopithecines, *H. habilis*, and *H. erectus/ergaster* (like the great apes today) grew rapidly and skipped adolescence. Even though *H. erectus/ergaster* walked erect and had a relatively large brain, this creature did not have the time provided by adolescence for additional brain growth and learning.

H. erectus/ergaster now appears to have had more in common with apes than with human beings.

Brain Development
A recent study on the brain development of *H. erectus* stretches the distance between human beings and the erectines. This work used computed tomography (CT technology) to image the skull of the *H. erectus* infant called the

"Mojokerto child" (recovered in Indonesia and dated at 1.8 million years in age). From the CT image, the brain size of the Mojokerto child measures 663 cm^3, about 84 percent of the size of an adult *H. erectus* brain.[21]

In humans, the brain size at birth is only 25 percent of the adult brain size. By one year of age, the brain size is 50 percent of an adult's. In contrast, the brain of apes at birth is 40 percent the size of an adult ape's, and at one year of age, about 80 percent of the size. Paleoanthropologists believe the Mojokerto child was between 0.5 and 1.5 years old when it died. On this basis, it appears as if the erectine brain developed much more like an ape's than like a human's.

The Boy Who Never Was

The latest advances in *H. erectus* biology (anatomy, developmental patterns, and genetics) render these hominids as side branches and dead ends in the evolutionary framework. Mounting morphological and developmental evidence also widens the gap between humans and the erectines. Ironically, one of the hominids with the most abundant fossil record is no longer considered by many paleoanthropologists to be part of modern humans' evolutionary lineage. The status of *H. erectus* leaves evolutionary biologists with a rather sparse fossil record to piece together the evolutionary pathway that led to humanity. The textbook perception of Turkana boy (and *H. erectus* in general) as a transitional form between hominids and humans increasingly lacks scientific support.

These new insights into *H. erectus/ergaster* biology fit well with the RTB model, which identifies all hominids as animals created by God yet distinct from humanity (see "Who Were the Hominids?" on page 53). These hominids existed for a time then went extinct, disappearing (in almost all cases) before Adam and Eve were created. The biological separation between humans and *H. erectus/ergaster*, now recognized by the scientific community, is anticipated by the RTB model.

Hominids were *not* made in God's image. This distinction is reserved only for human beings (*Homo sapiens sapiens*), according to the RTB model. As a consequence, hominid behavior and culture should be crude and qualitatively different from that of humankind. Only human beings should display behavior and culture that reflect their creation in God's image. While biological characteristics are significant in drawing a distinction between humans and hominids, they are not the only or most important criteria—behavior is. Archeological evidence recovered from *H. erectus/ergaster* sites yields important insight into the behavior and culture of these hominids.

A Crude Culture

Homo erectus/ergaster produced Acheulean technology, which consisted of extremely crude stone tools. This technology (which first appears in the archeological record around 1.6 million years ago) was only a small step upward in sophistication from the earliest discernible tool use (see "Tool Time"). Acheulean tools consisted of stones flaked on both surfaces to form a sharp point. Paleoanthropologists refer to teardrop-shaped stone tools as hand axes and to those with a longer sharp edge as cleavers. Once Acheulean tools appeared in the archeological record, they underwent relatively minor changes over the course of the next 1.3 million years.[22] Scientists are unsure of how *H. erectus/ergaster* used hand axes and cleavers. Likely these hominids cut into wood and animal hides and removed meat from bones with these tools.

Some paleoanthropologists suggest that *H. erectus/ergaster* mastered fire use.[23] One of the most high-profile pieces of evidence for this behavior consists of burned animal bones in the same layers as Acheulean stone tools in the Zhoukoudian Cave near Beijing, China. The layered depths containing the bones and tools date between 500,000 and 200,000 years old. Other paleoanthropologists, however, claim that no ash or charcoal was found at the site and attribute the burning to naturally ignited fire.[24]

Other archeological evidence for fire use comes from Africa (near Kenya) and dates at 1.5 million years in age. However, as with the Zhoukoudian site, no ash or charcoal has been recovered. Again, brushfires might have caused the baked sediment.[25]

Tool Time

Most scientists think the first hominids to use tools were *H. habilis*. Others argue that *Australopithecus garhi* were the first.[26] The original tool users employed stone tools that consisted of sharp-edged stone flakes that were battered away from a stone core using a "hammer" stone.

Paleoanthropologists refer to the tools produced by these earliest toolmakers as Olduwan technology. Most researchers agree that the first toolmakers had greater interest in the flakes than in the core. The Olduwan culture first appeared in the archeological record around 2.6 million years ago and persisted unchanged until about 1.6 million years ago.[27]

Flores Man: Human or Hobbit?

Most people know that Middle Earth is not a real place. Humans, dwarves, elves, and hobbits never lived together. But in the fall of 2004, paleoanthropologists from Australia and Indonesia reported on fossil and archeological evidence for hobbit-sized hominids that coexisted for a time with modern humans.[28]

Skeletal remains of these hominids, recovered on Flores Island, Indonesia, indicate that these creatures were just over three feet tall, with an australopithecine-like brain size (415 cm^3). Comparisons of *Homo florensiensis* brain structure (determined from a virtual endocast generated by CT scans) with other hominids and modern humans indicate that its brain shape is most like that of *H. erectus*. Yet, the *H. floresiensis* brain possesses unique features as well.[29] Their cranial and facial features were erectine and their post-cranial skeleton combined features of both the australopithecines and *H. erectus*.[30] These unusual traits prompted the paleoanthropologists who recovered these remains to classify them as a new hominid species, *H. floresiensis*. This hominid species is considered to be closely related to other erectine hominids.

The most remarkable specimen recovered was a nearly complete skeleton of a female (ironically nicknamed the Flores man) that dates to about 18,000 years in age. Other fossil and archeological evidence indicates that *H. floresiensis* existed on Flores Island from about 95,000 to 12,000 years ago, when volcanic eruptions on the island presumably drove this hominid to extinction. It appears that *H. floresiensis*, like the Neanderthals, coexisted with modern humans. Still, paleoanthropologists are not sure if the hominids had any contact with human beings after humans migrated into Southeast Asia.[31]

Archeological evidence and animal remains associated with *H. floresiensis* fossils indicate that these hominids hunted and scavenged the dwarf elephants on the island as well as fish, snakes, frogs, birds, and tortoises. Just like *H. erectus*, they used tools that belong to the Acheulean, or Mode II, industry.[32]

This unusual and unexpected discovery causes little difficulty for the RTB human origins model. *H. floresiensis* is clearly distinct from modern humans, not only in morphology, but in behavior as well. Like *H. erectus*, *H. floresiensis* behaved in nonhuman ways. The RTB model considers these hominids in the same vein as the great apes—nonhuman creatures made by God (before He created human beings) that later became extinct.

Recently, however, paleoanthropologists from Israel claimed to have found solid evidence for fire use (presumably by *H. erectus/ergaster*) as early as 790,000 years ago.[33] These researchers recovered burned flint, wood, and seeds from the

Gesher Benot Ya'aqov site. Because only a small portion (less than 2 percent) of the remains were charred, they concluded that the burning was localized and controlled. The small percentage of burned materials seems to rule out the possibility that natural fires were responsible for the burned items.

Still, several archeologists have cautioned that natural fires can never be completely ruled out as the source of fire. Eleai Asouti (from the Institute of Archaeology in London) notes that definite proof for fire use would require "the wood fragments [to come] from the same locations as the burned flint."[34] This requirement has not been met in these *H. erectus/ergaster* sites. To date, the first undisputed evidence for fire use in the archeological record dates to about 200,000 (± 50,000) years ago, well after the time when *H. erectus/ergaster* became extinct.

The Prick Draws No Blood

The archeological evidence indicates that *H. erectus/ergaster* was an exceptional creature, advanced compared to the animals and hominids that came before. Still, this primate's behavior was not human. Though *H. erectus/ergaster* used tools, the implements were crude and unsophisticated compared to those employed by human beings. Evidence that *H. erectus/ergaster* used fire remains controversial. Moreover, fire use may not be a marker for human behavior (and God's image). *H. erectus/ergaster* fire use might have consisted of the opportunistic exploitation of naturally occurring fires. While no existing animals exploit fire in this way, the hominids found in the fossil record are unique. No animals alive today (including the great apes) are like *H. erectus/ergaster*. Nevertheless, no links between them and human beings have been established. And the disconnect grows wider with time as the evidence accumulates.

But what about Neanderthals? Could they be the transitional intermediates that evolved into humans? The next chapter explores Neanderthals' identity and how they fit with the RTB creation model.

Chapter 12

Who Were the Neanderthals?

Alas, poor Yorick! I
Knew him, Horatio, a fellow
Of infinite jest, of most
Excellent fancy. He hath bore
Me on his back a thousand times,
And how abhorr'd in my imagination
It is! My gorge rises at it.
Here hung those lips that I have
Kiss'd I know not how oft.
Where be your gibes now, your gambols,
Your songs, your flashes of merriment,
That were wont to get the table
On a roar?
                        —*Hamlet* Act 5, scene 1

If Neanderthals had survived extinction, would anybody want to sit next to one in a subway car? French paleoanthropologist Marcellin Boule probably would have taken a seat as far away as possible. Based on his examination of a nearly complete skeleton specimen, Boule concluded that Neanderthal was a slouching brute that made no immediate contribution to human origins.[1]

Boule's work on the La Chapelle-aux-Saints Neanderthal in 1908 was the first detailed comparison between human beings and these enigmatic hominids. Some scientists, however, disagreed with Boule's assessment.

According to William Straus (Johns Hopkins University) and A. J. E. Cave (St. Bartholomew's Hospital Medical Center), no one would notice a Neanderthal in the subway, "provided that he were bathed, shaved, and dressed in modern clothing."[2] These two anthropologists offered their commentary at a symposium held in 1956 commemorating the 100th anniversary of the

Neanderthals' discovery.

After reanalyzing the La Chapelle-aux-Saints fossils, Straus and Cave concluded that Boule's interpretation stemmed from his failure to recognize severe arthritis in the specimen's spine. Their reinterpretation presented the Neanderthal as a close relative to modern humans in the evolutionary framework. Based on this (and subsequent work), anthropologists for a time considered the Neanderthal "rehabilitated," a likely transitional form that immediately preceded human beings.

But what about now? For anthropologists and laypeople alike, controversy and intrigue surrounds the Neanderthals' status and fate. Since this creature's discovery in 1856, people have wondered, did Neanderthals evolve into modern humans? Like human beings, did they employ language and symbolic thought? Did they bury their dead and engage in religious expression? Stunning new advances in the study of Neanderthal biology can now provide some answers to these questions.

"I Knew Him, Horatio"

Neanderthals are classified as archaic *Homo sapiens* that lived (based on the fossil record) roughly between 150,000 and 30,000 years ago. They occupied Europe, the Middle East, and parts of Asia.[3]

In contrast to other hominids, the Neanderthal fossil and archeological records are rich. Fossil hunters have recovered nearly 30 complete skeletons and numerous partial remains.[4] The abundance of fossils and artifacts gives researchers powerful clues about Neanderthal biology and culture and, ultimately, comparative status with human beings. The data are sufficient to rigorously assess whether an evolutionary connection exists between Neanderthals and modern humans.

Anatomical similarities between the two seem obvious. This resemblance, as well as the time frame for Neanderthals' existence and their overlap with that of the first European humans, shaped paleoanthropologists' view of Neanderthal as a transitional form leading to modern humans (or at least to Europeans, in the multiregional model).

At Least I Thought I Did

Though anatomically similar in many ways, Neanderthals and humans exhibit significant morphological differences. In some instances, Neanderthals display a unique combination of features, unknown in any other hominid.[5] Compared to human beings, Neanderthals displayed:[6]

- an extraordinarily long face
- a pronounced midface projection
- a poorly developed chin
- a highly developed brow ridge
- large, round eye sockets
- an extremely long nose
- cavernous sinuses
- larger front teeth
- a retromolar gap
- an occipital bun
- a brain flatter and smaller in the front and more bulged in the back and sides
- a flatter skull
- an elongated foramen magnum (opening in the skull for the spinal cord)
- a higher larynx
- thicker bones
- a more compact body with a barrel chest and shorter limbs

The Neanderthals' brain size slightly exceeded that of humans, but their brain-size to body-mass ratio was smaller. In other words, encephalization was less extensive in Neanderthals than in human beings.

For a time, anthropologists who saw an evolutionary connection between Neanderthals and modern humans didn't consider the differences particularly meaningful. These scientists claimed that (to a large extent) the anatomical distinctives could be explained by the Neanderthals' lifestyle and environmental influences. In other words, the researchers didn't think the Neanderthals' unique characteristics were inherent. Rather, they presumed these features resulted from nongenetic factors.

The Neanderthals lived in a cold climate, and many of their facial and bodily attributes allowed them to thrive in harsh conditions. Modern human populations that have historically occupied frigid environments (such as the Inuits) display similar facial and body features. According to Bergmann's rule and Allen's rule, people found in cold environments naturally possess smaller, more barrel-shaped bodies and shorter limbs than do human populations with historical connection to warm climates. Stockier bodies with shorter arms and legs (according to these rules) help retain body heat. In warm climates, long limbs and elongated trunks make heat dissipation more efficient.[7] Therefore, some paleoanthropologists have claimed that the Neanderthals' unique anatomy may simply reflect cold adaptation, not fundamental genetic differences.

Stanford University researcher Timothy Weaver recently provided new insight along these lines. Neanderthal femurs are distinct from those of other hominids and human beings. By carefully examining the relationship between human morphology and climate, Weaver concluded that Neanderthal femur anatomy stems from environmental effects, not inherent genetic factors.[8] His data shows, however, that the cold-adapted features of these leg bones are extreme compared to the femurs of the Inuit and Aleutian peoples—the most well-adapted inhabitants of today's coldest climates.

This extreme degree of difference seems to be the case for practically all Neanderthal cold adaptations. They are similar to the climate-based variation of modern humans, but exceptional in that they lie outside the range seen in current populations. In light of Bergmann's and Allen's rules, anthropologists refer to the Neanderthal body plan as *hyperpolar* or *hyperarctic*, acknowledging this observation.

Not My Brother

Many paleoanthropologists acknowledge that climate effects may account for some anatomical differences between humans and Neanderthals. However, some of these same scientists maintain that the Neanderthals' unique features represent a profound distinction: Not only must Neanderthal be considered a separate species, but it must also be viewed as an evolutionary side branch, a dead end. In other words, the scientists claim that Neanderthals have no evolutionary connection to humanity.

This view gained significant support in 1992 when Yoel Rak discovered the skeleton of a Neanderthal infant in a limestone cave in Israel. The 50,000-year-old specimen manifested the same unique anatomical features as an adult Neanderthal. This similarity convinced Rak (along with the majority of paleoanthropologists) that Neanderthals are inherently distinct from human beings. The infant's morphology establishes that the anatomical differences stem largely from genetics, not exclusively from environmental and lifestyle effects.[9]

An anatomical study published in 2004 further confirms the conclusions of Rak and others. Using a recently developed statistical technique that incorporates and preserves the relative three-dimensional spatial orientation of anatomical features (during the data treatment), a team of paleoanthropologists compared the skull anatomies of Neanderthals and modern humans.[10] They found that Neanderthal and modern human data points formed distinct clusters. These investigators showed that the separation between the clusters was too great to allow classification as subspecies. Rather, they concluded, the anatomical distinctions between Neanderthal and human skulls indicate separate species. In fact, Neanderthals showed no closer anatomical affinity to modern Europeans than to any other human population group. This work "strongly implies that they [Neanderthals] were not ancestral to any extant human populations."[11]

Based on morphology alone, paleoanthropologists increasingly view these hominids as an evolutionary side branch. Their extinction meant the end of their kind.

Anthropologist Richard Klein quipped, "In the buff, Neanderthals would garner stares in any modern health club. It has sometimes been said that if they were properly dressed, they would go unnoticed on the New York subway, but even this is doubtful…unless like many New Yorkers, they made a point of minding their own business."[12]

Hitting the Mother Lode

In 1997, researchers from the Max Planck Institute and Pennsylvania State University reported the first genetic comparison of modern humans and Neanderthals.[13] During this groundbreaking study (which has been described as "science at its very best"), two independent teams isolated, amplified (with the polymerase chain reaction), and sequenced mitochondrial-DNA (mtDNA) fragments from the right humerus of the first-discovered Neanderthal specimen. These procedures were carried out using a fossil recovered in 1856 from the Neander Valley, Germany.

From the DNA fragments, each team pieced together the sequence for what is known as mtDNA's hypervariable I (HVI) region. This region consists of roughly 360 base pairs (genetic letters). The scientists then compared the Neanderthal HVI sequence to the corresponding sequence from 2,051 human and 59 chimpanzee samples. The human specimens came from 570 Europeans, 494 Asians, 478 Africans, 167 Native Americans, and 20 Australians and Oceanic individuals. The research revealed only an eight-base-pair difference, on average, for human-to-human comparisons (range: 1 to 24) but a 27-base-pair difference, on average, for Neanderthal-to-human comparisons (range: 22 to 36).

Most importantly, the locations and types of variations observed for the human-to-human comparisons were distinct from those for the Neanderthal-to-human. When the researchers compared the Neanderthal sequence to corresponding sequences in the various human subpopulation groups, they found an average 28-base-pair difference between Neanderthals and Europeans, a 27-base-pair difference between Neanderthals and Africans, a 27-base-pair difference between Neanderthals and Asians, and a 28-base-pair difference between Neanderthals and Native Americans.

In other words, Neanderthals were no more closely related to Europeans or any other population group than to human beings as a whole. This potent genetic data casts serious doubts upon the multiregional hypothesis (chapter 2). That hypothesis predicts a noticeably greater affinity between Neanderthals and modern European peoples.

Shortly after the 1997 report was published, the team from the Max Planck Institute extended their human-to-Neanderthal genetic comparison by including a second segment of mtDNA, called the hypervariable II (HVII) region.[14] This DNA sequence consists of about 340 base pairs. As with the first study, the HVII mtDNA fragments were isolated and amplified from the right humerus bone of the first Neanderthal specimen discovered. When examined alongside the corresponding HVII region from 663 modern humans, this segment differed, on average, by 35 base pairs (range: 29 to 43). For this study, human-to-human comparisons yielded an average difference of 10 base pairs (range: 1 to 35).

As with the HVI results, the research team found that the identity of the human subpopulation did not matter. Comparisons of Neanderthal DNA with human population groups yielded, on average, a 36-, 34-, and 34-base-pair difference between Neanderthal HVII and the samples from Europeans, Asians, and Africans, respectively.[15]

The extent and nature of the genetic differences make a powerful case that Neanderthals and humans are distinct species. Neanderthals did not make any genetic (and hence evolutionary) contribution to humanity, not even to Europeans as the multiregional model predicts. In fact, using the HVI for one estimate and the combined HVI and HVII DNA sequences for another, the Max Planck researchers found (from an evolutionary perspective) that Neanderthals and modern humans are so genetically diverse that they diverged from a common ancestor between 690,000 and 550,000 years ago and between 741,000 and 317,000 years ago, respectively.

Despite the power of the Planck team's case, several paleoanthropologists expressed unease.[16] For them, the conclusions of these two initial studies seemed too far-reaching. The work involved only a single Neanderthal specimen. These scientists also expressed concern about possible contamination.

The remains of the Neanderthal specimen had been extensively handled over the past 150 years. Each touch could transmit skin oils, skin cells, and so forth (which contain trace levels of modern human DNA), contaminating the fossil's surface. Given the age of the Neanderthal remains (perhaps 100,000 years old), only trace amounts of Neanderthal DNA should have survived. In fact, the surviving Neanderthal DNA was likely near the same level as the traces of contaminating DNA from the human handlers. Even though steps were taken to clean the fossil's surface before the Neanderthal DNA was extracted, and even though the DNA samples were obtained from the bone's interior, these scientists wondered how the Planck team could be so sure they didn't amplify and sequence human contaminant DNA. The polymerase chain reaction used to amplify the DNA is sensitive to such contamination.

Another concern had to do with errors that can occur during the amplification process. The polymerase chain reaction can make mistakes from time to time that lead to erroneous DNA sequences. If an error occurred early in the amplification process, then the differences between the Neanderthal and human DNA sequences might be due to a faulty process rather than to inherent genetic differences between the two species.[17]

Many of these legitimate concerns were laid to rest when teams from the University of Stockholm and the University of Glasgow each independently isolated, amplified, and sequenced the HVI and HVII mtDNA regions from the remains of a second Neanderthal fossil. This infant specimen, dated at 29,000 years old, was recovered from a cave in the northern Caucasus, the easternmost part of the Neanderthals' range.[18] Both teams obtained identical results. As with the first Neanderthal genetic study, these analyses noted a 22-base-pair difference between the northern Caucasus specimen's DNA and a modern human mtDNA reference sequence for the HVI region. They also found close agreement between their Neanderthal DNA sequence and the one obtained by the team from the Max Planck Institute (a mere 3.48 percent difference).

Since these two studies, the Planck team has isolated, amplified, and sequenced mtDNA from seven additional Neanderthal specimens—three dated at 42,000 years ago, recovered in Croatia; two dated near 40,000 years ago, recovered in the Neander Valley of Germany; the Engis 2 specimen, recovered in Belgium; and the La Chapelle-aux-Saints specimen, recovered in France.[19] The mtDNA sequences from these seven additional specimens closely agree with the sequences that were determined from the earlier studies.

The nine Neanderthal DNA sequences display only a 3.7 percent genetic difference—nearly the same variation observed among human mtDNA. In fact, the limited Neanderthal genetic diversity implies that, like humans, Neanderthals began as a small population in a single region that rapidly expanded and spread to fill its range.

The uneasiness that researchers felt about the results of the original study in 1997 has largely dissipated now that researchers have mtDNA sequences from nine separate Neanderthal specimens. Several independent laboratories, each essentially obtaining the same result on specimens representing different time points in the Neanderthals' existence, make it difficult to dismiss the Neanderthal genetic data as an artifact of contamination or error introduced during the amplification process. The cumulative weight of genetic evidence appears to decisively sever the link between Neanderthals and humans. At the same time, these data deal a significant blow to the multiregional hypothesis. The conclusion seems obvious—Neanderthals could not have given rise to modern European populations nor to any other human population group.

Not So Fast

As compelling as the evidence seems, a minority of paleoanthropologists remain unconvinced. They consider the genetic data insufficient to rule out a connection between Neanderthals and humans. Some researchers point out that the genetic studies rely exclusively on mtDNA comparisons. They ask whether the results would be the same in a comparison of nuclear DNA.

According to the challenges, while the mtDNA of modern humans and Neanderthals differ, the much more important chromosomal DNA found in the cell's nucleus may be highly similar and reflect a deep evolutionary connection between the two species. These holdouts maintain the possibility that Neanderthal mtDNA sequences disappeared from the modern human gene pool due to genetic drift and isolation, followed by extinction. Or perhaps (they think) the connection was lost because Neanderthal males selectively mated with modern human females (mtDNA has an exclusively maternal inheritance). In each of these cases, the scientists believe, Neanderthal nuclear DNA could still be a part of the human genome, even if the mtDNA sequences were lost.[20] If this scenario were true, then perhaps Neanderthals could still be considered a transitional intermediate.

Work done by paleoanthropologists from Australia seemingly supports this challenge.[21] These researchers isolated, amplified, and sequenced mtDNA from 10 human fossils recovered in Australia. Nine of these date between 2,000 and 15,000 years in age. The tenth specimen, known as "Lake Mungo man," tentatively dates somewhere between 40,000 and 60,000 years ago. The age remains controversial because of the dating technique applied (see chapter 8).[22]

The Lake Mungo man mtDNA sequence was found to be distinct from the other aboriginal fossils and from modern people. It looks as if Lake Mungo man's mtDNA sequence became extinct. If so, other mtDNA sequences might have been lost throughout human history. And perhaps that happened with the Neanderthals.

If the Neanderthals' mtDNA sequence was lost, the genetic continuity between them and modern humans would have been disrupted over time. In the distant past, the continuity would be readily evident. The apparent connection would then diminish until it disappears. Comparisons between Neanderthal and currently existing human populations thus might reflect the end of this decay process. In order to test this idea, paleoanthropologists must compare Neanderthal mtDNA sequences with ancient remains of humans that date as close as possible to the time when Neanderthals existed.

A scientific team from Spain and Italy recently performed this type of comparison. They isolated, amplified, and sequenced mtDNA from two human remains recovered in Italy and dating to 25,000 and 23,000 years in age.[23] These people lived within the Neanderthals' range and soon after the hominids disappeared. The researchers discovered that the mtDNA sequences of these ancient humans were characteristically identical to those of contemporary humans and yet were distinct from Neanderthal mtDNA.

The two ancient human mtDNA sequences differed from four previously published Neanderthal sequences by 22 to 28 base pairs. In other words, as soon as human beings appeared in Europe, sharp genetic differences existed between them and Neanderthals. The DNA from Neanderthals does not appear to be human DNA that became extinct.

By including mtDNA data from human remains dated to 14,000 and 5,500 years ago (data obtained via earlier studies), these researchers carefully tracked changes in human mtDNA sequences from about 24,000 years ago all the way to the present day.[24] The mtDNA sequences were characteristically identical. And in all cases, the mtDNA was distinct from Neanderthal mtDNA. That discontinuity remained unchanged through time.

The Italian and Spanish scientists also examined the Lake Mungo man's mtDNA sequence in their study.[25] The numerical parameters that characterize the Lake Mungo man DNA sequence closely cluster with those that describe modern human DNA sequences, and at the same time they reside an appreciable distance from the Neanderthal DNA cluster. Although the specific DNA sequence for Lake Mungo man does not occur in the contemporary human gene pool, it still is characteristically a human DNA sequence. Neanderthal DNA sequences do not possess the telltale features of human DNA.

Again, the evidence shows that Neanderthal DNA is not modern human DNA that became extinct. It is DNA characteristic of a separate species.

Concern remains, however, over the fact that comparative genetic studies focus only on mtDNA, and it's unlikely that in the near future technology will progress to the point that nuclear DNA sequences can be isolated from Neanderthal remains. In the absence of this capability, an international team recently conducted a broad-based comparison of Neanderthal and human genomes.[26] These researchers compared the propensity of Neanderthal DNA fragments (isolated from two specimens) and ancient human DNA fragments to physically associate (using a technique called southern blot hybridizations). The more similar two DNA sequences are, the more tightly they associate. While its methodology has been debated, this study appears to indicate that the genetic difference between Neanderthals and modern humans extends beyond their mtDNA and involves other parts of the genome as well.[27]

An Odd Couple
Despite this compelling accumulation of evidence, a minority of paleoanthropologists still believe Neanderthals might have made a genetic contribution to modern humans through interbreeding. Their case relies exclusively on morphological evidence.

The first suggestion that humans and Neanderthals might have interbred came in 1999 when a team of paleoanthropologists reported on a fossil find from Portugal (near Lapedo Valley) dated to 24,500 years ago. This find consists of the complete skeletal remains of a young male child recovered from a burial site.[28] These scientists interpreted the anatomy of the "Lagar Velho child" to consist of mixed modern human and Neanderthal features. From this observation, the researchers concluded that these two species must be closely related and that they regularly met and mated with one another.[29]

The interpretation of the Lagar Velho child as a relatively recent human-Neanderthal hybrid has been greeted with skepticism by most paleoanthropologists. Commenting on this discovery, Ian Tattersall and Jeffrey Schwartz state, "The analysis ...of the Lagar Velho child's skeleton is a brave and imaginative interpretation, of which it is unlikely that a majority of paleoanthropologists will consider proven."[30]

The reasons for such a response from the anthropological community are many. First, no one can easily or definitively project what a modern hu-man-Neanderthal hybrid would look like.[31] Second, the case for interbreeding among Neanderthals and humans rested on a *single* find that dates well after the time of the Neanderthals' extinction (about 30,000 years ago). If interbreeding were the case, evidence should be abundant. Paleoanthropologist Christopher Stringer points out, "Numerous fossils of early modern humans show no signs of Neanderthal contacts."[32]

If the Lagar Velho child specimens were a hybrid, one could reasonably expect that the fossil would show at least *some* distinctly Neanderthal features. It doesn't.[33] Furthermore, some of the traits (such as the mastoid and juxta-mastoid eminences) interpreted as intermediate characteristics between mod-ern humans and Neanderthals are known to be highly variable within species. Others (like limb proportions) are considered unreliable diagnostic features for species assignment.[34] What's more, the burial site that yielded the Lagar Velho child is typical of the graves used by humans living at that time. The Lagar Velho child simply represents either an unusually stocky human child or one who experienced some type of abnormal growth.[35]

This same team of paleoanthropologists claimed in 2003 to have discov-ered yet another example of a human-Neanderthal hybrid. This specimen, re-covered in Romania, consists of a single lower jaw that dates to about 35,000 years ago—a time when humans and Neanderthals likely coexisted in Europe. Again, these researchers interpreted the jaw and dental anatomy to be a mosaic of archaic hominid, Neanderthal, and modern human features. And again, the scientists maintain that this integration indicates continuity among the three populations and extensive interbreeding among modern humans and Nean-derthals.[36]

The same criticisms leveled at the hybrid status of the Lagar Velho inter-pretation apply in this case as well. To consider this specimen a second example of a human-Neanderthal hybrid is unwarranted, especially given that the in-terpretation for the Lagar Velho child was largely discredited. Again, the case for interbreeding between modern humans and Neanderthals rests on a *single* jawbone that displays not even one diagnostic feature of Neanderthals. Given that certain anatomical features of both Neanderthals and humans fall within the same (wide) continuum, it's much more reasonable to interpret this speci-men as a human jawbone with somewhat unusual dimensions.

A study by researchers from the Max Planck Institute published in 2004 supplies direct evidence that Neanderthals and humans likely did *not* interbreed.[37] This work compared mtDNA recovered from four

Neanderthals with mtDNA isolated from the remains of five human fossils. The Neanderthal and human specimens all date within the same time period (between 40,000 and 30,000 years ago), and they were found in corresponding geographical locations.

Based on morphological features alone, proponents of the multiregional hypothesis had considered two of these fossils to be transitional intermediates between Neanderthals and modern humans. However, the Planck investigators readily attained Neanderthal-type DNA from the Neanderthal specimens and detected no Neanderthal DNA in the human remains. The mtDNA sequences isolated from the two "transitional intermediate" specimens contained no "hybrid" Neanderthal-human sequence. Rather, one possessed a characteristically Neanderthal mtDNA sequence, and the other possessed a characteristically human mtDNA sequence.

Using a simple model, Max Planck Institute researchers concluded that Neanderthals could not have made a genetic contribution to the human gene pool at a rate any larger than 25 percent.

Recently, two Swiss researchers addressed the question of interbreeding between humans and Neanderthals by performing a more sophisticated and realistic analysis of the genetic data. From their modeling, the Swiss scientists concluded that the maximum interbreeding rate between humans and Neanderthals was 0.1 percent, not 25 percent. They estimated that over the course of 12,000 years of potential contact, no more than 120 interbreeding events could have taken place between humans and Neanderthals.[38]

More Differences
Not only does morphological and genetic evidence break the hypothesized evolutionary ties between humans and Neanderthals, but developmental dissimilarities do also. Computerized reconstructions of fossilized Neanderthal infant skulls expose another significant distinction. In 2001, researchers from the University of Zurich generated three-dimensional computer reconstructions of 16 Neanderthal skulls from specimens ranging in age (at the time of death) from six months to young adulthood.[39] Their objective was to compare Neanderthal skull development with human skull development. For the human data set, they produced CT reconstructions using both fossils and still-living human skulls.

This study revealed that dramatic differences in the skull and jaw anatomy appear quite early in the development process. Neanderthals underwent a much more rapid craniofacial development along a completely different developmental trajectory. The Swiss scientists noted a highly consistent developmental pattern for the 16 specimens studied, even though they represent remains through time and across the Neanderthals' range. This stability shows a developmental pattern inherent to Neanderthals and associated with their first appearance.

In 2004, a team of French and Spanish scientists compared Neanderthal and human development using tooth anatomy.[40] Dental development that closely corresponds to overall development and life history makes such an evaluation possible. Moreover, some microanatomical tooth features result from the regular deposition of enamel that occurs every nine days or so. These microlayers provide a proxy for growth rates and patterns.

This comparison also showed that Neanderthals matured much more rapidly than humans. And again, the researchers attested that Neanderthals and humans must be distinct species. (This same study additionally determined that humans develop more slowly than did *Homo antecessor* and *Homo heidelbergensis*.)

Though the textbook view considers Neanderthals to be a part of humanity's lineage, the preponderance of scientific evidence strongly positions them off to the side—a separate branch in any evolutionary framework. Strauss and Cave argued in 1956 that the public perception of the Neanderthals is incorrect. Instead of being rehabilitated as modern humans, the Neanderthals have been rendered extinct hominids with no bearing on humanity's origin.

A Cultured Beauty or a Beast?

The RTB model readily accommodates scientific insights into Neanderthal biology. It identifies these hominids as created by God—with some similarities to human beings and yet distinct (see page 50). Hominids existed for a time, then went extinct. The biological separation, now recognized by the scientific community, is what the RTB model anticipates.

This biblical record of origins states that only one creature was made in God's image. That distinction belongs solely to humans (*Homo sapiens sapiens*). As a consequence, the RTB model predicts that Neanderthal behavior and culture will be qualitatively different from humankind's. Only people should display behavior and a culture that reflect God's image. As with *Homo erectus/ergaster*, behavior is the most important criteria for drawing a distinction between humans and Neanderthals.

Archeological evidence from Neanderthal sites has yielded important insight into their behavior and culture. Claims that Neanderthals used sophisticated tools, possessed language, and engaged in artistic and musical expression abound. They might have buried their dead. And there's a widespread perception that Neanderthals engaged in religious activity. If these claims are accurate, the RTB model needs major adjustment. What does the archeological record say?

Hand me a spearhead

The Neanderthals' tool kit belongs to the Mousterian culture (also known as the Middle Stone Age and Middle Paleolithic). This technology appeared about 250,000 years ago and disappeared around 30,000 years ago when the Neanderthals vanished. Relatively few Middle Stone Age sites are known outside Europe. Mousterian technology primarily relied on stones and wood. The archeological data seem to indicate little if any use of bone, antlers, or ivory. In contrast to Acheulean technology (used by *H. erectus/ergaster*), the stone flakes taken from rock cores were fashioned to a greater degree to form a larger collection of tool shapes.

Stone tools were much more standardized in the Mousterian culture than in the Acheulean. Some paleoanthropologists think that stone flakes might have been used as spearheads, indicating that Neanderthals were effective hunters.[41] Hand axes (used by *H. erectus/ergaster)* were absent from the Mousterian tool kit.[42] Still, compared to the tools used by the earliest human beings, Neanderthal implements were relatively unsophisticated. According to paleoanthropologist Richard Klein, "The archeological record suggests that they [Neanderthals] were behaviorally far less innovative [than modern humans]."[43]

A somewhat controversial study reported in 2001 offers one possible (or perhaps partial) explanation for the simplicity of the Neanderthals' tools: Neanderthals might not have possessed the manual dexterity needed to fashion and use sophisticated tools.[44] This conclusion (based on multivariate statistical analysis of metacarpal bones, which would be involved in grip) implies significant behavioral differences between Neanderthals and humans.

Let's do lunch

Differences in dietary habits also suggest behavioral and cognitive dissimilarities between Neanderthals and the earliest humans. By analyzing different forms of carbon and nitrogen (isotopes) from bone collagen (fibrous proteins in bones), paleoanthropologists from the United States and the United Kingdom identified the protein sources in the diets of these two species. They found that the protein in the Neanderthal diet came almost exclusively from the consumption of terrestrial herbivores. In contrast, early people who lived 40,000 to 30,000 years ago ate a varied diet including fish, fowl, mollusks, and herbivores from freshwater, wetlands, seacoasts, and dry terrestrial regions.[45]

These people displayed a far greater proficiency at obtaining food from their environment than Neanderthals ever did. Thus these dietary differences may reflect an important disparity in cognitive capability. Early human ability to acquire protein from a wide range of sources suggests a superior intelligence. Neanderthals apparently lacked the means to adjust their diet as circumstances demanded.

"Where be your gibes?"

When it comes to cognitive ability, no issue is more contentious among paleoanthropologists than the Neanderthals' ability to communicate. The anatomical evidence, while not entirely conclusive, increasingly indicates that Neanderthals lacked the capacity for speech and language. The structure of the Neanderthal skull base was not conducive for speech.

Compared to hominids, human beings have a shorter skull base. This faculty allows for a lower larynx, leaving a larger air space above it. The expanded air space allows people to produce the range of sounds needed for spoken language. Considering the structure of the Neanderthals' skull base, its larynx appears too high to allow for speech. This feature enhanced the Neanderthals' ability to live in a frigid environment because it limited the amount of cold air they "gulped" when they breathed.[46]

Some anthropologists point out, however, that the hyoid bones of Neanderthals and of modern humans are identical. This U-shaped bone connects to muscles of the jaw, larynx, and tongue and may provide the vocal tract's shape. This disputed conclusion may be taken as evidence that Neanderthals could speak.[47]

The hypoglossal canal guides the nerve that controls the tongue muscles. A high-profile study published in 1998 maintained that, based on the size of their hypoglossal canal, Neanderthals had the same vocal capabilities as humans.[48] The researchers who conducted this study argued that the more richly the tongue muscle is supplied with nerves (thus necessitating a larger canal), the better the motor control of the tongue—a key requirement for speech.

Other paleoanthropologists have demonstrated that this intriguing idea lacks validity. Two follow-up studies demonstrated that no correlation exists between canal size and vocal ability.[49] As Roger Lewin notes in his textbook on human evolution, "The notion that Neanderthals had poorly developed language abilities has become the majority position among anthropologists."[50]

Most anthropologists think language is necessary to develop and sustain advanced culture and technology. Without it, Neanderthals simply could not behave like human beings.

Where be "your songs, your flashes of merriment"?
Neanderthals lacked not only speech but also symbolic thought. Artistic and musical expression reflects this capacity. Klein states, "Unlike Upper Paleolithic Cro-Magnons [modern humans], Middle Paleolithic Neanderthals left little compelling evidence for art or jewelry."[51]

Despite a lack of evidence, some highly publicized claims have been made for Neanderthal artistic expression. One of the most widely known is the so-called Neanderthal flute recovered from a cave in Slovenia in 1995.[52] The paleo-anthropologists who made this find interpreted an 11-centimeter bone fragment from a cave bear's femur (leg bone) as a flute. This bone shaft had four evenly spaced circular openings on one side. Subsequent analysis, less publicized, revealed that these openings were more likely perforations to the bone caused by carnivores.[53]

The dearly departed
Highly touted claims of Neanderthals' ritual behavior and even religious expression have also appeared in the media. Their chief basis? Graves. Neanderthal remains have been uncovered in close association with tools and other artifacts or in an exaggerated fetal position that seems to have been deliberately arranged at the time of burial.[54]

One of the most widely known Neanderthal burial sites was excavated in Iraq between 1957 and 1961. Researchers there found pollen beneath the Neanderthal specimen. This discovery was taken to indicate that flowers had been placed around the corpse during a ritual burial.[55]

Other paleoanthropologists hesitate to conclude that Neanderthal burials were ritualistic. Natural causes could account for many of the features of Neanderthal "graves." A cave roof's collapse on live occupants (or abandoned bodies) could have buried them. Some scientists have suggested that wind might have blown the pollen in the Neanderthal grave onto the remains, or a rodent might have carried the pollen to the burial site.[56]

Paleoanthropologists struggle to interpret hominid behavior from a sparse archeological record. Conclusions drawn from limited data are speculative and far-ranging, often beyond what the evidence can sustain (as in the case with the pollen). Based on the data, it is not outlandish to conclude that Neanderthals buried their dead, at least occasionally, but to interpret these "burials" as deliberate, established rituals appears unwarranted and unsubstantiated. Neanderthal burials likely reflect the fact that these hominids possessed some limited emotional capacity, but this fact does not necessarily imply that they were spiritual beings.

Support for the idea that Neanderthals possessed some emotional capacity comes from some Neanderthal remains that have severe skeletal injuries that appear to have healed before death. This find is taken as evidence that Neanderthals cared for their sick and injured, assuming they couldn't have cared for themselves while healing.[57] However, this interpretation again involves far-reaching extrapolation from the evidence at hand.

A study published in 2002 indicates that Neanderthals might have used stone tools in violent acts of aggression against one another.[58] Scientists from Switzerland and France detected a healed fracture in the skull of a Neanderthal specimen. Detailed analysis of the fracture indicates it resulted from the impact of a sharp implement. Though their work is speculative, these researchers interpreted the find to indicate that Neanderthals used stone tools for aggression against one another as well as to hunt and process animal remains. Some paleoanthropologists consider violence among Neanderthals as an indicator of ritual behavior.

A few paleoanthropologists have conjectured that Neanderthals engaged in cannibalism. The idea arose in 1999 when an international team of paleoanthropologists unearthed the remains of six Neanderthals in a cave in France from deposits dated 120,000 to 100,000 years in age. These specimens displayed "butchery" marks and a hint that the skeletons had been cut apart to obtain meat.[59] While this finding could be evidence of ritual killing, in a more realistic scenario, cannibalism reflects an expected response to food shortages often suffered by Neanderthals living in extremely cold environments. Cannibalism would have been an obvious way to avoid starvation.

One of the most fanciful pieces of evidence cited in favor of Neanderthal religious expression came from caves in Switzerland and France that contained large and seemingly orderly collections of bear skeletons. A few paleoanthropologists interpreted the bear skeletons as a type of altar and initially took this evidence to indicate that Neanderthals worshiped as part of a "bear cult." Closer study, however, indicates that the remains had simply accumulated in the caves when bears died there during hibernation (perhaps over a period of years), with natural processes causing the apparent sorting of the bones.[60]

When all archeological evidence is critically considered, it appears as though Neanderthals possessed some capacity for emotional expression and a level of intelligence, similar to that of the great apes today. Yet they clearly lived in nonhuman ways. To say that Neanderthals behaved like spiritual beings made in God's image stretches the evidence beyond reasonable limits. The archeological evidence more closely coincides with the RTB model's perspective on these creatures—they behaved more like animals than like humans.

A Cave Full of Confusion

Despite unambiguous archeological evidence to the contrary, a minority of paleoanthropologists propose that, just prior to extinction, the Neanderthals acquired a culture virtually identical to that of human beings. Their primary evidence comes from a cave in France (Arcy-sur-Cure) that contains layers from both the Middle and Upper Paleolithic time frames. At layers that date 34,000 years in age (which corresponds to the end of the Neanderthals' existence), a Neanderthal specimen was recovered in what appears to be the same layer containing artifacts identical to those made by human beings.[61] The interpretation of this find represents an obvious challenge to RTB's model.

However, not all paleoanthropologists are so quick to conclude that Neanderthals eventually achieved technology and behavior comparable to those of modern humans. Some point out the various problems with this supposition. First they caution that, because several layers from different time periods lie close together, mixing might have jumbled contents, particularly for juxtaposed layers. Also, it's possible for two separate layers to be misinterpreted as one, even with the most careful excavation.

Another explanation relies on the idea that Neanderthals and humans coexisted. It's conceivable that Neanderthals might have mimicked—or borrowed—the technology of people. A more likely scenario is that Neanderthals came upon a cave site previously occupied and abandoned by human beings. Or perhaps the hominids took these artifacts from nearby human sites.[62] (Monkeys like to "steal" and play with human tools, pottery, and jewelry.)

When for nearly 120,000 years Neanderthal behavior seemed stagnant and unchanging, it would seem implausible to conclude that, just before their extinction, they suddenly and dramatically made a quantum leap in their cognitive capacity and developed human technology and culture. With more plausible explanations available (see chapter 5), the Arcy-sur-Cure cave artifacts raise no serious threat to the RTB model.

"Abhorr'd in My Imagination"

Two recent studies conducted by Italian and Spanish scientists employed multivariate statistical analysis to compare the brain shapes and structures of archaic *H. sapiens* (such as *H. heidelbergensis*), Neanderthals, and modern humans.[63] The team used both computer-generated models and physical brain endocasts in their analysis. They discovered that the brain shape and structure for Neanderthals and the "archaic" *H. sapiens* were essentially identical. The only difference? The Neanderthals' brains were larger.

Human brain shape and structure, however, are distinctly different. Compared to Neanderthals' brains, the human brain has a larger parietal lobe. This brain region plays a vital role in language, math reasoning, sense of self-identity, and religious experience.[64]

Such a profound biological distinction explains the behavioral difference between Neanderthals and people. The Neanderthals' brain shape and structure provided no capacity for behaving the way human beings behave. Neanderthals lacked the necessary brain structure to think and act in a way that reflects God's image.

Recent scientific advances have shuffled "Neanderthal man"—one of evolution's most popular icons—off center stage in the unfolding drama of human origins. The next chapter discusses what many people consider the most potent evidence for human evolution and the most difficult challenge yet encountered by RTB's creation model—the genetic similarity between humans and chimpanzees.

Chapter 13

What about Chimpanzees?

For that I am some twelve
Or fourteen moonshines
Lag of a brother? Why bastard?
Wherefore base?
When my dimensions are as well compact,
My mind as generous, and
My shape as true, as honest madam's issue?
Why brand they us?
With base? With baseness?
Bastardy? Base, base?
Who, in the lusty stealth of nature, take
More competition, and fierce quality,
Than doth within a dull, stale, tired bed
Go to th' creating a whole tribe of fops,
Got 'tween asleep and wake?
—*King Lear* Act 1, scene 2

"I kept thinking the project was a disaster because I couldn't find any difference," mused Mary-Claire King. Ironically, the absence of a difference made her PhD project a notable success.[1]

While working at the University of California, Berkeley, in the early 1970s, this burgeoning geneticist compared the amino acid sequences, as well as the immunological and physical properties, of several proteins isolated from both humans and chimpanzees. These three measures indicated to King and her doctoral supervisor, Allan Wilson, that only a small genetic distance separates the two species.[2] (An organism's genetic material directly specifies each protein's structure and hence its physical and immunological properties.)

According to King's results, humans and chimpanzees share a closer genetic relatedness than anyone had anticipated. King uncovered a 99 percent agreement in the amino acid sequences of several proteins.

Though King was disappointed with her inability to unmask any genetic and/or biochemical differences between humans and chimpanzees, the scientific community was not. *Science* (one of the world's most prestigious science periodicals) featured King and Wilson's article on its cover. Inside, they presented a detailed account of the molecular comparison between humans and chimpanzees.[3]

So Close

The 99 percent genetic similarity has been enshrined as a cultural icon. For many naturalists, this resemblance represents one of the most compelling arguments for humanity's evolutionary origin. Presumably, the 99 percent sequence overlap for proteins and DNA proves that humans and chimps arose from a common ancestor some time in the relatively recent past. According to this view, the small genetic differences arose after the human and chimpanzee lineages split as a consequence of mutational changes within each species' genetic material.

Despite all the support the RTB model receives from genetic and archeological evidence, this challenge must be addressed—doesn't the compelling genetic similarity between humans and chimpanzees mean human evolution must be true? An in-depth answer to this question comes from an examination of the recent comparative studies of human and chimp biochemistry and genetics. These studies uncover some unexpected surprises for both the RTB model and the evolutionary account of human origins.

For readers with little scientific background, the research findings cited in this chapter may at times seem complicated. Unfortunately, oversimplification detracts from the stunning detail that some readers will find essential to understanding the relationship between humans and chimpanzees. A couple of devices accommodate lay-level readers. Text boxes offer help for those who want to grasp the science. (For example, "Proteins, DNA, and Genes" on page 206 provides a quick refresher course.) Other readers may wish to skip the technical information altogether and move to the Bottom Line sections, where the significance of each finding is summarized.

All in the Family

Charles Darwin was the first to argue that the features shared by humans and apes reflect their mutual evolutionary ancestry.[4] And yet long before Darwin, biologists recognized and acknowledged the similarity between humans and chimpanzees (as well as the other great apes). Carl Linnaeus (1707–1778), the father of the biological classification system still used today, grouped humans and apes together as primates.[5]

On the basis of anatomical features, legendary evolutionary biologist George Gaylord Simpson in the 1940s grouped humans and the great apes in the same superfamily, *Hominoidae*. Within this superfamily, Simpson distinguished two families: (1) *Hominidae*, which included humans and the extinct bipedal primates found in the fossil record; and (2) *Pangidae*, which housed the great apes—chimpanzees, gorillas, and orangutans.[6] For many biologists, this classification represents the standard evolutionary relationships among these primates and humans.

Today's evolutionary biologists find this qualitative analysis unsatisfying. Family assignment is based on a subjective characterization of complex morphological features. The use of proteins and DNA to decipher evolutionary relationships allows researchers, at least in principle, to make objective quantitative comparisons (see "Proteins, DNA, and Genes" on page 206).

Beyond the quantitative potential, many evolutionists consider the analysis of proteins and DNA to be the basis for much more important fundamental comparisons. The amino acid sequences of proteins and the nucleotide sequences of DNA reflect an organism's genetic makeup. Genetic information determines each organism's anatomical and physiological traits. Since King and Wilson's landmark work on human and chimpanzee proteins, evolutionary biologists have conducted a litany of genetic and molecular analyses of humans and the great apes. Chromosome-to-chromosome and gene-to-gene comparative studies attempt not only to identify evolutionary relationships but also to understand what distinguishes humans from apes.

Chromosome to Chromosome

The cell houses DNA in its nucleus (a spherical structure near the cell's center) in packages called chromosomes (see "Chromosomes" on page 208). Around the time King was studying human and chimp proteins, geneticists developed staining techniques that allow them to visualize the fine structure of chromosomes. Each chromosome displays a unique banding pattern when exposed to certain dyes. These banding patterns permit geneticists to identify each chromosome.[7]

Evolutionary biologists began to exploit these staining techniques in an attempt to discern evolutionary relationships among various species based on

Proteins, DNA, and Genes

Proteins—the workhorse molecules of life—take part in virtually every cellular and extracellular structure and activity. They help form structures inside the cell and the surrounding matrix. Among their other roles, proteins catalyze (assist) chemical reactions, store and transport molecules, harvest chemical energy, and assemble the cell's structural components.[8]

Proteins are chainlike molecules that fold into precise three-dimensional structures. The protein's three-dimensional shape uniquely determines its functional and/or structural role.[9] A cell's biochemical machinery forms protein chains by linking together smaller molecules (amino acids) in a head-to-tail fashion. Biochemists refer to amino acids as subunits. The amino acid subunits are the links in the protein chain.[10]

The cell uses 20 different amino acids to build proteins. Amino acids that constitute proteins possess a range of chemical and physical properties.[11] The cell's machinery joins together these 20 amino acids in a wide variety of combinations. Each sequence produces a protein chain with a specific chemical and physical profile along its length. The protein chain's physicochemical properties determine (to a large extent) the way it folds three-dimensionally. In other words, the amino acid sequence determines the protein's structure, which in turn determines its function (see figure 13.1).

DNA stores the information used by the cell's machinery to make proteins. Like a protein, DNA is a chainlike molecule. It consists of two molecular chains that align themselves parallel to one another.[12] The paired DNA chains twist around each other to form the well-known DNA double helix.

The cell's machinery forms DNA by linking together subunit molecules called nucleotides. The cell uses four nucleotides (abbreviated A, G, C, and T) to form DNA's molecular chains (see figure 4).

The nucleotide sequences of DNA's molecular chain specify the amino acid sequences of proteins. Biochemists refer to the nucleotide sequence that specifies the entire amino acid sequence for a single protein as a gene. Through the use of genes, DNA stores the necessary information to make all the proteins an organism requires to function.

chromosome banding patterns.[13] Even though the patterns provide a crude measure, most researchers believe these measures point to something fundamental, because chromosome structure indirectly reflects an organism's genetic makeup.

Figure 13.1: Protein Structure
Proteins are chainlike molecules that fold into precise three-dimensional structures.

Chromosomes

DNA and proteins interact to make chromosomes.[14] These structures become visible in the cell nucleus as the cell divides. Each chromosome consists of a single DNA molecule that wraps around a series of globular protein complexes. These wrapped complexes repeat to form a supramolecular structure resembling a string of beads (see figure 13.2). Biochemists refer to the "beads" as nucleosomes.

The chain of nucleosomes further coils to form a structure called a solenoid. The solenoid condenses to form higher-order structures that constitute the chromosome. Between cell division events, the chromosome exists in an extended diffuse form that is not detectable. Prior to and during cell division, the chromosome condenses to form its readily recognizable compact structures.

All the genetic material (DNA) in the cell's nucleus is distributed among numerous chromosomes. The number of chromosomes in its cells is a characteristic feature of each species. For example, in the nucleus of each cell, chimpanzees possess 48 chromosomes, while humans possess 46.

Because DNA contains genes at specific locations along its length, each gene is found at a characteristic location on the chromosome. The banding patterns of chromosomes serve as landmarks, helping geneticists locate individual genes.

In the early 1980s, evolutionary biologists compared the chromosomes of humans, chimpanzees, gorillas, and orangutans using two staining techniques called G-banding and C-banding.[15] These studies revealed an exceptional degree of similarity between human chromosomes and chimp chromosomes. When aligned, the human and corresponding chimpanzee chromosomes appeared virtually identical. They displayed practically the same banding pattern, band locations, band size, and band stain intensity. To evolutionary biologists, this resemblance speaks of human and chimpanzee shared ancestry.

The researchers making these comparisons also identified differences between human and chimp chromosomes. These differences were interpreted, however, within an evolutionary framework. They were accounted for by chromosomal mutations after humans and apes diverged. For example, human chromosomes 1, 4, 5, 9, 12, 15, 16, 17, and 18 all manifest what appears to be a single inversion. This characteristic is assumed to result from the reversal of a chromosome segment due to a breakage and reunion event after human and chimpanzee lineages diverged.[16]

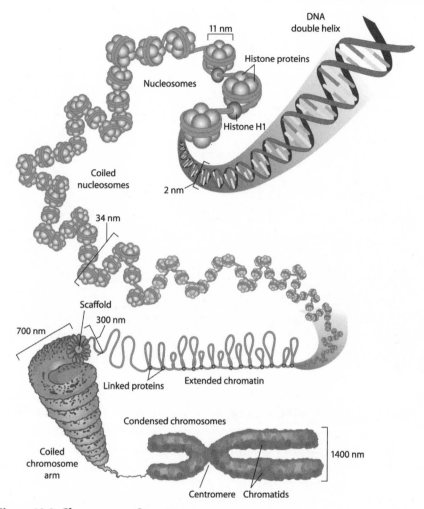

Figure 13.2: Chromosome Structure
DNA and proteins interact to make chromosomes.

Changes in the amount of centromeric DNA (located near the chromosome's central region) and telomeric DNA (located at the chromosome's tips) are also evident. These changes are explained by presumed amplification or reduction of chromosomal DNA after divergence from the shared ancestor. (DNA found in the chromosome's telomere and centromere does not contain genes. These two regions play a role in chromosome movement during cell division and help maintain the structural integrity of chromosomes.)

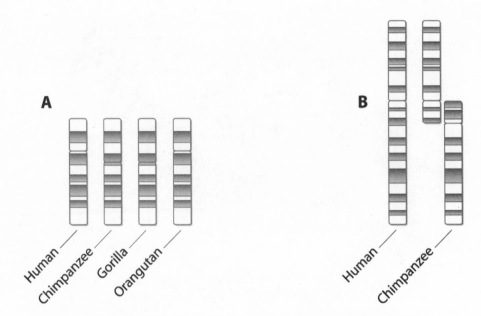

Figure 13.3: Human and Chimpanzee Chromosomal Comparison
(A) When aligned, human and corresponding chimpanzee chromosomes appear virtually identical. (B) Evolutionary biologists posit the fusion of two chimpanzee chromosomes to generate what is now human chromosome 2.

The most notable difference between human chromosomes and chimp chromosomes is the quantity: 46 for humans and 48 for chimpanzees. Evolutionary biologists account for this difference by suggesting that two chimp chromosomes fused. They think this fusion generated what is now human chromosome 2 (see figure 13.3).

Researchers continue to compare human chromosomes with those of other primates and mammals, using new techniques and technologies that allow more refined comparisons.[17] Still, the data and the conclusions are always viewed through the same lens—humans and chimpanzees share a high degree of chromosomal similarity because of their presumed evolutionary connection. Any difference in chromosomal structure is explained as the consequence of chromosomal mutations.

Evolutionary biologists have used chromosomal similarities and differences among primates to establish evolutionary relationships. According to these types of analyses, chimpanzees are the primate species most closely related to humans, with gorillas and orangutans the next closest relatives.[18]

Bottom line
Human and chimpanzee chromosomes display many structural similarities. Evolutionary biologists interpret these shared features as evidence that humans and chimpanzees evolved from a common ancestor.

"Wherefore Base?"
The chromosomal evidence for shared ancestry stands, at best, as a qualitative and indirect comparison of genetic material. Such information fails to offer any insight into the anatomical, physiological, and behavioral differences between human beings and chimpanzees. Evolutionary biologists therefore want a more direct and meaningful comparison at the molecular level.

Steps toward this goal have been taken through application of DNA-DNA hybridization. Begun in the 1970s at the California Institute of Technology, this technique gained importance in the early 1980s when two biologists from Yale University further developed the methodology and then used it to characterize bird origins.[19] This success encouraged biologists to begin using the technique to determine evolutionary relationships among primates.

DNA-DNA hybridization provides the means to make large-scale, though indirect, quantitative comparisons of DNA sequences. This procedure measures and compares the temperature required to separate the two strands that make up the DNA double helix (see "Proteins, DNA, and Genes" on page 206).

The DNA double helix is held together by interactions between the nucleotide side groups that extend from each individual chain's backbone. The side chain interactions are highly specific. Adenine (A) subunits of one strand always pair with the thymine (T) subunits of the other strand. Likewise, guanine (G) subunits on one strand always pair with the cytosine (C) subunits on the other strand (see figure 4). For the DNA double helix to have maximum stability, each subunit must pair with the corresponding subunit on the opposite DNA strand.

This requirement renders the nucleotide sequence of each DNA strand complementary to the other strand's sequence. Because of this complementarity, if biologists know the sequence of one DNA strand, they know the sequence of its companion strand.

When heated above a characteristic temperature (T_m), the two DNA strands of the double helix separate because heat breaks apart the bonds formed between A and T and between G and C on the complementary strands. DNA-DNA hybridization exploits this physical phenomenon. The first step in the process involves heating DNA from two different species to separate each DNA double helix. Once separated, the single DNA strands from each species are mixed and hybrid double helices form. One strand of the hybrid double helix comes from one species; the other strand comes from the other species.

These hybrid DNA molecules form "heteroduplexes." The side chains of the two DNA strands won't pair exactly because the DNA sequence of the two species is different, but the more similar the DNA sequences are, the more completely and tightly the two strands pair. The heteroduplexes are then carefully heated in a controlled fashion to determine precisely the temperature at which they separate (T_m).

The difference between the separation temperatures of the heteroduplex and DNA double helix for each species (ΔT_m) reflects their degree of genetic similarity. Evolutionary biologists use ΔT_ms to chart relationships among species with genetic similarity as an indicator of evolutionary relatedness.[20]

DNA-DNA hybridization studies show that, among the primates, chimp DNA has the highest degree of similarity to human DNA. The ΔT_m is 1.6°C for the human-chimpanzee heteroduplex.[21] By comparison, the ΔT_m for the human-gorilla heteroduplex is 2.3°C and 3.6°C for the human-orangutan heteroduplex. Scientists take these results to signify a deep evolutionary connection between humans and chimpanzees.

While DNA-DNA hybridization studies generally agree with chromosome comparisons, controversy has surrounded them. Both the reliability of the technique and the statistical analysis of DNA-DNA hybridization data have been hotly debated by biologists.[22] Currently, few evolutionists use this technique or consider it informative. DNA-DNA hybridization studies have mostly historical interest. Still, some people point to these studies as part of the body of evidence that humans and chimpanzees share a common ancestry.

Bottom line

Human and chimpanzee DNA tightly associate when mixed together. Evolutionary biologists have historically viewed this interaction as evidence that humans and chimpanzees possess a high degree of genetic similarity and thus a close evolutionary connection.

Gene to Gene

Most evolutionary biologists see direct comparisons of DNA sequences as the best approach to discern genetic and hence evolutionary relationships among organisms. The technology to conduct DNA sequence analysis became available only in the mid-1980s. Prior to this time, scientists could only gain access to DNA sequence information indirectly through the amino acid sequences of proteins, much like the work done by King and Wilson.

Comparison of amino acid sequences of numerous proteins from humans, chimpanzees, and other primates indicates a greater than 99 percent genetic similarity between humans and chimps and suggests a deeper evolutionary connection than between chimps and gorillas.[23] Evolutionary biologists are not satisfied, however, with the conclusions drawn from protein-to-protein sequence comparisons. They typically express concern that this approach overestimates genetic similarity because mutational changes to a protein's amino acid sequence (thought to account for the 1 percent genetic difference) most likely alter its three-dimensional structure and hence its function.

Nonoptimal protein function potentially has far-reaching consequences. Mutations often cause organisms to lose fitness, which leads to reduced survivability and reproduction failure. Because of these problems, changes in amino acid sequences are less likely to be passed on to the next generation. Natural selection weeds out mutations and renders the amino acid sequences of proteins resistant to change.[24]

Direct gene-to-gene comparisons yield these same concerns. Yet evolutionary biologists still conduct this type of comparison. In the spring of 2003, Morris Goodman (from Wayne State University) and his research team made headlines with one such study. His team took advantage of recently available DNA sequence data from the human and chimpanzee genome projects.

Goodman and his collaborators examined 97 genes collectively comprised of 90,000 base pairs (genetic letters)—perhaps one of the most extensive human-chimp gene-to-gene comparisons ever made. Their work revealed a 99.4 percent sequence similarity for genetic differences that alter the amino acid sequence of the protein coded by the gene (non-synonymous). The research also showed a 98.4 percent sequence similarity for genetic differences that leave the amino acid sequence unchanged (synonymous).

Given this likeness, Goodman maintains that, genetically speaking, chimpanzees and humans belong to the same genus, *Homo*.[25] However, the scientific community has been reluctant to embrace Goodman's proposal because genetic comparisons are not the sole criteria for biological classification. Humans and chimpanzees display obvious anatomical, physiological, behavioral, and cultural differences that form a basis for their assignments to separate genera. In spite of the shortcomings with gene-to-gene comparisons (whether direct or indirect), the high level of genetic similarity suggests to evolutionary biologists that humans and chimpanzees share ancestry.

Bottom line
When scientists compare corresponding human and chimpanzee genes, they find that DNA sequences typically vary by no more than 2 percent. Evolutionary biologists take the 98 to 99 percent similarity to be clear evidence that humans and chimpanzees evolved recently from a common ancestor.

Noncoding DNA

In addition to genes, vast amounts of noncoding DNA form an organism's genome. Roughly 95 percent of the human genome is noncoding. For evolutionary biologists, noncoding DNA is far more susceptible to genetic change (at least in principle) because it does not code for functional proteins.

Noncoding DNA offers the best way to probe for genetic relatedness among organisms. According to this line of reasoning, changes to noncoding DNA are free from the influence of natural selection. They should occur in roughly a clocklike fashion from the time two species diverge from a common ancestor.

One of the best-known studies of this sort used DNA sequence comparisons of the β-globin gene cluster. The genes found in this cluster code for oxygen-binding hemoglobin proteins. Evolutionists consider the β-globin gene cluster to be an excellent marker for evolutionary studies because 85 to 95 percent of this gene cluster consists of noncoding DNA. The noncoding DNA resides both within the β-globin genes (noncoding DNA within a gene is called an intron) and in large stretches between genes (intergenic regions). Comparison of β-globin cluster DNA reveals a 98.4 percent genetic similarity between humans and chimps.[26]

A more comprehensive study of noncoding DNA conducted recently yielded similar results. Researchers compared 53 DNA segments (totaling more than 24,000 base pairs) located throughout the human genome with corresponding segments from chimpanzees, gorillas, and orangutans. They found a 98.76 percent genetic similarity for humans and chimpanzees. Gene-to-gene comparisons uncovered a 98.66 percent genetic similarity for humans' and chimpanzees' coding DNA.[27] Again, evolutionary biologists take the results to indicate a close evolutionary connection between humans and chimpanzees.

Bottom line
When scientists compare corresponding regions of nongenic, noncoding DNA taken from humans and chimpanzees, they find a 98 to 99 percent sequence similarity. Because noncoding DNA presumably is not influenced by natural selection, evolutionary biologists take this similarity as compelling evidence

for human evolution from an earlier primate.

Divergence Time

Anthropologists maintain that genetic relatedness can also be used to determine how long ago two primates diverged from a common ancestor. The basis for this assertion hinges on some important assumptions. Along with the understood supposition that evolution accounts for the origin and diversity of life's major groups, evolutionary biologists assume that mutations cause the genetic differences among organisms. They also believe these mutations to the genetic material occur at a roughly constant rate over long time periods.

If these assumptions are correct, then organisms that share an ancestor in the recent past will display fewer genetic differences. On the other hand, organisms that share ancestors in the more distant past will have accrued more mutations and display greater genetic disparity. If mutation rates are known, then the divergence time can be readily calculated once the genetic difference between two organisms is determined.[28]

University of California, Berkeley biologists Vincent Sarich and Allan Wilson conducted one of the first molecular clock studies of primate origins about a decade before King's comparisons of human and chimpanzee proteins. In their study Sarich and Wilson used the immunological properties of serum albumins as a surrogate for genetic relatedness. Anthropologists at that time were shocked by their results. Instead of humans and chimpanzees diverging between 20 and 15 million years ago (as most anthropologists had thought), Sarich and Wilson measured this split as occurring only 5 million years ago.[29]

This result ignited a controversy.[30] Over time, however, anthropologists came to accept this result and similar findings from other molecular clock studies. DNA-DNA hybridization places the timing of the human-chimpanzee split at between 7.7 and 5.7 million years ago.[31] Mitochondrial-DNA analysis places the human-chimpanzee common ancestor at around 5 million years ago, and DNA analysis of nuclear DNA sequences typically places the divergence time at between 6 and 4.5 million years ago.[32]

Bottom line

The various genetic comparisons made between humans and chimpanzees appear to construct a powerful case for human evolution despite the genetic, archeological, biochemical, geophysical, and even astronomical evidence that supports the biblical creation model. The genetic comparisons of humans with other primates often cited in support of human evolution, however, do not tell the whole story. Many recent studies provide a potent counter to the genetic evidence that seemingly supports a shared ancestry for humans and the great apes—chimpanzees in particular.

Differences That Matter

For the last three decades, the 99 percent genetic similarity between humans and chimpanzees has stood as an unassailed "fact," seemingly confirmed time and time again by evolutionary biologists. However, several recent studies strongly indicate that humans and chimpanzees actually display substantial genetic differences. Biologists are uncovering these differences as they transition from performing individual gene-to-gene comparisons to performing studies that involve significant portions of, if not the entire, human and chimpanzee genomes.

Studies that reveal a 99 percent genetic similarity between humans and chimpanzees have stacked the deck in a way that guarantees a high degree of likeness. Comparisons made between corresponding regions of the human and chimpanzee genomes, which researchers already suspected to be nearly identical, showed striking similarity. But when researchers made unbiased comparisons of larger regions of these two genomes, differences began to emerge.

One of the first studies to make a genome-to-genome comparison between humans and chimpanzees was reported early in 2002 by the International Consortium for the Sequencing of Chimpanzee Chromosome 22.[33] To make this whole-genome comparison, the Chimpanzee Genome Project team cut the chimp genome into fragments, sequenced them, then compared them to corresponding sequences found in the Human Genome Database. For those chimp DNA fragments that were able to align with sequences in the Human Genome Database, the project team found that the sequences displayed a 98.77 percent agreement. However, the project team found that about 15,000 of the 65,000 DNA fragments did not align with any sequence in the Human Genome Database. They appear to represent unique genetic regions.

A few months later, a team from the Max Planck Institute achieved a similar result when they compared over 10,000 regions (encompassing nearly 3 million nucleotide base pairs). Only two-thirds of the sequences from the chimp genome aligned with the sequences in the human genome. As expected, in those that did align, a 98.76 percent genetic similarity was measured, and yet one-third found no matches.[34]

The Chimpanzee Genome Project team discovered another difference between genomes during a detailed comparison of the chimpanzee genome DNA fragments with human chromosome 21. The team found that this human chromosome possesses two regions apparently unique to the human genome.[35]

Until recently, evolutionary biologists have looked for only a single type of difference between human and chimpanzee DNA sequences, namely substitutions of one nucleotide for another. When researchers expand the comparison to include differences that involve insertions and deletions (called indels), marked dissimilarities between human and chimpanzee genomes become evident. For example, a study that compared five regions of the chimpanzee genome collectively (encompassing about 780,000 nucleotide base pairs) with corresponding regions of the human genome found a 1.4 percent difference when substitutions were considered. But a 3.4 percent difference appeared when these five regions were examined for indels. Both types of differences combined show a 95 percent genetic similarity, not 99 percent.[36]

Another study that used this type of approach found a much more limited genetic similarity when a 1,870,955-base-pair segment of the chimpanzee genome was compared with the corresponding human genome region. When only substitutions were considered, the sequence similarity proved about 98.6 percent. Including indels in the comparison dropped the similarity to 86.7 percent.[37]

As research continues, indels appear to account for substantial differences between human and chimpanzee genomes. A comparative analysis of 27 million base pairs of human chromosome 21 with the corresponding chimpanzee chromosome (number 22) identified 57 indels ranging in size from 200 to 800 base pairs. Twenty-one of these indels were found in regions that contained genes.[38]

In the spring of 2004, the International Chimpanzee Chromosome 22 Consortium affirmed this initial observation when they generated a detailed sequence of chimpanzee chromosome 22 and compared it to human chromosome 21.[39] They discovered a 1.44 percent sequence difference when they lined up the two chromosomes and made a base-by-base comparison. But they also discovered 68,000 indels in the two sequences, with some indels up to 54,000 nucleotides in length.

Another study achieved similar results. This work compared a 1.8-million-base-pair region of human chromosome 7 with the corresponding region in the genomes of several vertebrates. Only a third of the differences between humans and chimpanzees involved substitutions. Indels accounted for roughly two-thirds of the sequence differences between these two primates. Of these indels, about one-half were greater than 100 base pairs long.[40]

As for mitochondrial DNA (mtDNA), a 91.1 percent sequence similarity was seen when the entire sequence was compared, not a 99 percent similarity.[41] This factor promises to be significant because mitochondria play a role in energy metabolism. Several neurodegenerative and muscular degenerative diseases actually stem from mutations in mtDNA.[42]

Bottom line

Although human and chimpanzee genomes display great similarity, that similarity has been magnified to some extent by research methodology. Researchers are starting to uncover significant differences. Results of large-scale comparisons must be considered preliminary, as it's not yet clear what the genetic differences mean in terms of anatomical and behavioral characteristics. However, greater clarity will likely come as research progresses. Already the newly recognized genetic differences between humans and chimpanzees complicate the picture for biologists who view the high degree of genetic similarity between humans and chimpanzees as proof of shared ancestry. If 99 percent genetic similarity represents a close evolutionary connection, what does the more recently measured 86.7 percent genetic similarity mean?

Small but Significant

While advancing research is uncovering what appear to be extensive genetic differences between humans and chimpanzees, it's important to remember that sometimes even single genetic differences can be significant. Separate studies conducted at the University of California, San Diego (UCSD), the Max Planck Institute, and the University of Chicago supply important examples. This work demonstrates that subtle genetic differences translate into marked disparities in human and chimpanzee brain biochemistries. Researchers think these discrepancies may explain, at least in part, the unique qualities of the human brain.

On the surface

One noteworthy biochemical difference between humans and the great apes is the absence in people of a particular cell-surface sugar, N-glycolyl-neuraminic acid (GL-neur).[43] This sugar is found in virtually all mammals, including chimpanzees. Sugars in the cell surface play a critical role in a number of physiological processes. For example, they serve as the binding site for many pathogens. The absence of GL-neur explains the immunological distinction between humans and other mammals, including chimpanzees.

Cell-surface sugars also mediate cell-to-cell communication and may play a role in development. While GL-neur occurs at high levels in all body tissues in mammals, including the great apes, its levels are relatively low in brain tissue. This fact has led the UCSD scientists to speculate that the absence of GL-neur in humans may explain, in part, differences in human and chimpanzee brain development, structure, and capacity.[44] Experiments are underway to test this idea.

GL-neur forms when an enzyme (called CMP-N-acetylneuraminic acid hydroxylase) adds an oxygen atom to N-acetylneuraminic acid (AL-neur).[45] According to evolutionary biologists, this enzyme (found in other mammals) became nonfunctional in humans due to a mutation that deleted 92 base pairs from the gene that encodes CMP-N-acetylneuraminic acid hydroxylase.[46]

From an evolutionary perspective, researchers think this deletion occurred when a mobile piece of DNA (an *Alu* sequence) replaced a segment of the gene that encodes the hydroxylase enzyme.[47] Molecular clock analysis and the recovery of AL-neur (but not GL-neur) from Neanderthal remains have led evolutionary biologists to speculate that this mutation occurred around 2.2 million years ago, right before the *Homo* hominids appeared and brains became larger.[48] While this explanation appears to buttress the evolutionary paradigm for human origins, its support is superficial.

Molecular biologists consider *Alu* replacements and insertions the cause of genetic disasters because the loss of a gene usually has catastrophic consequences. The critical role cell-surface sugars play in cell-to-cell communication and development makes these problems even worse.

It's difficult to think that a genetic change with such potentially far-reaching effects could occur in the just-right way to sustain brain expansion along with an accompanying coherent advance in brain function. Interpretation of these results from a creation model perspective will come shortly, but for now the point is this: A single gene difference can have profound anatomical and physiological consequences. The just-right nature of these changes (required by a human evolutionary perspective) renders them highly improbable, if not impossible, through natural means alone.

Just a little off

Further indication of significant differences come from the discovery that a subtle variation in the DNA sequence of a single gene (the so-called language gene) has far-ranging consequences. This revelation came when the Max Planck Institute team compared the DNA sequence of the *FOXP2* genes from humans, chimpanzees, gorillas, orangutans, rhesus monkeys, and mice.[49]

The *FOXP2* gene codes for a DNA-binding protein. These types of proteins regulate gene expression (when they bind to DNA) by turning genes on and off. The FOXP2 protein plays a key role in the development of a number of mammalian organ systems and exists at high levels in fetal brain tissue.

In the fall of 2001, a research team from the United Kingdom reported that mutations in the *FOXP2* gene cause severe language disorders. People suffering from this genetic defect can't properly control their lips and tongues, which affects their ability to talk. Neither can they use and understand grammar, nor can they understand many speech sounds.[50] Presumably the FOXP2 protein plays a key role in controlling the development of brain structures that support key aspects of human language capacity.

This gene is not the only one responsible for human language. Language most likely derives from a complex network of gene interactions that dynamically vary through the course of development. The *FOXP2* gene represents only one of these genes. If it or any other gene that plays a role in human language ability becomes defective, then a breakdown occurs in the ability to communicate verbally.

The *FOXP2* gene can be compared to an automobile engine part. If that part is defective, the engine won't run properly, or at all. Still, the function of that particular part doesn't explain how the engine works. An engine consists of numerous components, each playing a critical operating role as it precisely interacts with other components in a carefully orchestrated fashion.

If an auto mechanic tries to figure out how an unfamiliar type of engine works, the failure of an individual component can actually help. When a part stops working, the symptoms displayed by the car's engine provide valuable understanding, not only as to what that component does, but also as to how the engine operates in its entirety.

With human language abilities, researchers have yet to catalog all the genes involved, let alone figure out how the genes interact to produce language capacity. Still, the *FOXP2* gene gives researchers important insight into human language development and abilities, even if the understanding is limited. Knowledge will increase as new genetic defects that affect language ability are identified.

Scientists from the Max Planck Institute were motivated to study the *FOXP2* gene closely because of its key role in aspects of brain development essential for human language capacity. These researchers discovered that, of the 715 amino acids that comprise the FOXP2 protein, only three differences exist between the human and mouse proteins. Only two amino acids differ between the human protein and that of the great apes.[51]

Reflecting an evolutionary perspective, the researchers concluded that because of the key role the *FOXP2* gene plays in development, it has been highly resistant to mutational change. Presumably, any mutation that alters its structure and, hence, function would be so disruptive to the development process that death would result. In other words, natural selection would have prevented mutations from occurring in the *FOXP2* gene.

Using protein-structure prediction methods, the Max Planck team determined that the human FOXP2 protein adopts a different shape from that of the mouse or great ape proteins. Also, they noted that this shape difference creates a phosphorylation site on the protein. Such sites serve as locations where the cell's machinery can attach phosphate groups to proteins. As a result of phosphorylation, the protein's shape—and therefore function—becomes altered, sometimes dramatically. By attaching and removing phosphate groups, the cell's machinery can cause a protein to switch back and forth between two functional states, on and off.

The altered shape of the human FOXP2 protein and the presence of a phosphorylation site led the Max Planck scientists to conclude that the *FOXP2* gene influences gene expression and hence development in dramatically different ways in humans compared to the great apes and other mammals. This characteristic accounts for the aspects of brain structure that allow humans to possess unique language capacity.

The Max Planck researchers explained the structural and functional differences between human and great ape versions of the FOXP2 protein as a consequence of mutations to the *FOXP2* gene. According to these investigators, molecular changes led to the (sudden) evolution of human language. Employing molecular clock analysis, these scientists concluded that the mutations occurred less than 200,000 years ago—in other words, around the time modern humans first appeared. (Interestingly, from an evolutionary perspective, this event happened well after the time humans and Neanderthals allegedly split from a common ancestor. According to this view, Neanderthals could not have possessed a humanlike *FOXP2* gene and therefore did not have language ability.)[52]

This evolutionary explanation seems to account, at least partially, for the origin of human language. However, as with the loss of the CMP-N-acetylneuraminic acid hydroxylase activity in humans, this explanation for the evolutionary origin of human language is tenuous at best. Could the *FOXP2* gene have been resistant to mutation for over 70 million years because of its central role in development? Then, just when modern humans appear, could two *just-right* changes occur in the gene in such a way as to significantly alter the structure of the FOXP2 protein? Could these just-right events adjust the FOXP2 protein so that it now precisely regulates the complex network and sequences of gene interactions necessary to generate the intricate brain structures that make human language and speech possible? Or does it seem more likely that a divine hand redesigned the FOXP2 protein to give humans, made in God's image, the gift of language?

Another slight problem
Three separate teams of geneticists have discovered yet another single-gene difference that appears to have a far-reaching impact on human and great ape brain chemistries.[53] These researchers focused their attention on the *ASPM* (Abnormal Spindle-Like Microcephaly Associated) gene. Defects in this gene cause microcephaly, a disorder characterized by an extreme reduction in the size of the cerebral cortex.[54] This brain region controls the ability to plan and to perform abstract reasoning.

The investigators surmised that during human evolution, changes in this gene caused an expansion of the cerebral cortex that led to the human ability to reason abstractly. To test this idea, the scientists compared the DNA sequence of the *ASPM* gene from a number of different mammals. The research team detected no significant differences in the *ASPM* gene among cows, sheep, cats, dogs, rats, mice, and lower primates. They did note, however, that the human *ASPM* gene does differ. Its differences alter the structure and function of the ASPM protein. The investigators concluded that these features in the *ASPM* gene DNA sequence emerged spontaneously within the human lineage and produced the cerebral cortex.

As with the *FOXP2* language gene, this evolutionary explanation stretches the bounds of credulity. How is it that any structural and functional change in the ASPM protein would benefit an organism when mutations to this gene typically lead to a devastating disorder? Furthermore, the *ASPM* gene for a large number of mammals shows remarkable stability. Could the *just-right* changes have altered the ASPM protein in the *just-right* way to support the expansion of the cerebral cortex, an incredibly complex brain structure? Could this *just-right* change have happened spontaneously to support advanced cognitive functions? Or does it seem more likely that a purposeful Creator remade the ASPM protein to allow for abstract reasoning when He made humans?

There's more
Recent large-scale comparisons indicate that the subtle yet biologically significant genetic differences between humans and the great apes are not confined
exclusively to the CMP-N-acetylneuraminic acid hydroxylase, FOXP2, and
ASPM proteins. Numerous human genes have been altered in ways that yield
important biological effects. A research team recently compared 7,645 human,
chimpanzee, and mouse genes and discovered nearly 3,000 human and chimpanzee genes with structural alterations that cause biological differences.[55]
When the International Chimpanzee Chromosome 22 Consortium conducted
a detailed comparison of human chromosome 21 with chimpanzee chromosome 22, they discovered that 47 of the 231 genes residing on this chromosome
differ in structurally and hence functionally substantial ways.[56]

Bottom line
Though humans and chimpanzees share a high degree of genetic similarity,
several recent studies demonstrate that even subtle genetic differences can
manifest themselves dramatically in terms of an organism's anatomy, physiology, and behavior. This finding compels the question addressed in the next
section (one that all readers can appreciate): What do genetic differences and
similarities really mean?

"True, as Honest Madam's Issue"
Anthropologist Jonathan Marks addresses the genetics question in his book
What It Means to Be 98% Chimpanzee.[57] Marks maintains that comparisons
based on the percentage of similarity (or difference) of DNA sequences are
largely meaningless. He points out the fact that humans and daffodils possess a
35 percent genetic similarity. According to Marks,

> In the context of a 35% similarity to a daffodil, the 99.44% of the
> DNA of human to chimp doesn't seem so remarkable. After all,
> humans are obviously a heck of a lot more similar to chimpanzees
> than to daffodils. More than that, to say that humans are over one-
> third daffodil is more ludicrous than profound. There are hardly any
> comparisons you can make to a daffodil in which humans are 33%
> similar.[58]

Comparison of the mouse genome (reported in December 2002) with the
human genome supports Marks's point. Of the 30,000 genes found in each of
the human and mouse genomes, around 99 percent are the same. Only 300

genes are unique either to mice or to humans. Gene-to-gene DNA comparisons for humans and mice reveal roughly an 80 percent sequence similarity.[59] Are humans 80 percent similar to mice? Are mice 80 percent similar to humans?

Given that humans and mice essentially possess the same genes, something more than genes and genetic similarity must define organisms. Biologists are starting to look to differences in gene expression as a way to account for anatomical, physiological, and behavioral differences among organisms. As part of this effort, anthropologists are examining and comparing the gene expression patterns in humans and the great apes. The results of these studies are worth noting.

In "Lag of a Brother"?

Scientists from the Max Planck Institute conducted the first comparison of gene expression. (Gene expression describes which genes are turned on and off in a given tissue or at a given point in time.) This German team showed that the gene expression patterns for liver and blood tissues from humans, chimpanzees, orangutans, and rhesus monkeys are quite similar. So is the gene usage in the brain tissue of chimpanzees, orangutans, and rhesus monkeys.[60] However, the researchers observed a distinctly different gene expression pattern in human brain tissue. According to the team's lead investigator, "Among these three tissues, it seems that the brain is really special in that humans have accelerated patterns of gene activity."[61]

The research community views these results with both interest and concern. Some scientists point out that the number of samples used in this study was limited and that variation within species was not properly taken into account. Also, the detection methods were optimized for human genes but not for those of the great apes.[62]

To correct for these problems, a team from the United States compared gene expression patterns in cultured fibroblasts from humans and great apes. Fibroblasts are cells found in connective tissue. They secrete materials that form the extracellular matrix. (Researchers routinely use fibroblasts cultured in the laboratory to study metabolic disorders and the aging process.) By using cultured fibroblasts, the researchers were able to account for variation within each species due to age and gender and were able to compare a single cell-type.

The investigators from the United States demonstrated that gene expression occurs at an accelerated rate in human fibroblasts compared to the rate in great apes. These scientists also identified the specific genes that were expressed at higher levels in humans. Genes known to be defective in neurological diseases and cranioskeletal and muscular disorders were differentially expressed.[63] These genes play a role in brain biology and in the muscular and skeletal systems. This process potentially accounts for the differences in cognitive ability between humans and the great apes. It also may explain why people walk erect and the great apes knuckle-walk on all fours.

Since this study, other researchers have compared the gene expression patterns of specific brain regions. For example, a team of collaborators from a number of labs measured the gene expression profiles for the human cerebral cortex and the chimpanzee cerebral cortex.[64] This brain structure is responsible for cognitive activity. These researchers noted a number of differences in gene expression, and they determined that in the cerebral cortex of humans, genes were expressed at higher levels (up-regulated). They interpreted this finding to indicate that the human brain has characteristically higher neuronal activity than the chimpanzee's brain.

A team from Wayne State University compared gene expression profiles of humans', chimpanzees', and gorillas' anterior cingulated cortex.[65] In humans this brain region displays increased activity during cognitive tasks. Researchers noted that the gene expression patterns of the human and chimpanzee anterior cingulated cortex were less distinct from one another than either was from the gorilla's. Still, there were significant differences in gene usage between the humans' and chimpanzees' anterior cingulated cortex.

A recent study by German researchers compared gene expression patterns in three regions (the cerebellum, caudate nucleus, and cerebral cortex) of the human and chimpanzee brains. These investigators noted that, for both humans and chimpanzees, each of these three brain regions displayed a characteristic and different gene expression pattern. For humans, the extent of the differences in gene expression for the various brain regions was greater than for chimpanzees. While these scientists failed to detect any specific difference between the three regions of the human and chimpanzee brains, they did note that on average the gene expression rates in the human brain were all about 10 percent greater than those of the chimpanzee's brain.[66]

The International Chimpanzee Chromosome 22 Consortium also detected significant differences in gene expression when they compared the usage of the 231 genes found on human chromosome 21 with the corresponding genes on chimp chromosome 22.[67] The researchers noted that in the liver, nine of these genes—and in the brain, 12 of the genes—function at different levels in humans and chimps.

The Max Planck Institute team that pioneered the human-chimpanzee comparative gene expression studies also measured the methylation pattern of DNA in human and chimpanzee blood, liver, and brain tissues.[68] DNA methylation (the addition of a methyl chemical group) plays an important role in regulating gene activity.[69] These investigators found a much greater difference between humans and chimpanzees in the DNA methylation patterns of their brain tissue than in their blood and liver.

Researchers are just beginning to gain knowledge of gene expression patterns in humans and the great apes. Yet these initial studies already indicate that anatomical, physiological, and behavioral differences between humans and chimpanzees (as well as the other great apes) result much more from differences in gene expression than from DNA sequence disparities.[70] In many instances, it's not the genes present that are important but the way they function.

What does it mean to be 98 percent chimpanzee? In terms of evolution, essentially nothing.

Beyond the Bottom Line

The 98 percent genetic similarity between humans and chimpanzees remains among the most widely recognized evolutionary arguments. However, recent advances (such as the one discussed in the previous section) threaten to tarnish this icon. The most comprehensive genetic comparisons indicate that humans and chimpanzees share a genetic similarity closer to about 85 percent than to 99 percent. From an evolutionary perspective, if a 99 percent genetic similarity reflects a close evolutionary connection, then an 85 percent genetic similarity distances humans from chimpanzees.

Other recent studies demonstrate that even small genetic differences (such as the presence or absence of a single gene or an altered gene structure) translate into significant biological differences. These help explain why humans stand apart from the great apes. Additionally, studies now show that gene expression patterns in the human and chimpanzee brains (and other tissues and organs) also differ. In other words, the difference between human biology and behavior and chimp biology and behavior likely depends to a large extent on the difference in gene usage, not the types of genes present.

These discoveries are just the iceberg's tip. Based on the trend line, future work will likely identify other important genetic differences between humans and chimpanzees. Recent studies, for example, identified recombination hot spots in the human genome that are absent from the chimpanzee's genetic makeup.[71] Differences in recombination affect mutation rates and biological variation within a species. Another recent study determined that the human genome has 200 times more copies of a class of noncoding DNA (referred to as *Alu Yb8*) than does the chimpanzee genome. As discussed in the next chapter, *Alu Yb8* DNA (a subclass of SINE DNA) plays a role in stress response and gene regulation.[72]

Such discoveries may not necessarily invalidate human evolution, but they do make evolutionary explanations for human origins less plausible and more difficult to accept. From an evolutionary perspective, the scientific data indicate that substantial genetic change must have occurred within an exceptionally short time frame (6 to 5 million years at most). More problematic are the growing number of instances in which small differences in human genes produce the just-right biological effects necessary to account for profound biological and behavioral differences between humans and chimpanzees.

The complexity and the intricacy of biological systems, especially those in the brain, underscore the improbability that random mutations could bring about the exacting changes in gene structure necessary to support new biological functions, particularly when structure-altering mutations to single genes more often result in devastating diseases and disabilities.

The same is true for changes in gene expression. As indicated by the data, differences in gene usage play an important role in generating the differences between humans and chimpanzees. The intricacy of gene-to-gene interactions and the biological effects manifested when gene expression is altered make it difficult to envision how coordinated and extensive changes in gene expression could occur to generate the anatomical and physiological characteristics that define humanity. Changes in gene expression are frequently harmful and play a role in the etiology of many diseases.

Each new discovery coming from genetic comparisons between humans and chimpanzees seems to weaken the case of evolution. What do the newly recognized genetic similarities and differences mean for the RTB model?

Legitimacy

Rather than struggling to accommodate the data from human-chimpanzee genetic comparisons, the RTB model predicts it. As chapter 3 describes, a careful reading of Genesis 1:26–27 and 5:1–2 in the original Hebrew leads to the expectation that anatomical, physiological, biochemical, and genetic similarities exist between humans and animals, including chimpanzees. God created male and female (humans) in an *'āśâ* fashion (see pages 47–48). He made them from previously existing designs, presumably biological in nature.

These biblical passages also state that humans possess unique qualities compared to animals—characteristics that reflect the Creator's image. There-fore, it stands to reason that significant physical differences also exist between human beings and animals. These differences provide biological support for humanity's expression of likeness to God.

From a physical standpoint, many of the qualities that define man's like-ness to God stem from the brain's structure and activities. Even in the midst of substantial genetic similarities, significant differences exist in the brain bio-chemistries of humans and the great apes. In some cases, these disparities result from subtle genetic differences, such as seen for the CMP-N-acetylneuraminic acid hydroxylase, ASPM, and FOXP2 language proteins. Other incongruities stem from gene expression patterns. Based on all indicators, these differences appear to have far-ranging consequences and may help explain the advanced cognitive behavior of humans.

Emerging genetic data, when viewed from a creation model perspective, provide some understanding of how God might have created humanity. It ap-pears that when the Creator made (*'āśâ*) humanity's physical component, He employed similar design features and the same building blocks (genes) as He used to fashion the great apes and other animals. It also appears that God re-designed certain building blocks or revised their function via genetic changes. He introduced new building blocks (gene duplications followed by genetic changes), cast aside other building blocks (gene deletions), and used the build-ing blocks in radically different ways (gene expression and gene regulation) to produce humanity's unique features.

Why Do Humans, Chimps, and Other Animals Have the Same Genes?

The large number of shared genes found among the genomes of humans, chim-panzees, mice, rats, and other animals reflects elegant design efficiency. The Cre-ator appears to have selected a gene set that could be used to construct a wide range of organisms.

This design principle is commonplace. A child with a set of building blocks may be observed to take advantage of this approach. Depending on the child's wishes, he or she can make numerous structures from the same set of blocks. Com-puter engineers produce computers with fixed hardware that can be programmed with software for an enormous array of functions. Even human languages rely on this principle. A relatively small set of words can be used to communicate an im-measurable number of ideas and concepts.

This speculation seems most plausible when it comes to human brain bio-chemistry relative to the great apes. Because the brain is the primary physical component that supports humanity's spiritual nature, this idea makes sense. With the physical framework of the brain in place, God created (*bārā'*) male and female (humans) as unique spiritual creatures, in His image (see pages 47–48).

The RTB model faces yet another challenge: junk DNA. The next chapter explains why junk DNA appears to support human evolution and also describes some new discoveries that have caught evolutionary biologists by surprise.

Chapter 14

What about "Junk" DNA?

All that glisters is not gold,
Often have you heard that told;
Many a man his life hath sold
But my outside to behold.
Gilded tombs do worms infold.
—*The Merchant of Venice* Act 2, scene 12

"God don't make no junk!" This once-familiar T-shirt and bumper sticker slogan conveys an age-old theological truth: God's creative work is ideal.[1] If (as the songwriter David expressed in Psalm 8) the all-powerful, all-knowing Creator made the universe and all that's in it, then people can expect to see superior designs throughout the natural realm.

For those who agree with Darwin's view, any example of nature's imperfection contradicts the notion of a divine creation. As a result, many naturalists regard "junk" DNA as among the most potent evidences for biological evolution.[2] According to this perspective, junk DNA results when undirected biochemical processes along with random chemical and physical events transform a functional DNA segment into a useless molecular artifact. This junk piece of DNA remains part of an organism's genome solely because of its attachment to functional DNA. In this way, junk DNA persists from generation to generation.[3]

Evolutionists emphasize that, in many instances, identical segments of junk DNA appear in a wide range of related organisms. Identical junk DNA segments often reside in precisely the same locations within the genomes of these different creatures. For evolutionists, this feature clearly indicates that these organisms shared a common ancestor. The junk DNA segment supposedly arose prior to the time when the organisms diverged from their shared evolutionary progenitor.[4]

The obvious question arises, why would a perfect Creator introduce non-functional, junk DNA at the same location within the genomes of different, but seemingly related, organisms? The answer to this question necessitates a trek through some technical details. Once again, however, readers who want only the bottom line can look for it at the end of each section.

Pseudogenes, LINEs, SINEs, and Endogenous Retroviruses, Oh My!

Evolutionary biologists consider pseudogenes, endogenous retroviruses, and repetitive LINE and SINE DNA sequences shared among humans and the great apes to be the most compelling evidence that these primates evolved from a common ancestor. Molecular biologists generally believe that these four types of noncoding DNA sequences arose through a variety of random biochemical events. Because these segments presumably lack function and are found in both human and chimpanzee genomes, evolutionists argue they must be the molecular artifacts of a shared evolutionary history.[5]

Pseudogenes

Biochemists view pseudogenes as the dead, useless remains of once-functional genes. According to this view, severe mutations destroyed the capacity of the cell's machinery to read and process the information contained in these genes. Despite being nonfunctional, pseudogenes possess the telltale signature that allows molecular biologists to recognize them as genes.[6]

Three distinct classes of pseudogenes have been identified (see figure 14.1). The relatively rare unitary pseudogenes occur as single copies in an organism's genome.[7] The loss of the gene that degenerated into a unitary pseudogene wouldn't compromise the organism's fitness if its lifestyle no longer depended on that gene.

The classic example of a unitary pseudogene is the one that presumably encoded the enzyme L-gulono-γ-lactone oxidase (GLO) in primates. In other mammals (except guinea pigs), GLO plays a role in ascorbic acid (vitamin C) biosynthesis.[8] However, primates do not have a functional GLO enzyme. Rather, they possess a GLO pseudogene. According to the evolutionary paradigm, mutations corrupted this gene, rendering vitamin C biosynthesis impossible for primates. The inability to produce vitamin C does not hamper their fitness, however, because plenty is available through dietary sources.

The primate GLO pseudogenes have many of the same mutations that occur in the human GLO pseudogene.[9] The evolutionary model maintains that these "mutations" occurred in the ancestral species shared by all primates. The

Figure 14.1: Pseudogenes
Evolutionary biologists consider pseudogenes to be the dead, useless remains of once-functional genes.

alterations were then propagated as different primate species diverged from their common ancestor. Evolutionary biologists have identified several identical unitary pseudogenes shared among humans and other primates.[10]

Duplicated pseudogenes form the largest pseudogene class. Molecular biologists suggest that these DNA segments arose when genes underwent duplication in the genome. Afterward, the copies experienced severe mutations that rendered them unrecognizable as a functional gene by the cell's machinery. Loss of the duplicated gene's function has little, if any, effect on an organism's fitness, since an intact functional copy still exists.[11]

As with unitary pseudogenes, great apes and humans share numerous duplicated pseudogenes with identical "mutations." According to the evolutionary models, shared duplicated pseudogenes indicate the evolutionary relatedness of humans and the other primates.[12]

Processed pseudogenes are the third pseudogene class. The pathway that produces processed pseudogenes (as conceived by molecular biologists) is complex. The mechanism that generates processed pseudogenes overlaps with the one that the cell's machinery uses to synthesize proteins. Genes contain the information that the cell needs to make proteins. As the first step in protein synthesis, the cell's machinery duplicates the gene in the form of RNA (a biomolecule class that structurally resembles DNA). The RNA message migrates to a ribosome (a subcellular particle). Here the cell's machinery reads the information stored in the RNA message to form the protein encoded by the messenger RNA (mRNA).[13]

Before the RNA message relocates to the ribosome, the cell's machinery alters it in several ways. This change includes removing segments in the RNA message that correspond to noncoding regions of the gene (introns), splicing together the RNA segments that correspond to the gene's coding regions (exons), and modifying and making additions to the ends of the RNA molecule.[14]

Processed pseudogenes are thought to arise when a particular enzyme (reverse transcriptase) generates DNA from the processed RNA message. Once produced, this newly formed DNA gets inserted back into the genome. Now called a processed pseudogene, the newly inserted DNA resembles the gene from which it originated. However, the gene also contains telltale signs of having been processed. This type of pseudogene is nonfunctional because it lacks the regions that surround functional genes—regions used by the cell's machinery to initiate the production of the RNA message.[15]

As with unitary and duplicated pseudogenes, primate species share several identical processed pseudogenes with humans. And in some instances, the location where the processed pseudogene appears to have entered the human genome corresponds to the exact location in the genomes of other primates.[16] For evolutionary biologists, the shared identical unitary, duplicated, and processed pseudogenes found in the human and chimpanzee genome make sense only from an evolutionary perspective.

The mere presence of unitary, duplicated, and processed pseudogenes in the human genome doesn't necessarily challenge a creation model, because mutations and errant biochemical processes could generate these noncoding forms of DNA after humans were created. What evolutionary biologists find so convincing is the fact that *identical* pseudogenes with many of the *same* mutations occur in humans, chimpanzees, and other primates.

SINEs and LINEs
Evolutionists also point to the distribution of short interspersed nuclear elements (SINEs) and long interspersed nuclear elements (LINEs) in the human and chimpanzee genomes as evidence for shared ancestry. These two types of noncoding DNA are called transposable elements—pieces of DNA that jump around the genome, or transpose. In the process of moving around the genome, transposable elements direct the cell's machinery to copy themselves and consequently increase in number (see figure 14.2).[17] SINEs and LINEs belong to a class of transposable elements called retroposons. Molecular biologists believe that these DNA elements duplicate and move around the genome through an RNA intermediate and by the work of reverse transcriptase.

SINEs range in size from 100 to 300 base pairs (genetic letters). In primates the most common SINEs are the so-called *Alu* sequences. There are about 1.1 million *Alu* copies in the human genome (roughly 12 percent of the genome). An *Alu* sequence contains a segment that the cell's machinery can use to produce an RNA message. In this way SINEs can duplicate and move around the genome as reverse transcriptase converts SINE RNA back into DNA.[18]

Twenty percent of the human genome consists of LINEs. The most common LINE in the human genome (called *L1*) consists of about 7,000 base pairs. LINE segments contain the gene for reverse transcriptase and, like SINEs, can duplicate and move around the genome.[19]

Molecular biologists have discovered numerous instances in which both SINE and LINE segments occur at identical locations in the genomes of humans, chimpanzees, and other primates.[20] Because the duplication and movement of SINE and LINE DNA appear to be random, evolutionists note the unlikelihood that these would occur in exactly the same way independently in

Figure 14.2: SINEs and LINEs
SINEs and LINEs are pieces of DNA that jump around the genome, or transpose.

humans and chimpanzees (and some other primates). Given their supposed nonfunctional nature, SINE and LINE DNA in humans and chimpanzees would seem to reflect common ancestry.[21] In fact, evolutionary biologists have used SINE *Alu* sequences to guide the construction of primate evolutionary trees.[22]

Endogenous retroviruses

Evolutionists also maintain that shared endogenous retroviruses in human and chimpanzee genomes make a convincing case for evolutionary connection. These retroviruses have become permanently incorporated into the host organism's genome.

Retroviruses, like all viruses, consist of protein capsules that house genetic material (either DNA or RNA). Viruses infect organisms by invading specific cell types of the host organism. After viruses attach to the target cell's surface, they inject their genetic material into the healthy cell. The viral genetic material exploits the cell's machinery to produce viral genetic material and proteins. Once formed, these materials combine to form new viral particles. When the newly formed viruses escape from the host cell, the infection cycle repeats (see figures 14.3A and B).[23]

RNA is the genetic material used by retroviruses. After it's injected into the host cell, reverse transcriptase uses the retroviral RNA to make DNA. This newly made DNA can then direct the production of new retroviral particles.[24] (HIV, the virus responsible for AIDS, is a retrovirus.)

The DNA copy of the retroviral genetic material can also incorporate the host cell's genome. (The retroviral DNA possesses two noncoding regions on each end called long terminal repeats [LTRs]. This DNA also contains genes for reverse transcriptase and the virus capsule.) If the retroviral DNA suffers severe mutations, the retrovirus becomes disabled. The retrovirus DNA then remains in the host genome as, presumably, nonfunctional DNA. It is

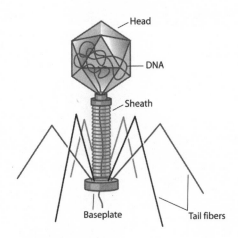

Figure 14.3A: Virus
Viruses consist of protein capsules that house genetic material.

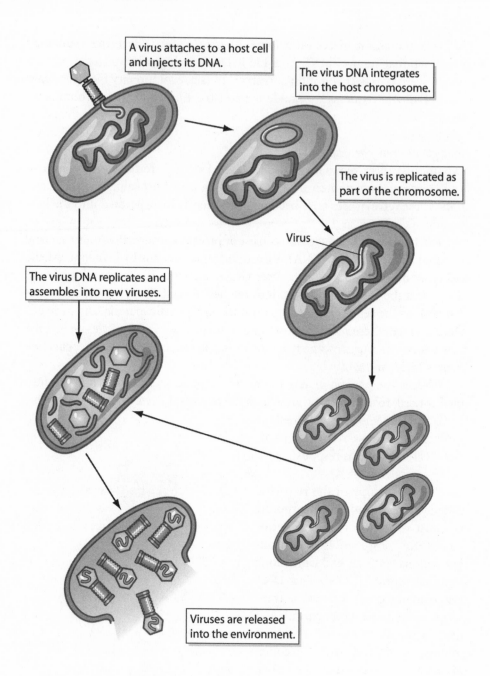

A virus attaches to a host cell and injects its DNA.

The virus DNA integrates into the host chromosome.

The virus is replicated as part of the chromosome.

Virus

The virus DNA replicates and assembles into new viruses.

Viruses are released into the environment.

Figure 14.3B: Virus Life Cycle
Viruses infect organisms by invading specific cell types of the host organism.

then referred to as an endogenous retrovirus (see figure 14.4).[25] Roughly 1 percent of mammalian genomes consist of endogenous retroviruses.

While examples of endogenous retroviruses shared among humans and other primates are few, evolutionary biologists have identified some. As with SINE and LINE DNA sequences, these endogenous retroviruses have highly similar sequences. They are found in identical locations in human and primate genomes.[26]

The evolutionary model explains this data by asserting that the human-chimpanzee shared ancestor, for example, became infected by retroviruses. Later these retroviruses suffered mutations that disabled them in this organism's genome. According to the model, the endogenous retroviruses shared by humans and chimpanzees represent the molecular artifacts of infections that occurred millions of years ago and left their imprint on contemporary genomes via this (presumed) shared ancestor.

Bottom line
Evolutionary biologists maintain that the pseudogenes, SINEs, LINEs, and endogenous retroviruses shared among humans and the great apes provide persuasive evidence that these primates arose from a common lineage. The crux of this argument rests on the supposition that these classes of noncoding DNA lack function and arose through random biochemical events. For evolutionary biologists, it makes little sense to attribute "junk" DNA to the Creator.

"Gilded Tombs"

For several years, the nonfunctional DNA elements—pseudogenes, SINEs, LINEs, and endogenous retroviruses—shared among humans and the great apes have appeared to make an ironclad case for common evolutionary ancestry. Recent studies on noncoding DNA, however, provide a challenge that evolutionists find surprising and yet hard to deny.

Noncoding DNA regions (including pseudogenes, LINEs, SINEs, and endogenous retroviruses) aren't really junk after all. These elements possess function. An alternative explanation, besides evolution, may reasonably account for the presence of noncoding DNA classes in the genomes of humans and great apes.

Pseudogenes
Judging from the characteristics of pseudogenes, few molecular biologists would ever have thought this class of noncoding DNA played any role in the

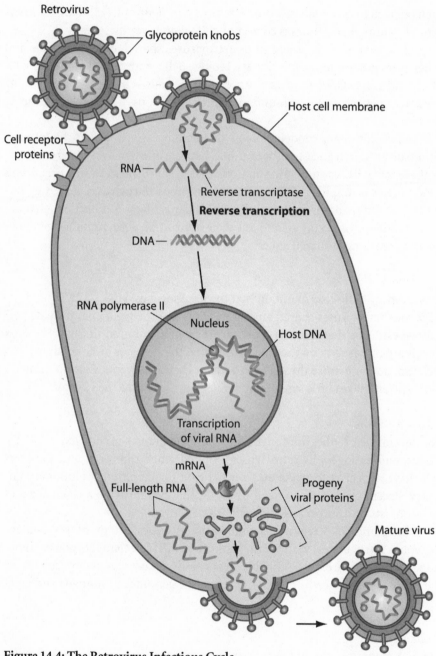

Figure 14.4: The Retrovirus Infectious Cycle
Pseudogenes

cell's operation. And yet several recent studies identify functions for both duplicated and processed pseudogenes. One high-profile example was announced in the spring of 2003 by an international research team. These investigators demonstrated that if the pseudogene *Makorin-1-p1* is disrupted in a mouse, the mouse dies. This fatal consequence indicates the critical importance of this pseudogene.[27]

The *Makorin-1-p1* pseudogene exists as a partial copy of the *Makorin-1* gene (which codes for a protein that controls gene expression). Evolutionary biologists argue that the *Makorin-1-p1* pseudogene originated after the gene became duplicated in the genome and suffered a catastrophic mutation that deleted an important portion of the copied gene. It turns out, however, that the partial structure of the *Makorin-1-p1* pseudogene factors significantly into its operational mechanism.

To utilize the gene's encoded information in protein production, the cell's machinery first makes a copy of the gene in the form of an RNA molecule. This mRNA migrates to the ribosome, where it directs protein synthesis. When researchers disrupted the *Makorin-1-p1* pseudogene, the Makorin-1 mRNA became degraded before it could direct the production of the Makorin-1 protein.

The team discovered that for the cell to produce the Makorin-1 protein, the cell's machinery had to make mRNA copies of both the *Makorin-1* and *Makorin-1-p1* gene and pseudogene. The Makorin-1-p1 mRNA somehow protects the Makorin-1 mRNA from breakdown. Makorin-1-p1 mRNA exerts its protective effect only when it exists in a partial form that bears some resemblance to the *Makorin-1* gene.

When these researchers published their work on the *Makorin-1-p1* pseudogene, they thought their study was the first to demonstrate pseudogene function. They predicted that researchers would discover other duplicated pseudogenes working in partnership with corresponding genes. Their hunch was based on awareness that the cell's machinery makes copies of other pseudogenes (like *Makorin-1-p1*) in the human genome.[28]

The high-profile nature of their report prompted two molecular biologists to carefully review the scientific literature on pseudogenes. To nearly everyone's surprise, they found numerous examples in which pseudogenes played a role in gene regulation and expression.[29] The team that conducted the work on *Makorin-1-p1* later issued a correction to their original paper. They acknowledged that pseudogene function had been identified prior to their work, as far back as 1999.[30]

Along similar lines, molecular biologists now acknowledge that processed pseudogenes encode functional proteins. Scientists from the University of Chicago and University of Cincinnati reported in 2002 that a processed pseudogene (*Phosphoglycerate mutase,* or *PGAM3*) found in the human genome actually produces a functional protein.[31] This processed pseudogene seems to have originated through haphazard biochemical events from processed mRNA. However, the pseudogene possesses the DNA elements required for the cell's machinery to recognize it as a functional gene and read it to produce a mRNA copy. The research team also experimentally detected mRNAs from the *PGAM3* processed pseudogene. All their data indicate that this pseudogene must be functional.

Currently, *PGAM3* represents only one of a handful of processed pseudogenes that molecular biologists have identified as functionally active. Still, the research team from Chicago and Cincinnati anticipates that, because a large number of processed pseudogenes exist in the human genome, the identification of purpose for them is just starting to unfold.

As researchers continue to uncover function for pseudogenes, it becomes apparent that the evolutionary perspective on noncoding DNA as junk has thwarted scientific advance. In the spring of 2004, a research team discovered a new class of antifreeze proteins in fish that prevent ice from forming in biological tissues and allow fish to live in subfreezing environments. However, researchers failed to recognize this new type of antifreeze protein for nearly 30 years because they had assumed its gene was a pseudogene. Only after researchers realized that the previously identified antifreeze proteins were insufficient for fish to survive in icy polar waters were they motivated to search for additional types of antifreeze molecules.[32]

Bottom line

The discovery that some pseudogenes are actually functional means the evolutionary paradigm no longer offers the only viable explanation for their existence. Critical pseudogene activity in the cell makes an equally plausible case that the Creator intentionally incorporated this class of DNA into the genomes of humans, chimpanzees, and other organisms for reasons the scientific community is only now beginning to grasp.

SINEs

Molecular biologists now recognize that SINEs (found in the genomes of a wide range of organisms) play an important role in regulating gene expression and protecting the cell during times of distress. Researchers from University of California, Davis, demonstrated that, for silkworms, mice, and humans, the cell's machinery makes RNA copies of SINE DNA at higher levels when the creatures are stressed by heat shock (hyperthermia), viral infection, and physiological insults (such as high levels of ethanol).[33] Presumably, the cell's increased production of SINE mRNA protects it.

As part of these studies, the researchers showed that SINE mRNA binds to a particular enzyme (called double-stranded RNA-regulated protein kinase PKR) that regulates protein synthesis and other cellular activities.[34] These results provide some initial insight as to how SINE DNA helps the cell deal with stress.

The UC Davis team identified another potential function for SINE DNA—regulation of gene expression during the course of an organism's development. Machinery within the cell attaches methyl chemical groups to certain regions of SINE DNA. This methylation process turns genes off. SINE DNA isolated from different types of tissue displays varying patterns of DNA methylation, a characteristic that implicates SINEs in the differential gene expression that occurs during development.[35]

Evolutionary biologists speculate that SINE DNA arose, acquired the ability to increase in number, and moved throughout the genome when a random biochemical event inserted a piece of DNA into the proto-SINE sequence. This DNA was needed for the cell's machinery to make RNA copies of it. Given that SINE DNA plays a functional role in the cell, evolutionists maintain that this function evolved after SINE DNA emerged.

While superficially plausible, this explanation seems inadequate to some scientists, especially because SINE DNA appears to have such an integrated and far-reaching role in gene regulation. Carl Schmid, head of the UC Davis research team that produced many of the new insights about SINE DNA, stated, "Since *Alus* have appeared only recently within the primate lineage, this proposal [of SINE function] provokes the challenging question of how *Alu* RNA could have possibly assumed a significant role in cell physiology."[36]

Bottom line
Molecular biologists have recently discovered functional roles for SINE DNA. The DNA elements help protect the cell when stressed and regulate gene expression. Given its importance to the cell, SINE DNA may more likely represent the Creator's handiwork.

LINEs

Much in the same way as the scientific community came to acknowledge function for SINE DNA, molecular biologists have begun to recognize that long interspersed nuclear elements (LINEs) critically regulate gene expression. One of the first scientific reports to describe the importance of LINE DNA came from Case Western Reserve University scientists in the summer of 2000. These researchers identified a central role for LINE DNA in X-chromosome inactivation.[37]

This inactivation occurs in healthy females as a way to compensate for duplicate genes found on the two X chromosomes.[38] (Females have two X chromosomes; males have an X and a Y chromosome.) The inactivation of one set of the X-chromosomal genes ensures proper levels of gene expression in females. If this inactivation doesn't occur, genetic disorders result.[39]

Scientists are beginning to understand the molecular mechanisms of X-chromosome inactivation.[40] This process starts at a location on the X chromosome called the inactivation center. The site contains the *XIST* gene. The cell's machinery copies this gene to produce mRNA. Unlike most RNA messengers, the XIST RNA does not migrate from the cell's nucleus to ribosomes to make proteins. Rather, multiple copies of the XIST RNA coat the X chromosome. They first bind to the inactivation center and from there spread along the remainder of the X chromosome. This initial buildup at the inactivation center causes the X chromosome to form a highly condensed structure called a Barr body. Once it forms, none of the X-chromosomal genes can be expressed.

Only one of the X chromosomes is inactivated. The other one remains in an extended state with all of its genes active. The *XIST* gene that is part of the functional X chromosome is obviously turned off. Otherwise, this chromosome would also be converted into a Barr body.

The work of the Case Western Reserve University research team implicates LINEs as the binding site for XIST RNA. The X chromosome contains a significant enrichment of LINE DNA compared to other chromosomes, with the greatest concentration being near the inactivation center.

Since this group of scientists reported their results, molecular biologists have shown that the regulatory role of LINE DNA extends beyond X-chromosome inactivation. The scientific community now suspects that LINE DNA controls monoallelic gene expression.[41] This term refers to the situation in which only one of the two genes inherited from an organism's parents is used. The other gene is completely turned off.

Many biologists explain LINE DNA as the consequence of molecular evolution. But as with SINE DNA, the seemingly pervasive role that LINE DNA plays in gene regulation raises doubts. It's difficult to envision how the supposed artifacts of random biochemical events could be so elegantly co-opted to perform vital regulatory functions.

Further exacerbating an evolutionary explanation for LINE DNA is another surprising discovery made by the Case Western Reserve University team. Assuming an evolutionary perspective, these researchers discovered that LINE DNA first appeared in placental mammals just when they supposedly separated from marsupial mammals.[42] Instead of gradually accumulating, LINE DNA appeared suddenly and seems to perform identical functions among all placental mammals.

Bottom line

Biochemists now recognize that LINE DNA plays a strategic role in an organism's development, turning genes off in X-chromosome inactivation and in monoallelic gene expression. Because it regulates gene expression, LINE DNA may represent an intentionally designed feature of humans' and animals' genomes.

Endogenous retroviral DNA

The scientific community is also well on its way to uncovering functional roles for endogenous retroviruses and their compositional elements. Recent advances indicate that, in addition to regulating gene expression, this class of noncoding DNA helps the cell ward off retroviral infections.

Retroviruses comprise a class of viruses that exploit RNA as their genetic material. Once the retrovirus infects the cell, its RNA genome is converted to DNA by the reverse transcriptase enzyme. The retroviral DNA can then become incorporated into the host's genome.[43]

One of the first suggestions that endogenous viral DNA may protect the cell from retroviral infections came in 1989 from a molecular biologist studying the distribution of LINE DNA in the human genome. This scientist noted that the cell's machinery increases its production of LINE RNAs when retroviral infections occur.[44] The RNA derived from LINE DNA presumably interferes with the retroviral life cycle because it shares structural similarity with retroviral RNA. Evolutionary biologists believe that LINE DNA originated from a retrovirus that suffered disabling mutations after it had been incorporated into its mammalian host's genome.

More recent work has identified genes that share structural similarity to those found in retroviruses. These genes take part in disrupting the life cycle of invading retroviruses. In such instances the genes appear to code for proteins that interact with and disrupt the assembly of the retroviral capsid.[45] Researchers investigating these anti-retroviral proteins in human and monkey cells observed that an infection with one type of retrovirus inhibits infection by other retroviruses, presumably due to competition.[46]

Researchers have also suggested that another noncoding DNA class called long terminal repeats (LTRs)—thought by evolutionary biologists to originate from endogenous retroviruses—perform an anti-retroviral function as well.[47] All these studies make a strong case that endogenous retroviruses found in humans and other organisms perform in a protective capacity.

Along different lines, researchers have developed evidence that LTRs help regulate gene expression.[48] Because LTRs share structural features with endogenous retroviruses, perhaps endogenous retroviruses are also involved in regulating gene expression.

A team of French scientists has found that endogenous retroviral elements function in yet another capacity, beyond providing retroviral protection and regulating gene activity.[49] These investigators showed that the retroviral component ERVWE1 is *not* noncoding DNA but rather functions as a gene. Its protein product plays a role in the functioning of the human placenta.

Bottom line
It now appears that endogenous retroviruses play a wide range of roles in the cell. One of their chief functions is protection against retrovirus infections. These DNA elements appear to be an elegantly functioning component of the human genome.

Junk DNA and Human Evolution
The plethora of discoveries that identify functions for virtually all classes of noncoding DNA undermine evolution's case. Instead of compelling an evolutionary interpretation, the shared features of human and chimpanzee noncoding DNA can easily be explained as useful features fashioned by the Creator for the benefit of a wide range of organisms, including humans and chimpanzees.

Many scientists now maintain that even though they can't directly identify functional roles for some classes of noncoding DNA, these DNA segments must be functional because they are shared among a wide range of distantly related and even unrelated organisms.[50] Apparently these noncoding DNA classes operate in a critical capacity. If they didn't, mutations would readily accrue in them. The mutations would have rendered the DNA nonfunctional. Any change would be deleterious to the organism. Ironically, this reasoning supports the concept that shared genetic features reflect the Creator's work, not common ancestry.

The scientific community now recognizes that noncoding DNA is functional. This realization greatly weakens one of the mainstays for human evolution and for the shared ancestry of humans and chimpanzees.

Junk DNA and the RTB Model

Because the various classes of noncoding DNA all perform functional roles, it's unnecessary to evoke a common evolutionary history to explain their shared presence in the human and chimpanzee genomes. The RTB model maintains instead that the existence of similar noncoding DNA sequences in these genomes reflects the Creator's use of common design features when He miraculously made humans and chimps. The common geography of noncoding DNA sequences in the human and chimp genomes likely stems from their role in regulating gene activity. These DNA sequences must be precisely positioned (relative to the genes they control) to exert their proper influence.

What about the genetic material without a known function, such as the GLO unitary pseudogenes that humans and chimpanzees share? Currently the RTB model offers no explanation for this feature. The model does predict, however, that as with other classes of noncoding DNA, function will one day be discovered for these uniting pseudogenes.

Recent scientific discoveries about junk DNA leave no ironclad arguments for evolution. Rather than supporting Darwin's perspective of humanity's origin, many scientific discoveries and viable arguments give credence to David's position on creation.

Chapter 15

Humanity's Identity Materializes

The play's the thing
Wherein I'll catch the conscience
Of the King.
—*Hamlet* Act 2, scene 2

For Shakespeare's Hamlet, the death of his father threw the world into chaos. When an apparition appeared, it drove the prince of Denmark to pursue the truth about his father's death. Was the specter a "damned ghost" intent on devilish deception, or was it a tormented spirit crying out for justice?

The desire to know led Hamlet to devise a plan to test the spirit's true identity. Testing becomes even more crucial in the real world.

Over a hundred years ago when Darwin wrote *The Descent of Man, and Selection in Relation to Sex*, it threw society's view of humankind into chaos. An underlying message implied that—as an accident of nature—humanity possessed no meaning, no purpose, no value. The vision of humankind as a special creation no longer informed the scientific quest for humanity's origin. Man's eternal significance, which David sang about 3,000 years ago, became lost. Instead, scientists explained human origins as a chance outcome in the naturalistic process of evolutionary descent from an apelike ancestor.

The Ghost Vanishes

Over the years, however, attempts to account for humanity's origin through an evolutionary process appear to be much like Hamlet's ghost—a presence that begs to be authenticated. Scientific investigation demonstrates that while paleontologists have discovered a menagerie of hominids, scientists have failed to establish the necessary evolutionary connections (see chapter 9). Without these connections, human evolution cannot be declared a fact. Instead of solidifying evolutionary hypotheses about human origins, each new hominid find generates further turmoil.

Paleoanthropologists cannot adequately account for the evolutionary emergence of bipedalism or brain size, generally considered to be humanity's two most significant anatomical characteristics (see chapter 10). Instead of emerging gradually, bipedalism appears suddenly in the fossil record, coincidently with the first appearance of hominids. Instead of gradually increasing in the fossil record, hominid brain size shows discontinuous jumps as new hominid species successively enter the fossil record. These sudden steps are relatively small from hominid to hominid until modern humans appear. With humans' advent, brain size dramatically increases.

Paleontologists now have definitive evidence that Homo erectus and Neanderthals, long regarded as central figures in the human origin sequence, were evolutionary side branches and dead ends (see chapters 11 and 12). Neither Neanderthals nor H. erectus made genetic (thus evolutionary) contributions to modern humans. Such discoveries annul the multiregional hypothesis—the familiar assertion that modern humans evolved around the world from different hominid populations. (According to this view, H. erectus gave rise to Asian and Oceanic peoples. Homo neanderthalensis produced Europeans, and archaic Homo sapiens in Africa evolved into African peoples.) For nearly 50 years, this evolutionary model was the standard explanation for humanity's origin. It no longer has merit.

For many scientists, the "99 percent genetic similarity" between humans and chimpanzees has represented compelling evidence for human evolution by natural process. Here, too, recent advances undermine this supposed certainty. The most comprehensive genetic comparisons to date indicate that humans and chimpanzees share a genetic similarity of about 85 percent, not 99. If a 99 percent genetic similarity reflects a close evolutionary connection, then from an evolutionary perspective an 85 percent genetic similarity shows a decisive distance.

Other recent studies demonstrate that even small genetic differences translate into significant biological variations. These discoveries help explain why humans stand apart from the great apes. Several studies now show that the gene expression patterns in human and chimpanzee brains (and other tissues and organs) vary significantly. In other words, the biological and behavioral distinctions between humans and chimpanzees likely depend to a large extent on the differences in gene activity, not the types of genes present (see chapter 13).

Evolutionary biologists maintain that endogenous retroviruses, LINEs, SINEs, and pseudogenes shared among humans and the great apes provide persuasive evidence that these primates arose from a common ancestor. This argument rests on the supposition that these classes of noncoding DNA arose through random biochemical events and that they lack function. For many biologists, it makes little sense to attribute "junk" DNA to the Creator's handiwork.

And yet a plethora of discoveries have identified functions for virtually all classes of noncoding DNA. Instead of leading to an evolutionary interpretation, the shared features of human and chimpanzee noncoding DNA find ready explanation as a common design feature in the genomes of these two species (see chapter 14).

In light of all this research, the case for human evolution begins to dissipate. Does creation, then, offer a better explanation for humanity's beginning?

Under Scrutiny
Forming and testing hypotheses (the scientific method) is an effective way to discover truth. The scientific community places great importance on developing hypotheses and models so they can be tested. Research continues even on well-established theories.

Scientists produce models in the hope that they adequately represent the realities of the natural realm. For properly conceived models, logical outworkings become the predictions that scientists use to further assess the model's validity. Models that successfully account for scientific results and observations (through predictions) are considered valid. Models that fail to make successful predictions are appropriately discarded.

The notion that Adam and Eve were historical individuals created by God as the first man and woman has long been regarded by the science community (or at least a large part of it) as an ancient Hebrew myth. Because faith appeared to be the only basis for accepting it, this view played no role in most scientists' quest for the truth. For creation to be taken seriously by the scientific community, the creation explanation must be recast in the form of a scientific model. And that is what this book does.

Substance over Speculation
Creation does not have to be blindly accepted based on faith alone. The biblical explanation can be tested (see chapter 3). Statements about God's creative work and passages that speak about Earth's and life's natural history can be

framed in the form of a scientific description or model. The logical consequences and outworkings of the biblical text expressed in this manner provide a way to establish creation's validity. The RTB model can be tested by the scientific community to access—and further assess—truth about the natural realm.

Application of the creation model approach to humanity's origin makes a way for biblical ideas and concepts to gain entry into the scientific arena. Within science's domain, new discoveries can be used to evaluate the validity of the RTB model (and, along with it, the biblical account of humanity's beginnings). In turn, the RTB model provides the means to guide future scientific investigation through the predictions it makes (see chapter 3).

The RTB model views Adam and Eve as historical individuals—the first human beings—originating by God's miraculous intervention approximately 70,000 to 50,000 years ago. Adam and Eve's descendants formed a small initial population that eventually gave rise to all human population groups around the world.

This biblical approach places the origin of humanity in or near the Garden of Eden. While theologians have yet to reach a consensus on the Garden's exact location, it likely existed in Mesopotamia and might have extended into northern and eastern Africa.

After Noah's flood (described in Genesis 6–9), the first humans rapidly spread from the Middle East into Africa, Europe, Asia, and eventually the Americas. During the course of this global migration, the size of the first human population dramatically expanded.

The RTB model regards humans as qualitatively different from animals, including the great apes and hominids. This distinction does not primarily refer to physical differences. Although such differences exist, the RTB model maintains that humans and all other animals (including hominids and the great apes) share at least some biochemical, genetic, physiological, and anatomical similarities. One main distinctive, however, separates human beings from the animals: Only humans bear God's image. People use their minds to reason and contemplate the future. People create, imitating their Creator. People, male and female, worship the Creator as God.

Adam and Eve Steal the Show

A litany of scientific advances in genetics, biochemistry, archeology, and even geology and astronomy comport with the RTB model, which predicts this reflection of God's image. Genetic studies of human population groups signify that humanity had a recent origin in a single geographical location from a small population, with genetic links back to a single man and single woman (see chapter 4). The research also demonstrates that humanity and human civilization arose relatively recently near (or in) the Middle East to fill the earth (see chapter 8).

These studies suggest a scenario for human origins that agrees with the RTB biblical view. In fact, the first genetic ancestors of humanity are referred to in the scientific community as "Y-chromosomal Adam" and "mitochondrial Eve."

This still-controversial idea (referred to as the out-of-Africa model or the Garden-of-Eden hypothesis) is gaining acceptance among biologists even though it runs counter to traditional human evolutionary models and fits uncomfortably within the current evolutionary framework. In many respects, the out-of-Africa model is the RTB model forced into a naturalistic construct. The ambiguities lingering over the evidence for human evolution give the creation model an edge over the out-of-Africa hypothesis.

Archeological evidence also supports this biblical view (see chapter 5). Though hominids that lived as far back as 2 million years ago employed tools and possessed a culture of sorts, their technology and lifestyle must be described as crude and simple. This way of life remained static for hundreds of thousands of years at a stretch. When new modes of technology and culture appear in the archeological record, the advances represent relatively small-step changes upward, again followed by long periods of stasis. In short, the archeological record does not display a gradual evolutionary emergence of modern human intellectual and artistic capabilities. At 50,000 years ago, advanced human culture appeared out of nowhere. The archeological record reveals a veritable explosion of human culture—anthropology's "big bang"—which marks the appearance of God's image.

New astronomical and geophysical studies indicate that human beings appeared on Earth at a special time in cosmic history (see chapter 6). Humanity arrived within an amazing number of astronomical, geological, and biological time windows that not only provide Earth with the necessary benign conditions needed for survival but also ensure an abundance of the natural resources that make advanced civilization possible. This timing of humanity's appearance indicates that human beings have a high purpose.

Scientific evidence harmonizes remarkably well with the predictions that logically flow from the RTB model. Even the long life spans described in Genesis 5 and 11 (an undeniable part of the RTB model) find possible scientific explanation in recent breakthroughs in the biochemistry of aging and new astronomical findings about changes in Earth's radiation environment several tens of thousands of years ago (see chapter 7).

At no other time in human history has the biblical account of humanity's origin held greater scientific credibility than it does today. Advancing scientific research in the months and years to come will provide even more opportunities to test the credibility of biblical models for human origins. Putting the biblical view of humanity's origin to the test in the form of a scientific creation model affirms David's claim—man is the crown of God's creation. And that is a conclusion worth singing about.

Psalm 8

> O LORD, our Lord,
> how majestic is your name in all the earth!
> You have set your glory
> above the heavens.
> From the lips of children and infants
> you have ordained praise
> because of your enemies,
> to silence the foe and avenger.
> When I consider your heavens,
> the work of your fingers,
> the moon and stars,
> which you have set in place,
> what is man that you are mindful of him,
> the son of man that you care for him?
> You made him a little lower than the heavenly beings
> and crowned him with glory and honor.
> You made him ruler over the works of your hands;
> you put everything under his feet:
> all flocks and herds,
> and the beasts of the field,
> the birds of the air,
> and the fish of the sea,
> all that swim the paths of the seas.
> O LORD, our Lord,
> how majestic is your name in all the earth!

PART III

THE
TEN-YEAR
UPDATE

Chapter 16

Why This Update?

To vouch this is no proof,
Without more wider and more overt test
Than these thin habits and poor likelihoods
Of modern seemingly do prefer against him.
                                        —*Othello* Act 1, scene 3

To his dismay, Brabanito has just learned that his daughter Desdemona has married Othello. He accuses the Moor of winning her over with some kind of special potion or magical spell. The Duke of Venice, however, is not convinced by these arguments and determines that they need "more wider and more overt" tests. Testing is the way to get to the bottom of things. And it is the way of science.

Testing the Model
Scientists don't rest on their laurels. No matter how well established, scientific theories are continually subjected to further testing. Each new discovery provides the opportunity to test the reigning paradigm. Good theories will anticipate and readily accommodate these advances. But if they cannot, they must be modified or, in some instances, abandoned altogether. Science progresses through the never-ending cycle of testing, revision, and testing—again and again.

The purpose of Part III is to bring *Who Was Adam?* up-to-date by discussing how scientific advances impact Reasons to Believe's (RTB) model. We opted to let the original work stand (aside from minor editorial corrections) as written in 2005 and to focus on the most salient new discoveries of the past decade. Rather than simply describe the new finds, we will use them as a way to subject our model to wider, more overt tests.

What's New?

One challenge for this endeavor was to limit the testing in the face of mounting discoveries. Here are some of the breakthroughs that we have chosen as the focus of our attention.

Genetic dating of humanity's origin

Advances in molecular anthropology allow for greater accuracy when estimating the dates for "mitochondrial Eve" and "Y-chromosomal Adam." Scientists have established a more robust date for humanity's genesis. Was the RTB model close in its original estimate? And was there indeed a genetic bottleneck at the flood of Noah, as the model maintained?

Origin of sophisticated behavior

Archeological finds have yielded important new insights about the origin of sophisticated behavior in modern humans. Many anthropologists consider sophisticated behavior to be a hallmark of symbolic thought, which we take as evidence for the image of God. From caves along South Africa's coast, archeologists have recovered artifacts, presumably made by modern humans, which date to about 70,000 to 80,000 years in age. These advances and others discovered in Asia help define the mode and tempo for the appearance of modern human behavior. Do they support or challenge RTB's view?

Hominids

This past decade has been unprecedented in the history of paleoanthropology. Investigators have unearthed and characterized exciting new hominid finds attributed to: *Ardipithecus ramidus, Australopithecus afarensis, Australopithecus sediba, Homo gautengensis, Homo habilis, Homo georgicus, Homo erectus, Homo antecessor, Homo heidelbergensis,* and the Red Deer Cave people. Scientists have analyzed ancient skulls, jawbones, teeth, partial skeletons, footprints, and more. We will explain what these fossils show.

Ancient hominid DNA

Breakthroughs in genomics have enabled researchers to reconstruct—from ancient pieces of DNA—a high-quality sequence of the entire nuclear genome for Neanderthals. They have also identified the Denisovans, possibly a new hominid species, from DNA fragments extracted from a small finger bone, dating 74,000 to 82,000 years in age. Abundant new data have afforded researchers the unprecedented opportunity to conduct detailed comparisons between the human genome and that of Neanderthals and Denisovans. Along with other important discoveries, the trove of data yields a new perspective on hominid behavior and cognitive abilities.

In recent years, researchers also surprised the scientific world with genetic data indicating that humans interbred with Neanderthals, and possibly with Denisovans as well. Popular news outlets have run with this titillating idea. Did it happen? Is so, what does it mean?

Great ape behavior
Primatologists have made remarkable observations of chimpanzees, bonobos, and gorillas in the wild and in captivity. This work provides new understanding of great ape behavior and a better context for understanding modern human behavior as compared to Neanderthals', erectines', and habilines' behavior.

Great ape genomes
Geneticists have sequenced the genomes of chimpanzees, bonobos, orangutans, and gorillas, and have used this massive data to carry out detailed comparisons of the human genome with those of the great apes. What have scientists discovered about the widely touted "99 percent similarity" between humans and chimps? Do meaningful comparisons also entail a description of the difference between genetic similarity and genetic expression?

Junk DNA
Long considered an evolutionary standout, is it time for junk DNA to stand down? New understanding of *Alu* sequences and pseudogenes reveals surprises. Plus, the headline-grabbing ENCODE Project, involving 450 researchers and 1,650 experiments, produced a massive database that showed just how much of the human genome is functional and nonfunctional.

Criticisms of the model
Since RTB's human origins model has been in the public purview, like all scientific ideas, the model has received its share of criticism. Here we respond to six prominent criticisms of our model. Evolutionary biologists object to the idea of a primordial pair—the biblical Adam and Eve—and assert that humanity arose from a population. They also claim humanity emerged from multiple locations, not a single one purported to be the Garden of Eden. Does RTB's model withstand this type of scrutiny? And what about the argument regarding human chromosome 2?

New scientific questions

Science progresses at a frenetic pace—so much so, that models cannot incorporate every possible source of input for building a case. Where did the races come from? How did human diseases arise? Do extensive genetic similarities between humans and great apes support common descent? Ten years ago RTB's model did not address these questions. It does now.

While we anticipated some of the new insights from genomics when *Who Was Adam?* was first published, the growing prominence of genomics highlights the need for a theoretical framework that accounts for the similarities and differences in the genomes of organisms (specifically, in this context, those of humans, the great apes, Neanderthals, and Denisovans) from a creation/design standpoint. To address this need, we present the framework for such a model. The RTB genomics model stands on its own, but it should also be viewed as a companion to the RTB human origins model, given how important DNA sequence data have become in understanding the origin of humanity.

How Has the RTB Model Fared?

As we explained in the first edition of *Who Was Adam?*, considerable freedom exists within the creation model's framework for adjustments and fine-tuning as scientists and theologians make new discoveries and gain fresh insight. A decade of scientific advance affords RTB the opportunity to refine the model. More importantly, it provides *readers* with a chance to subject the model to "wider and more overt" testing. Here are some questions to bear in mind:

- Do these advances match the model's predictions?
- Can the RTB model accommodate all the new insights into humanity's origin?
- How about evolutionary explanations? How do they fare in light of the evidence?
- Which model *best* accounts for the available data?

Maintaining Integrity

Ultimately, the rationale for updating *Who Was Adam?* and not rewriting the book is to emphasize the fact that the RTB human origins model *is*, indeed, a scientific model. RTB's model exists within a highly dynamic environment, continually challenged by new discoveries from the fossil and archeological records and advances in molecular anthropology and comparative genomics. These advances have forced (and will force) revisions and refinements and have generated the need for extensions of the model.

But the same is true for any model in any scientific discipline. It is what makes science so exciting. Creation can indeed be science.

Better Dates for Humanity's Genesis

"What are the new dates for the creation of Adam and Eve?"
"How long ago do you believe Adam and Eve existed?"
"Will Reasons to Believe keep moving its dates for Adam and Eve back?"

These queries rank among the most frequent we encounter after speaking engagements or via social media. A real tension accompanies the questions. People wonder if the Reasons to Believe (RTB) model has withstood the wider testing of a decade of discoveries. Recent evidence from the field of molecular anthropology helps "shore up" the dates for when the first human beings lived.

Tracing Human Origins through Molecular Anthropology

As discussed in chapter 4, an ensemble of genetic markers collectively indicates that humanity originated recently from a single location (apparently East Africa, close to where theologians believe the Garden of Eden was located) and from a small population. Those markers include mitochondrial DNA (mtDNA) variants, and Y-chromosomal variants. Both types of DNA trace back to single ancestral sequences that some anthropologists take as corresponding to a single female ("mitochondrial Eve") and male ("Y-chromosomal Adam") individual.

Given such evidence, and to summarize some features of our earlier position, RTB maintained that

- remarkable agreement between the molecular anthropology data and our model predictions supported the biblical creation account of humanity;
- the ancestral mitochondrial and Y-chromosomal sequences corresponded to a primordial couple, the biblical Adam and Eve;

- the date for mitochondrial Eve was at 171,000 ± 50,000 years ago;
- the date for Y-chromosomal Adam was between 50,000 to 60,000 years ago; and
- the discrepancy between the dates for mitochondrial Eve and Y-chromosomal Adam may find explanation in the flood event described in Genesis 6–9.

Was There a Genetic Bottleneck?

As noted in chapter 4, many scientists reject the notion that humanity originated from one man and one woman. Rather, they maintain that a large population of modern humans (or the evolutionary predecessors to modern humans) suffered a catastrophic collapse. When this occurred, genetic diversity was lost and the first humans went through a genetic bottleneck. After the collapse, the remaining population experienced rapid growth and expansion to fill the planet.

Evolutionary biologists and anthropologists say that the genetic marker for this collapse remains imprinted on today's human population groups in the form of limited genetic variation. Accordingly, the passage of humanity through a genetic bottleneck, perhaps as recently as 100,000 years ago, creates the appearance that humanity arose from a small original population. Hence, the recent origin of humanity from a small population and a single location in Africa would merely reflect humanity's recovery from a population collapse.

Lucky Pair?

These scientists also reject the notion that humanity came from an "Adam and Eve." Instead they argue that many "Eves" and "Adams" existed. Thus, mitochondrial Eve and Y-chromosomal Adam were the lucky ones whose lineages just happened to survive. Their contemporaries' mitochondrial and Y-chromosomal genetic lines were lost over time.

Evolutionary biologists go further and assert that when other genetic markers are used to characterize humanity's origin, they too trace back to a single ancestral sequence that can be interpreted as corresponding to a single individual. They argue, however, that these "Eves" and "Adams" are not the same individuals as mitochondrial Eve and Y-chromosomal Adam. (These challenges to the RTB model are discussed in more detail later. See pages 347–352.)

Evolutionary biologists maintain that the discrepancy between the dates for mitochondrial Eve and Y-chromosomal Adam makes it impossible to square the scientific data with the biblical idea that humanity emerged from a primordial couple. The difference in dates indicates to them that mitochondrial Eve came from a population that existed earlier than the population to which Y-chromosomal Adam belonged.[1] (See "Why Eve Might Have Been an Older Woman" on pages 70–71.)

New Date for Mitochondrial Eve

However, recent studies in molecular anthropology potentially remove the discrepancy in the dates for mitochondrial Eve and Y-chromosomal Adam. In 2009, a group of researchers led by Phillip Endicott questioned the assumptions used to establish the mtDNA mutation rate.[2] They pointed out that the mutation rate employed in most studies relies on genetic comparisons between humans and chimpanzees. (This comparison assumes that humans and chimps share a common evolutionary ancestor.) To establish an average mutation rate, geneticists take the average number of genetic differences between human and chimp mtDNA and divide by 6 million because they assume humans and chimps diverged from their shared ancestor about 6 million years ago.

Endicott's team noted that using this mutation rate produces results that contradict the dates for events in human history derived from the fossil and archeological records. They believe the reason for the discrepancy stems from several factors. First, evolutionary biologists do not know when the human-chimp ancestor lived. Second, the mutation rate is not constant through time and it can vary based on geographical location. Finally, the mutation rate varies from region to region within the mitochondrial genome. The team determined a new mutation rate for mtDNA by taking these factors into account and using widely agreed upon dates from the fossil and archeological records to calibrate the mtDNA molecular clock. Their date for mitochondrial Eve comes in close to 108,000 years ago.

A more recent study by Aylwyn Scally and Richard Durbin challenged this revised date, claiming that mitochondrial Eve lived between 250,000 and 300,000 years ago.[3] Scally and Durbin reached their conclusion based on a much slower mtDNA mutation rate derived from a comparison of genome sequences from humans living today.

However, the validity of this recent approach is questionable because it fails to consider molecular clocks' stochastic (random events that overlay a long-term statistical trend) nature. Such clocks are not metronomic (regular); therefore, mutation rates cannot be reliably determined by comparing genomes of contemporaries or of several generations of people in the same family. Mutation rates must be established over much more significant time frames.

Yet another study published in 2013 describes a calibration of the mtDNA clock over a larger time frame without employing any assumptions. Scientists calibrated the mtDNA clock using genomes recovered through ancient DNA analysis from the fossil remains of 10 humans that lived over the span of about 40,000 years. These remains were confidently dated using carbon-14 methods. Using this calibration, the researchers concluded that mitochondrial Eve lived about 157,000 ± 40,000 years ago.[4] A related study conducted by researchers from the United Kingdom employed a similar approach to calibrate the mtDNA molecular clock.[5] Making use of a database of 350 complete genome sequences of mtDNA recovered from well-dated ancient human remains and contemporary individuals, the UK scientists estimated that mitochondrial Eve lived about 157,000 ± 30,000 years ago.

The recovery of a high-quality genome from the 45,000-year-old remains of an anatomically modern human femur demonstrates the accuracy of this new calibration of the mtDNA molecular clock.[6] Carbon-14 dating places the most likely age of the femur at 45,000 ± 2,000 years. Molecular clock analysis of the mtDNA recovered from the femur places its age at 49,000 ± 17,000 years old. Consequently, we have adjusted our date for Eve from between 10,000 to 100,000 years ago to about 150,000 years ago.

New Date for Y-chromosomal Adam

Scientists have also revised the date for Y-chromosomal Adam. A study conducted in 2011 and three more in 2013 made use of a larger portion of the Y chromosome and rare Y chromosome variants to estimate respective dates of Y-chromosomal Adam at: (1) 142,000 ± 16,000 years ago; (2) between 101,000 and 115,000 years ago; (3) between 120,000 and 156,000 years ago; and (4) 180,000 to 200,000 years ago.[7] These four studies fall in line with the best, most-recent dates for mitochondrial Eve.

Another 2013 study from University of Arizona (UA) created a stir when its authors reported a date for Y-chromosomal Adam between 237,000 and 581,000 years ago, with the most likely age for Adam at 338,000 years.[8] This estimate for Y-chromosomal Adam is about 200,000 years earlier than the first appearance of modern humans in the fossil record; thus, on this basis alone people have questioned the result.

One team of inquirers, scientists from University of Houston (UH) and from Johns Hopkins University (JHU), identified a number of flaws with the UA study.[9] Careful examination of the UA study's approach to calculating the date of Y-chromosomal Adam reveals that the mutation rate used by the UA investigators to calibrate the molecular clock was slower than that used in previous studies. The UA researchers based the mutation rate they used on whole genome sequence comparisons of people living today. As discussed previously with respect to mtDNA, this type of calibration is probably not valid. If the UA researchers had used the same mutation rate as previous investigators, their estimated date for Y-chromosomal Adam would be closer to 209,000 years ago. In fact, when the UH-JHU team reanalyzed the UA team's data, they generated a date for Y-chromosomal Adam of about 208,000 years in age, roughly consistent with the other recent studies.

The UH-JHU team identified other problems with the UA study. For example, the Arizona researchers used generation times that were unusually long, they compared DNA sequences of unequal length, and they employed unusual statistical methods in their analysis. All three factors contributed to the much older date for Y-chromosomal Adam.

Bottom line
Based on the best and most recent analysis of Y chromosome variants, it appears that the date for Y-chromosomal Adam is between 100,000 and 200,000 years ago, not—as we had thought—50,000 to 60,000 years ago.

Last Human Ancestors
Now that researchers have used better estimates of mutation rates for mtDNA, looked at larger regions of the Y chromosome, and included rare Y chromosome variants, the dates for mitochondrial Eve and Y-chromosomal Adam converge around 150,000 years ago. Added support for this conclusion comes from a study in which researchers determined that the last ancestor of all human males lived between 120,000 and 156,000 years ago and the ancestor of all human females lived between 99,000 and 148,000 years ago.[10]

From a scientific standpoint, the revised dates for mitochondrial Eve and Y-chromosomal Adam are gratifying because they both align with estimates of humanity's origin from the fossil record (between 100,000 and 200,000 years ago) and also comport fairly well with the archeological record. History places the first evidence for symbolism, which we take as a reflection of God's image in humans, between 70,000 and 80,000 years ago (and arguably as far back as 160,000 years). (See chapter 18, pages 274–276.)

Testing the Models

What does it mean for the RTB model to say that Adam and Eve both lived (with generous error bars) about 150,000 years ago? On one hand, this is good news. If mitochondrial Eve and Y-chromosomal Adam are the primeval biblical couple, then it is incumbent that they lived at the same time. If mitochondrial Eve and Y-chromosomal Adam lived at *different* times, then they must have been members of different populations, giving credence to the evolutionary interpretation—if for no other reason than the biblical view could not be correct if Adam did not "know" Eve. These new insights from molecular anthropology affirm the traditional biblical understanding of humanity's origin and spread.

On the other hand, these results do force us to revise a key part of the RTB model. In 2005, we said that humanity's female lineage should trace back to an earlier date than the male lineage. We made the point that although all humanity came from Adam and Eve, scientific dating of humanity's origin using genetic markers specific to the female lineage should measure older than those specific to the male lineage. The discrepancy was not because Eve came first, but because the male line experienced a more severe bottleneck at the time of the flood. We believe the Bible teaches that the flood destroyed all humanity except for Noah, his wife, his three sons (Shem, Ham, and Japheth), and their wives. The four men—but not necessarily the women—on the ark were blood relatives. Scientifically speaking, humanity's male lineage effectively traces back to Noah, whereas the female lineage traces back much farther, closer to Eve.

At that time, we took this inconsistency as fulfillment of a key prediction of the RTB human origins model. Unfortunately, the latest results from molecular anthropology show no direct genetic evidence for the flood and no longer allow us to make the claim we stated in chapter 3. That prediction was "the origin of the female lineage (Eve) predates the origin of the male lineage" (page 55). We were wrong.

However, this does not mean there is no evidence for the flood. For example, the pattern and timing of humanity's spread around the world (see chapter 8) comport well with the biblical account of humanity's forced spread around the world—an event that took place after the flood (Genesis 11).

The question arises at this point: are the new scientific dates compatible with the biblical date for human origins?

It must be emphasized that both scientific and biblical dates for human origins are inexact, to say the least. Even with improved accuracy, the uncertainties for the genetic dates for humanity's origin can be as great as ± 50,000 years.

Biblically, the genealogies help establish a chronological order of the key patriarchs, but they cannot provide precise dates for humanity's origin. Most biblical genealogies, including those found in Genesis 5 and 11, skip an unstated number of generations (see pages 50–51). As noted, the calendar date for Abraham and the carbon-14 date for the breaking of the Bering Land Bridge can be used to yield crude dates for Noah and Adam. However, those dates presume the passage of time for the Genesis 5 and 11 genealogies is proportional to the life spans mentioned there. That assumption may be incorrect.

The descriptions of the Garden of Eden (Genesis 2–3) and of Noah's flood (Genesis 7–9) imply that both events occurred during an ice age.[11] The last ice age took place 13,000–112,000 years ago, so it is reasonable to assume both Noah and Adam might have lived within this period, or Noah only during the last ice age but Adam and Eve during the preceding one (140,000–235,000 years ago).

Despite these uncertainties, both the biblical and scientific dates for human origins harmonize. Improving the precision of the scientific dating methods will prove to be a challenging, perhaps unattainable, goal; but still, both measurements converge roughly at about 150,000 years ago.

Speaking of Adam and Eve

Linguistics research supplies another line of evidence supporting a biblical account of human origins. Quentin Atkinson, a scientist from the University of Auckland in New Zealand, used linguistic analysis of language to trace humanity's origin. In doing so, he provided independent confirmation of the out-of-Africa model (see chapter 3) for human origins and, with it, support for the biblical creation model.[12]

The sounds of language—vowels, consonants, and tones—are referred to as phonemes. Linguists have discovered that languages spoken by larger populations tend to possess more phonemes than languages spoken by fewer people. Atkinson wondered if phonemes could be used to study humanity's origin. What motivated his question is the phenomenon in genetics known as the serial founder effect. When a subpopulation breaks off from the main population, that smaller group displays more limited genetic variability than the parent population. If the subpopulation, in turn, spawns another subpopulation, that resulting group of "breakaways" will display an even more reduced genetic variability.

When people began to migrate around the world, a small group left the site of humanity's genesis. Serial fracturing of the migrating population took place, thereby generating the serial founder effect. According to Atkinson's hypothesis, this phenomenon should be evident in the phonemes of the world's languages.

Atkinson analyzed 504 languages and discovered that African languages displayed the greatest number of phonemes. (African populations are the most genetically diverse and thought to be the oldest people groups.) He also determined that languages of people groups in South America and Oceania possessed the fewest number of phonemes. (These people groups are believed to be the youngest.) Atkinson also noticed a cline (a gradual decrease) in phonemes as the languages moved away from Africa and into Europe and Asia.

Where Does the Evidence Point?
The phoneme patterns Atkinson discovered closely match the genetic diversity data and independently support the out-of-Africa model. We stated earlier (see chapter 2) that this model could be recast as a biblical model. Thus, it is encouraging that a number of separate lines of evidence (genetic, archeological, and now linguistic) harmonize with the biblical account of human origins.

At this juncture we can say that "wider and more overt" tests over the past decade have mostly affirmed our model. However, we would be dishonest if we failed to mention that in retrospect our initial estimate for humanity's origin between 10,000 and 100,000 years ago was misguided, and should be retracted.

Now, what about modern human behavior? Does the archeological record show evidence for the image of God? The next chapter updates and explores the first appearance of sophisticated behavior.

Chapter 18

When Did Modern Human Behavior Begin?

How do we know humans are different from animals? This important question impacts how we view human dignity (including our own) and the ethical choices our society makes based on that view. One of the key features of the Reasons to Believe (RTB) human origins model centers on the idea that God made humans, and only humans, in His image (Genesis 1:26–28).

As discussed in chapter 3, two predictions stem from RTB's view: (1) human beings should display unique behaviors compared to other creatures (including hominids); and (2) these behaviors should appear suddenly in the fossil record, coinciding with the appearance of modern humans.

Sociocultural Big Bang

Ten years ago many anthropologists found evidence in Europe's archeological record for the dramatic emergence of sophisticated behavior for modern humans—an event labeled the "sociocultural big bang." Concomitant with the arrival of modern humans in Europe was the explosive appearance of sophisticated tools, body ornamentation, and artistic expression in the form of cave paintings, figurative art, and musical instruments. This record reflects the capacity for symbolic thought and perhaps even religious behavior, which we interpret to be a reflection of God's image.

When we first wrote *Who Was Adam?*, we concluded that modern humans emerged between 50,000 and 70,000 years ago, based on the evidence at that time. The sociocultural big bang, taking place around 40,000 years ago, squared well with the estimates for humanity's origin from genetics and the fossil record, particularly because most of the evidence for the emergence of advanced cognitive capability came from archeological sites in Europe and, presumably, modern humans already possessed the capacity for symbolism when they migrated into Europe.

Discordant Dates for RTB's Model?

The most recent dates for mitochondrial Eve and Y-chromosomal Adam (between 100,000 and 150,000 years ago), create a potential problem for RTB's human origins model. It appears that a discrepancy (of possibly up to 100,000 years) exists between the times modern humans first appeared (based on genetic and fossil data) and when symbolic capability first emerged (40,000 years ago).

Does new research *expose* or *close* that gap? The good news is that studies of archeological artifacts from caves in South Africa and recently re-dated cave art in Southeast Asia significantly close the gap between the fossil record and the archeological and genetic data—and in doing so helps to address this quandary for the RTB model.

Caves Reveal Evidence for Symbolism

Over the last decade, archeologists have uncovered artifacts from several coastal cave sites (Blombos, Sibudu, Pinnacle Point, and Diepkloof Rock Shelter) in South Africa. These discoveries reflect the activities of humans endowed with the capacity for symbolism.[1] The finds at these sites include red ocher with engravings, engraved ostrich eggs, jewelry beads, heat- and pressure-treated stones (which allows for easier flaking), use of adhesives, and bedding made from evergreens with insect-repellent properties. (Research reveals that the human occupants would periodically burn and then replace the bedding material with new bedding.)

Of particular note is a site at Pinnacle Point that yielded 27 tiny blades (microliths). By carefully dating the layers containing the microliths, researchers demonstrated that these artifacts were produced continuously over the span of 11,000 years, beginning about 71,000 years ago. Such continuity further supports the contention that the manufacturers of the blades employed symbolism, because they would have had to possess and pass on knowledge of the manufacturing process, which requires abstract thinking and language capabilities.[2]

Illumined by Luminescence

At the time this book was first written (2005), early reports of artifacts from Blombos Cave had been published. We were skeptical about these finds. To begin with, the reported dates (greater than 70,000 years ago) were measured by luminescence dating, which we considered a potentially unreliable technique (see "Luminescence Dating Methods" on page 85). And furthermore, if the initial Blombos Cave finds were valid, then they would have shown a disjointed archeological record. Human behavior would appear to have been localized in South Africa for tens of thousands of years before archeological records for other regions began to show similar cognitive ability.

A number of anthropologists, including Richard Klein of Stanford University, also expressed skepticism about the Blombos Cave finds. Klein was concerned about mixing between Blombos Cave layers. If mixing occurred, it would cause scientists to conclude mistakenly that sophisticated modern behavior arose earlier than thought.

Yet given the number of other cave sites that have been studied since 2005, it is now difficult to dismiss Blombos Cave as an anomaly. The most recent finds have also been dated using luminescence techniques, with ages clustering between 70,000 to 80,000 years ago. Again, given the number of sites that independently date to 70,000+ years, it seems that the luminescent dates for the artifacts should be taken seriously.

Early Southeast Asian Art

Recent re-dating of cave art specimens throughout Southeast Asia affirms the early appearance of symbolism. In 2014, an international team of scientists reanalyzed cave art found on the Indonesian island of Sulawesi.[3] Consisting of hand stencils and depictions of animals, this art was discovered in the 1950s and was originally dated to be about 10,000 years old.

When a new technique was developed more than 60 years after the initial discovery, researchers led by Maxime Aubert and Adam Brumm took the opportunity to re-date the Sulawesi art. The new method measures the age of calcite deposits overlaying cave art. These deposits form when water runs over the walls of a cave and leaves behind a calcite film. Trace amounts of radioactive uranium and thorium isotopes associated with the calcite can be used to date the mineral deposit, providing a minimum age for the artwork. The Sulawesi cave art dates to 35,000 to 40,000 years old—not 10,000 years in age, as expected. These results have recently been affirmed and extended in a second, independent study that dated rock art throughout China, Indonesia, Thailand, Cambodia, and Malaysia and found many of these specimens to be over 40,000 years in age.[4] These two studies indicate that modern humans possessed the capacity to produce art when they migrated into Asia about 50,000 to 60,000 years ago.

The Southeast Asia cave art is of the same quality and (roughly) same age as cave art found in Spain, France, and Germany (see chapter 5). Such a parallel suggests that humans possessed the capacity for symbolic expression *before* they began global migration, pushing the origin of modern human behavior prior to at least 60,000 years ago. Anthropologist Christopher Stringer of the Natural History Museum in London commented on the Southeast Asia art re-dating:

> It is a really important find; it enables us to get away from this Euro-centric view of a creative explosion that was special to Europe and did not develop in other parts of the world until much later…The basis for this art was there 60,000 years ago; it may even have been there in Africa before 60,000 years ago and it spread with modern humans.[5]

In light of Stringer's assessment, it is worth noting that researchers estimate that humans began migrating out of Africa about 72,000 years ago. They arrived at this date by using a mitochondrial DNA (mtDNA) clock calibrated with mtDNA isolated from the ancient remains of modern humans.[6] (See pages 265–267.)

Closing the Gap

The discovery of ancient art in Southeast Asia and the dates of the South Africa cave sites (if accepted as valid) mean that humans displayed advanced cognitive abilities almost 30,000 years earlier than previously thought (formerly 40,000, now 70,000 years ago). This recognition places the emergence of symbolic behavior much closer to the time anatomically modern humans first appeared (100,000 to 150,000 years ago) based on the fossil and genetic evidence. Such a reduction in the gap is consistent with the RTB model prediction that "human culture appears and expands explosively in the archeological record since humanity's origin" (see page 55). And given the patchiness of the archeological record, it is within reason to think that the gap might be even narrower. In fact, while not conclusive, a number of studies suggest that modern human behavior emerged earlier than 70,000 to 80,000 years ago.[7]

For example, researchers recovered beads made from marine shells in Israel (Skhūl) and Algeria. The shells were transported long distances before being made into jewelry. Thermal luminescence techniques placed the beads between 100,000 and 135,000 years in age.[8] In a second find, archeologists unearthed evidence of the use of red ocher and pierced marine shells that date about 92,000 years ago in the Qafzeh cave of Israel.[9] A third discovery showed evidence that the occupants of the Pinnacle Point Cave in South Africa used pigment as far back as 165,000 years ago.[10] All three artifact finds potentially reflect the capacity for symbolism. Again, if these observations withstand more testing, they will place the origin of modern human behavior fully in line with the genetic dates for humanity's physical origin.

Lines of Evidence Accord

Mounting recognition that symbolism (and hence, the image of God) might have been associated with occupants of the Skhūl and Qafzeh caves could eliminate another point of discomfort for the RTB human origins model. At the time *Who Was Adam?* was originally published we wondered how to make sense of the *near* anatomically modern humans (which are different from hominids; see chapter 19) found in the fossil record.

As discussed in chapter 5, some paleoanthropologists maintain that modern humans appear in the fossil record between 100,000 and 130,000 years ago based on the recovery of fossil remains from the Qafzeh and Skhūl caves in Israel, Omo Kibish in Ethiopia (between 105,000 and 190,000 years in age), and the Klasies River Mouth in South Africa (cranial fragments that date between 70,000 and 130,000 years in age). These remains bear much similarity to modern humans, but they also show differences. Such characteristics have led to differing interpretations among scientists. Some claim the creatures represented by these fossils *were* anatomically modern humans and others claim they *were not*, instead referring to them as *near* anatomically modern.

Ten years ago, we sided with those who viewed these remains as nonhuman, noting the associated archeological record revealed that these putative hominids engaged in behavior unsophisticated compared to that expected for modern humans. Yet, if the evidence for symbolism at these sites stands, then it would be best to regard the Qafzeh, Skhūl, Omo Kibish, and Klasies River Mouth people as anatomically and behaviorally modern humans. Once again, a slight correction to our model is in order as a consensus emerges among the fossil, archeological, and genetic lines of evidence.

Ability Versus Need

In light of this developing accord, it is important to consider the work of anthropologist John Shea, who rejects the idea that when anatomically modern humans appeared about 150,000 years ago, they exhibited only crude, cumbersome behavior until 40,000 years ago when modern behavior emerged suddenly. Instead he argues that the first anatomically modern humans were behaviorally modern as well. He bases his position on a careful study of the stone tool assemblage associated with the Omo Kibish remains and a detailed archeological survey of sites throughout Africa.[11] Shea points out that the first anatomically modern humans had the same capabilities that people have today. They simply did not *need* to make sophisticated tools. Instead they created items to meet the demands of their environment. Shea maintains that rather than a dramatic shift in cognitive ability occurring about 40,000 years ago, modern humans simply began to create with a greater degree of variability. Unused cognitive ability provided the means for creativity when needed.

Why No Mention of Humans in the Middle East?

How do these latest advances square with the geographical constraints found in Scripture? Did humans not emerge from somewhere in the Middle East? Clearly, the evidence for symbolism displayed by modern humans in the cave sites in South Africa cannot be viewed as corresponding to the creation of humanity. Rather, we argue that modern humans occupied these sites *after the flood*, as humans began to migrate around the world. However, given that theologians consider East Africa and (obviously) Israel as close to, if not constituting, the Garden of Eden, then we maintain that the archeological and fossil remains of the Qafzeh and Skhūl caves and the Omo Kibish site align closely with the timing and location for humanity's creation.

Model Implications

A decade of "wider and more overt" testing has helped determine the definitive emergence of modern human behavior. It also narrows the gap between the origin of humanity (100,000 to 150,000 years ago) and evidence for the image of God (now at 70,000 years ago if not earlier).

Turning from the archeological record to the fossil record, we next ask: Has a decade of discoveries helped the case for human evolution? The next chapter tracks the discoveries.

Chapter 19

New Hominid Fossils Provide Model Tests

The much-parodied *March of Progress* illustration depicts the evolution of man from a knuckle-walking apelike ancestor to a fully bipedal human striding purposefully forward. The image implies almost seamless transitions and reinforces the popular idea that human evolution is a given, well-founded fact.

In truth, it can be confusing for anybody—even scientists—to sort out the history of creatures that look like humans and walk upright. The tangle of interchangeable terms—such as "hominid," "hominin," "early humans," "transitional forms," etc.—used to refer to the various hominid species (as we will call them) described in the scientific literature demonstrates the potential for confusion. Do these creatures, which appear over lengthy spans of time, show a gradual progression toward the people we've become today? A decade of advances gives insight into these questions.

Hominid fossils unearthed since 2005 show that hominid natural history over the last 6 million years is far richer and more elaborate than anyone had imagined. In many respects, it is amazing that paleoanthropologists have discovered so many hominid remains. Though the hominid fossil record is still incomplete, scientists have learned much about the biology and biogeographical distribution of these creatures. Still, the question endures: do we have enough understanding to declare confidently that human evolution is a "fact"?

We argue in chapter 9 that paleoanthropologists cannot reasonably map out the evolutionary route that produced modern humans. Therefore, to consider human evolution anything more than a hypothesis based on the fossil record alone seems unwarranted. *That* human evolution occurred is as much a hypothesis as *how* it occurred.

So what are the new hominid fossils and how do the Reasons to Believe (RTB) and evolutionary human origins models account for them? It is not feasible to discuss every fossil discovery since this book was first published. Rather, we will focus on the most prominent breakthroughs, starting with the oldest fossils and proceeding to the most recent.

Backpedaling with *Ardipithecus ramidus*

A. ramidus fossils, dating to about 4.4 million years in age, were first unearthed in 1992. Initial fossils were few and fragmentary. However, in the fall of 2009, after fifteen years of work, a team of paleoanthropologists and geologists, in what amounts to a scientific tour de force, described a nearly complete specimen of this creature (nicknamed "Ardi") along with the partial remains of 36 other individuals.[1] The hominid fossils were recovered along with 150,000 additional fossils of plants, invertebrates, birds, and mammals—a trove that provides important understanding about the habitat of *A. ramidus*.

In a series of eleven scientific papers, the team presented a detailed characterization of the anatomy of *A. ramidus* and the paleoenvironment in which the creature lived.[2] Two observations flow from this rigorous work.

First, this hominid stood about four feet in height, weighed about 100 pounds, and had the brain size of a chimpanzee. It is presumed that *A. ramidus* evolved from knuckle-walking great apes. Ardi's skeletal anatomy displays no evidence of knuckle walking; instead, it looks like *A. ramidus* possessed full bipedal capabilities, albeit crude compared to the members of the *Homo* genus. This recognition pushes the emergence of upright locomotion closer to the supposed evolutionary divergence point between apes and humans.

The paleoecology data reported in 2009 also confirmed earlier studies that had indicated *A. ramidus* lived in a woodland environment. This means that bipedalism emerged in a forest, not an open savanna as the evolutionary paradigm has traditionally maintained (see chapter 10).

Second, the discovery of the Ardi specimen does more than challenge the traditional evolutionary model for the origin of bipedalism: it challenges long-held notions about the identity of the common ancestor shared by humans and chimpanzees. Some scientists believe *A. ramidus* gave rise to the australopithecines; thus, they speculate that *A. ramidus* should occupy a space in the lineage very close to the common ancestor shared by humans and chimps. But the anatomy of *A. ramidus* is quite different from a chimpanzee's and it shows no evidence for knuckle-walking behavior. This led the researchers who characterized Ardi to conclude that the last common ancestor was not an apelike, knuckle-walking primate. Instead, they argue that chimpanzee anatomy and behavior might be evolutionarily derived states, not ancestral ones. To put it more plainly, chimpanzees may well be the result of a long evolutionary history, not the starting point for human evolution.

That the discovery of a single hominid individual could have such far-reaching implications as to overthrow entrenched ideas about the origin of bipedalism and the characteristics of the human evolutionary ancestor demonstrates just how tentative and speculative the central tenets of human evolution are. New discoveries should solidify a well-established theory, not become a source of surprises.

Australopithecus afarensis: More Lucy Reruns?

The standard evolutionary view places *A. afarensis*, represented by the "Lucy" specimen, in the direct pathway from an apelike ancestor to modern humans. Presumably *A. ramidus* (~4.5 mya) gave rise to *Australopithecus anamensis* (~4 mya). In turn, this hominid evolved into *A. afarensis,* which later yielded *Homo habilis*, the first member of the genus *Homo*. Anthropologists believe that *A. afarensis* also produced a second evolutionary branch that included *Australopithecus africanus* and terminated with three species grouped into the genus *Paranthropus* (*P. boisei, P. aethiopicus, and P. robustus*). (See figure 2.3.)

However, since the first publication of this book in 2005, paleontologists have radically changed their views about *A. afarensis* based on three important new fossil finds and a more-detailed and updated analysis of an older discovery (the Laetoli footprints).

New place on the evolutionary path

Analysis of a jawbone from a recent *A. afarensis* find (discovered in 2002, about a mile from where paleontologists unearthed Lucy) indicates—from an evolutionary vantage point—that this hominid was exclusively part of the branch leading to *A. africanus* and *Paranthropus*.[3] Based on jawbone anatomy, Lucy could not have been in the direct line that led to modern humans. Thus, Lucy's new status introduces an uncertainty in the evolutionary pathway to the *Homo* genus that spans nearly 2 million years in the "evolutionary trajectory" between *A. anamensis* (~4.5 mya) and *H. habilis* (2.5 mya).

Obligate bipedalism

Two of the new discoveries, plus the updated review of the older find, indicate that *A. afarensis* employed obligate, not facultative, bipedalism (meaning bipedalism was its exclusive, or obligatory, means of locomotion rather than an optional means). (See chapter 10.) In the summer of 2010, a team of paleoanthropologists discovered a near-complete collection of *A. afarensis* postcranial remains, dating to about 3.6 million years in age.[4] Unlike the remains of the Lucy specimen (~3.2 mya), which indicated that *A. afarensis* was a diminutive creature (four feet in height) with apelike body proportions, the newly uncovered fossils clearly demonstrate that *A. afarensis* stood about five feet tall with body proportions very much like *Homo erectus*, the implication being that *A. afarensis* also walked like the bipedal *H. erectus*. That is, this species was an obligate biped.

Support for this new understanding of *A. afarensis'* biology comes from another team of researchers, who examined a fossil of the fourth metatarsal assigned to *A. afarensis*, dating about 3.2 million years in age.[5] The structure of the foot bone, recovered in the Afar region of Ethiopia, is diagnostic of the overall structure of the foot. The architectural features of this bone indicated that *A. afarensis* had an arched foot just like the members of the genus *Homo*.

Significant understanding of *A. afarensis'* gait stems from the Laetoli footprints found in Tanzania in the late 1970s. These trace fossils, dating to about 3.7 million years in age, were made by three individuals (believed to be an *A. afarensis* family) walking through volcanic ash. New analysis of the footprints indicates that *A. afarensis* must have walked like members of the genus *Homo*, employing obligate bipedalism.

Yet Lucy's skeletal anatomy indicates *A. afarensis* must have relied on a crude, facultative form of bipedalism. Which is it? Still another modeling study published in the summer of 2012 provides additional evidence that the Laetoli hominids were not facultative bipeds, but instead walked upright habitually like *H. erectus*.[6]

Lucy not easy to classify

It seems that Lucy—"poster girl" for *A. afarensis* and interpretive basis for the biology of other hominids in the fossil record—is anomalous and has misled paleoanthropologists for decades. It is sobering to think that the Lucy specimen, the gold standard when it comes to hominid fossils, turns out to be an aberrant *A. afarensis*. Perhaps this is why some paleoanthropologists have argued that Lucy has been improperly classified as a member of *A. afarensis*. In fact, they argue that she is actually a male that belongs to another hominid species.[7] Other researchers have disputed this claim,[8] but confusion remains.

Lucy's unusual anatomy has caused paleoanthropologists to formulate wrong views on the biology and behavior of *A. afarensis*, highlighting the incompleteness of the hominid fossil record. This incompleteness makes it difficult, if not impossible, to develop a clear understanding of hominid natural history and to establish evolutionary relationships among these creatures and modern humans.

Walking Too Fast?

This revised view of A. afarensis also has implications on the origin and natural history of bipedalism. These discoveries push back the appearance of obligate bipedalism from about 1.8 million years ago when H. erectus and Homo ergaster first appeared to at least 3.7 million years ago when A. afarensis made its entrance in the fossil record. In fact, it well may be that A. anamensis, precursor to A. afarensis, employed obligate bipedalism as well.

Also, A. ramidus, which presumably gave rise to A. anamensis, seems to have relied on a facultative form of bipedalism. If so, then the transition from facultative to obligate bipedalism happened relatively rapidly. (See chapter 10 for a review of the anatomical changes required for the emergence of bipedalism.) Instead of facultative bipedalism gradually giving way to obligate bipedalism over the span of a couple million years, it seems to have occurred abruptly—at least in biological terms.

RTB's model, which views bipedalism as occurring suddenly, optimally, and unaltered, seems validated by the latest research on A. afarensis. Let's take a look at another hominid.

Introducing Australopithecus sediba

In 2011, a research team from the University of Witwatersrand (South Africa) headed by paleoanthropologist Lee Berger created excitement when they presented a detailed anatomical analysis of Australopithecus sediba, a newly discovered hominid.[9] (Researchers first reported the discovery in the spring of 2010.[10]) Berger and his son stumbled upon two partial hominid skeletons while exploring the recently discovered Malapa Cave in South Africa. Excavations revealed the remains were from a juvenile male and an adult female.

The hominids were initially dated between 1.78 and 1.95 million years in age, but more careful dating placed the remains at 1.977 million years old. The Malapa fossils are well preserved and remarkably complete compared to most hominid finds, allowing paleontologists to perform a detailed anatomical analysis of the specimens.

Anatomical oddity

A. sediba represents an enigma of sorts. Overall it looks like an australopithecine. It has a small brain and long arms, designed for movement through trees. Yet it also shows features similar to *H. erectus*. Based on the pelvis and ankle joint, it appears *A. sediba* belongs to the genus *Homo*. Its hand seems to be designed for high-precision manipulation of objects, like a *Homo* hand, with a long thumb and short fingers. Even though the brain is small like that of an australopithecine, analysis of the *A. sediba* skull reveals unusual features in the frontal lobe that indicate the brain's structure is distinct.

Interpretive difficulty
Berger and his colleagues argue that their discovery makes things messy for paleoanthropologists, raising questions about conventional views of human evolution. Could *A. sediba* supplant Lucy (*A. afarensis*) as the transitional intermediate that gave rise to *H. habilis* and, in turn, *H. erectus*? Could *A. sediba*, and not *H. habilis*, be the direct ancestor to *H. erectus*? Berger and his colleagues note,

> None of these three species exhibits a comprehensive constellation of these features; thus when all three are viewed as a whole, they appear to form an adaptive mosaic. This conceivably implies an adaptive radiation of hominins at ~2.0 Ma. Under such a scenario, one would expect substantial homoplasy to be evident; consequently, we will face great difficulty in sorting out the phylogenetic relationships of several closely related species. In particular, discerning the specific ancestor of *H. erectus*, and placing this ancestor in the correct genus (i.e., *Australopithecus* versus *Homo*), will be a most challenging endeavor, especially when only fragmentary fossil remains are preserved.[11]

It is eye opening to realize how much uncertainty and speculation is associated with human evolutionary scenarios. The common perception is that anthropologists have a good understanding of how human evolution transpired—but perception is far from reality. Another discovery seems to complicate matters even more.

Homo gautengensis and a Temporal Paradox
Shortly after *A. sediba* was discovered in 2010, a researcher reported on the discovery of a group of fossils (also unearthed in South Africa) that was considered the holotype (single physical example of an organism) specimen of a new species dubbed *Homo gautengensis*.[12] This "creature," too, dates to about

2 million years in age and might represent the oldest member of the *Homo* genus. However, it is critical to note that most paleoanthropologists do not recognize *H. gautengensis* as an authentic species. Some argue the collection of specimens belongs to *H. habilis*. Others interpret it as an unusual *A. africanus*.

Whether *H. gautengensis* is an authentic species or is better classified as *H. habilis*, its mere existence as a holotype specimen perplexes those who see *A. sediba* as an important transitional form. Why? If it is a *Homo* specimen, then the *H. gauntengensis* holotype is *older* than *A. sediba* (or at best, coexisted with it), creating a temporal paradox. Simply put, as a transitional form, *A. sediba* should appear in the fossil record *before* any members of the genus *Homo*.

In addition to *H. gautengensis*, there are other finds in East Africa that also contribute to the temporal paradox for *A. sediba*.[13] At least two sets of fossil specimens assigned to *Homo* date to 2.4 and 2.5 million years in age, respectively. If these assignments stand, then they indicate that *Homo* existed in East Africa well before *A. sediba* arrived on the scene.

From an evolutionary perspective, the *A. sediba* discovery highlights uncertainty about evolutionary relationships among the hominids. It is clear that paleoanthropologists have no idea how many hominids existed, how these creatures relate to each other in an evolutionary sense, or which ones truly are part of the presumed evolutionary pathway that led to modern humans.

Homing in on *Homo habilis*

Another fossil discovery adds to the uncertainty. During the summer of 2007, a report appeared in the journal *Nature* questioning the traditional understanding of *H. habilis'* role in the human evolutionary drama.[14]

As noted in chapter 2, the standard evolutionary model for human origins views *H. habilis* as the first member of our genus (*Homo*). This hominid initially appeared in the fossil record about 2.6 mya and seemingly gave rise directly to *H. erectus* around 1.9 mya.

Researchers recovered fossil specimens consisting of the back of an *H. erectus* skull dated at 1.55 million years in age and a *H. habilis* jawbone dated to be 1.44 million years old. Analysis of both fossils recovered near Lake Turkana, Kenya, muddies the picture for *H. habilis'* role in human evolution. How?

The 1.44 million-year-old date for *H. habilis* means that this hominid must have coexisted with *H. erectus*. But that placement contradicts the standard model. If *H. habilis* gave way to *H. erectus*, then the two should not have coexisted. The fossils also indicate that *H. habilis* and *H. erectus* were morphologically distinct species that exploited different ecological niches within the same geographical region, reinforcing the conclusion that *H. habilis* did not directly transform into *H. erectus* and then disappear (a process called anagenesis).

From an evolutionary perspective, one possible explanation for the coexistence of these two hominids relies on a process called cladogenesis. Accordingly, *H. habilis* could have given rise to *H. erectus* via branching from the original population. It is possible that *H. habilis* and *H. erectus* could have shared a common ancestor. However, there is no support for this idea.

Discovery of the coexistence of *H. habilis* and *H. erectus* highlights two "truths" about the hominid fossil record and human evolutionary models: (1) time after time, a single fossil find overturns a "well-established" idea in human evolution; and (2) it is difficult to know which hominid fossils are transitional intermediates and which ones are not.

Dmanisi Skull Holds No Clues

During the fall of 2013, paleoanthropologists from the University of Zurich (UZH) described an intact skull recovered in Dmanisi, Georgia (the nation). The fifth skull recovered from the Dmanisi site, this find is one of the most complete skulls for early *Homo*. All five skulls date between 1.77 and 1.85 million years in age and have been ascribed to the hominid *Homo georgicus*. This recent find raises questions about the identity and place of *H. georgicus* in the human evolutionary scenario.[15]

The remains of all five skulls were deposited at this site within centuries of one another, providing paleoanthropologists with a rare opportunity to gain understanding about the biological variability of the Dmanisi hominids. The fifth skull possesses an unusual combination of features: massive jaws and teeth and a relatively small brain. In effect, all five of the Dmanisi individuals are conspicuously different from one another. This observation indicates that the Dmanisi population displayed significant morphological variability, but no more than that observed for modern humans. In fact, the range of variability of the Dmanisi fossils encompasses the differences among *H. ergaster*, *H. erectus*, and *H. georgicus*. On this basis, the UZH team concluded that all three hominids belonged to the *same* species.

That's a remarkable statement, considering that prior to this discovery, *H. georgicus* was considered a transitional intermediate between *H. habilis* and *H. erectus*. The coexistence of the latter two means the Dmanisi hominids cannot be transitional forms.

The discovery and characterization of the fifth Dmanisi skull offers further insight because reveals how little understanding paleoanthropologists have had about the biological variability of each hominid species. Again, it calls attention to the fact that scientists have no idea how many hominid species actually existed. According to Christoph Zollikofer, one of the senior members of the UZH team, "Had the braincase and the face of the Dmanisi fossil been found as separate fossils, they very probably would have been attributed to two different species."[16] Without an understanding of the biological variation within a species and the actual number of species, it is impossible to interpret the fossil record from an evolutionary perspective. Once again, a single fossil find can radically alter the account of human evolution.

Facing the Truth about *Homo erectus*

What about *H. erectus*, a closer presumed human ancestor? What has the last decade shown?

Recent analysis of a faceless *H. erectus* skull, dated at 1.55 million years in age widens the gap between *H. erectus* and modern humans.[17]

Large size disparity within a primate species is diagnostic for sexual dimorphism (a systematic size difference between males and females within a given species). The great apes (and the australopithecines that preceded *H. erectus* in the fossil record) display sexual dimorphism. In contrast, males and females in modern humans are relatively close in size.

To the surprise of paleoanthropologists, the new *H. erectus* fossil is far smaller than expected for an erectine specimen. With this find, the size variability for *H. erectus* widened suddenly to that observed for the great apes.

The sexual dimorphism in primates gives anthropologists important insight into the behavior and lifestyle of *H. erectus*. Primates that exhibit sexual dimorphism have a social structure centering around a dominant male that reproduces with a harem of females. On the other hand, primates that are characterized by limited sexual dimorphism form monogamous pairs.

Anthropologists have long thought that *H. erectus* was progressively becoming human-like in its behavior. The new find, however, means that the sexual behavior and lifestyle of *H. erectus* was apelike. This recognition confirms results of earlier studies that indicate the growth and maturation of *H. erectus* was apelike, not intermediate between apes and humans. (See chapter 11.) In other words, sexual dimorphism in *H. erectus* increases the separation between this hominid and modern humans.

Homo antecessor Strikes a Blow to the Evolutionary Jaw

Shortly after *Who Was Adam?* was first published, scientists recovered a fossilized hominid jawbone from the Gran Dolina site in northern Spain. This find raises questions about the identity of *H. antecessor* and its place in a widely held human evolutionary scenario.[18]

Between 1994 and 1996, paleoanthropologists found hominid fossils and stone artifacts at Gran Dolina that dated between 780,000 and 857,000 years old. The finds were assigned to a *H. antecessor*, a new species at that time. Based on cranial and dental features, many evolutionary biologists consider this hominid to be part of the transitional sequence leading to modern humans. According to this view, *H. ergaster* produced *H. antecessor*, which gave rise to *Homo heidelbergensis*, which then separately produced the lineage that led to Neanderthals and modern humans.[19]

The evolutionary identity of *H. antecessor* was based on analysis of immature jaw and facial features. To ensure its place in the human evolutionary pathway, paleoanthropologists needed access to the remains of adult individuals. This most recent *H. antecessor* find is just what paleoanthropologists had hoped for, an adult jawbone.

Analysis of the new jawbone, however, indicates that *H. antecessor* cannot be part of any evolutionary sequence that leads to modern humans. It has the wrong shape. This jawbone more closely resembles the erectine hominids found in Asia. In other words, from an evolutionary perspective *H. antecessor* is an insignificant side branch, a dead end.

This blow leaves a sore spot in the fossil record between *H. ergaster* and *H. heidelbergensis* and renders the putative human evolutionary pathway to modern humans sketchy at best. Will the Heidelberg man come to the rescue?

Homo heidelbergensis Falls into the Pit

Since the 1970s, *H. heidelbergensis* has assumed a central role in human evolutionary scenarios, representing a key transitional intermediate linking *H. erectus* to modern humans and Neanderthals. Some anthropologists believe the Heidelberg man is the common ancestor that gave rise to two separate lineages leading to: (1) modern humans; and (2) Neanderthals and the Denisovans (discussed in the next chapter). Others think that *H. heidelbergensis* led to Neanderthals and the Denisovans, with *H. antecessor* serving as the common ancestor to the modern human and Neanderthal-Denisovan branches of the human evolutionary tree.

Anthropologists believe *H. heidelbergensis* existed between 200,000 years ago and 800,000 years ago, making its home in Africa, Europe, and Asia. Support for *H. heidelbergensis* came from the discovery of 28 hominid individuals in Spain, recovered from the famous Sima de los Huesos ("the Pit of Bones"), dating to 430,000 years in age. These hominids were assigned to *H. heidelbergensis*.

Recent work on newly unearthed remains led to a reevaluation of the Sima de los Huesos hominids. It appears as if these individuals were much more Neanderthal-like than previously thought.[20] On the basis of this conclusion, the research team from Spain argued that the Sima de los Huesos specimens could not be *H. heidelbergensis*. This conclusion has led a number of anthropologists to argue that perhaps *H. heidelbergensis* never existed at all.[21]

What does it say about a theory when reanalysis of fossil specimens from one site can question the very existence of one of the key transitional intermediates in most human evolutionary scenarios?

Does a much more recent discovery restore order?

Red Deer Cave People

In March of 2012, a team of researchers from Australia and China made international headlines when they reported on the hominid remains recovered from two cave sites in southern China.[22] These hominids, dubbed the Red Deer Cave people (large deer were cooked in the hominids' cave), date between 11,000 and 15,000 years in age. They overlapped with modern humans and could have encountered modern humans when people first migrated into Asia about 50,000 years ago.

Detailed analysis of their remains indicates that these creatures were distinct from other hominids such as *H. erectus* and Neanderthals. Evolutionary scientists are not sure where to place these creatures. They had flat faces, broad noses, jutting jaws with no chin, prominent brows, and other features that make them distinct from modern humans. In other words, these newly discovered hominids further complicate the evolutionary landscape.

Up to this point the discussion of the fossil record has rightly focused on the hominids. But what about the chimpanzee evolutionary lineage? When *Who Was Adam?* was first published there was no record to document the emergence of chimpanzees and bonobos, but that changed shortly after the first edition went to press.

Chimpanzee Fossils Foil Paradigm

Where were you on September 1, 2005? While this date may not hold much meaning for you, it carries great significance for the scientific community. On this day *Nature* published the completed sequence of the chimpanzee genome.[23] (See chapter 24.) This remarkable achievement received ample publicity, since it paved the way for biologists to conduct detailed genetic comparisons between humans and chimpanzees.

Unfortunately, the fanfare surrounding the announcement overshadowed another significant discovery. In the same issue, *Nature* published a report describing the *first-ever* chimpanzee fossils.[24] This long-awaited scientific first barely received notice because of the chimp genome fascination. While evolutionary biologists declared the chimp genome as evidence for human evolution, paleoanthropologists were left wondering how humans and chimps could have evolved based on the *location* of the first-ever chimpanzee fossil find.

Rift in the theory

According to the evolutionary paradigm, humans and chimpanzees share a common ancestor. About 6 million years ago, this ancestral primate presumably spawned two evolutionary lineages, one leading to humans and the other to chimpanzees. Anthropologists considered the physical, geographical separation of *proto*-chimpanzees and hominids to be the "driving force" for the evolution of humans and chimpanzees. According to this scenario, the formation of Great Rift Valley (with its extensive ridge system) isolated the hominids in East Africa (hot, dry savannas) from chimpanzees in Central and West Africa (wet, warm jungles). Such geographical isolation presumably sent these two lineages along different evolutionary trajectories.

Evolutionary biologists think that fossil hominids like Lucy, *H. erectus,* and Neanderthals document the emergence of humans. (See pages 36–40.) Yet, until recently, paleoanthropologists had no corresponding fossils for the chimpanzee lineage.

The lack of chimp fossils was attributed to the environment in which these primates lived. The wet, warm jungles of Central and West Africa are not conducive to fossilization. In contrast, the hot, arid milieu of the East African savanna provides a better setting for fossilization to occur. Consequently, paleoanthropologists have an abundance of hominid fossils available to study.

Seeking a better explanation

Surprisingly, the first chimpanzee fossils were discovered not in West or Central Africa, but in East Africa, near Lake Baringo, Kenya. These fossils, which consist of three teeth, dated to 500,000 years in age, meaning that chimpanzees coexisted alongside hominids. Though formidable, Great Rift Valley was not an insurmountable geographical barrier. Thus, the discovery of the first chimpanzee fossils in East Africa fails to satisfy a key prediction of the human evolutionary paradigm. According to paleoanthropologist Sally McBrearty, who helped uncover the chimpanzee fossils, "This means we need a better explanation of why and how chimps and humans went their separate evolutionary ways... The discovery that chimps were living in semi-arid conditions as well as in the jungles seems to blow apart the simplistic idea that it was the shift to the savannah that led to humans walking upright."[25]

One decade of breakthroughs in physical anthropology has yielded phenomenal fossil finds. Yet, instead of creating greater certainty about the evolutionary history of the hominids, time and time again, these finds have forced a rewrite of human evolution.

Many evolutionary biologists, however, seem unfazed by the questions repeatedly raised by the new hominid finds. They argue that the fact of human evolution does not depend upon knowing the precise evolutionary sequence for the origin of modern humans. They argue that in the midst of uncertainty, there is still an array of specimens that show gradual transition over time and, therefore, constitute transitional forms. (See "A Presumed Connection" on page 146.)

To some degree, this view is valid. However, if an evolutionary explanation for humanity were correct, would it not be reasonable to think that greater clarity would emerge in the evolutionary pathway that led to modern humans?

From a creation perspective, RTB's model readily accommodates each of these hominid finds. We regard these creatures as the product of the Creator's handiwork. We expect humans would share some anatomical, physical, biochemical, and genetic similarities with extinct hominids and great apes, but we also possess biological differences. We will continue to examine this idea in the next chapter by applying wider, more overt testing to new insights gleaned over the past decade regarding Neanderthal biology and genetics.

Chapter 20

Are Neanderthals Similar to Humans?

Has a decade of research made the Neanderthal more human than ever? Some people think so. The Reasons to Believe (RTB) model, however, predicts that although Neanderthals share some biological similarities with humans, there remain important differences. The greatest distinction lies in cognitive and symbolic behavior and we maintain that the evolutionary connection between the two is tenuous at best. An avalanche of advances has provided new insights into Neanderthal biology, genetics, and behavior. Does "wider and more overt" testing earn the Neanderthal a place with us or does it relegate him to a museum diorama?

Gritting Teeth over the Ancestral Problem

Any evolutionary connection between Neanderthals and humans involves recognition of an ancestor species. In that quest, recent research by a team of collaborators from the United States and Europe highlights the problem paleoanthropologists face when interpreting the fossil record.[1]

The research team was trying to identify the common hominid ancestor (labeled MH-N LCA) shared by humans and Neanderthals. Relying on genetic comparisons, paleoanthropologists think humans and Neanderthals shared such an ancestor about 800,000 years ago. (Once the two lineages diverged, the one leading to Neanderthals split again about 650,000 years ago, producing Neanderthals and the mysterious Denisovans.) The prime candidates for the MH-N LCA are *Homo heidelbergensis* and *Homo antecessor* (though some data suggest *H. antecessor* is a side branch).

The strategy for identifying the MH-N LCA focused on comparative analysis of hominid teeth—no small feat. The team examined 1,200 fossil teeth representing 12 hominid species. Using new analytical techniques, the investigators reconstructed the dental anatomy of the putative MH-N LCA. They hoped to match the reconstructed dental features with those of the candidate species. Unfortunately, MH-N LCA's reconstructed dental features did not match those of *H. heidelbergensis, H. antecessor, Homo erectus,* or any other known hominid fossil—an unexpected result.

Based on their analysis, the researchers also concluded that MH-N LCA must have lived over 1 million years ago, earlier than the genetic data indicate. Aida Gómez-Robles, lead author of the study, said, "Our results call attention to the strong discrepancies between molecular and paleontological estimates of the divergence time between Neanderthals and modern humans... These discrepancies cannot simply be ignored, but they have to be somehow reconciled."[2]

The team accounts for the null result by speculating that dental anatomy might not be useful for ancestral reconstructions. Others have demonstrated that dental data cannot be used to build reliable evolutionary trees. (See pages 152–154.) If so, then this approach could be flawed fundamentally. The team also suggests they might not have been looking in the right location. They limited their analysis to fossil remains recovered in Europe, but they suggest African *H. heidelbergensis* specimens might match the dental data. However, no evidence indicates European and African *H. heidelbergensis* teeth would be different.

No Leg Up on Common Ancestor

Another possible candidate for ancestor species emerged from the recovery, sequencing, and analysis of mitochondrial DNA (mtDNA) from a 400,000-year-old hominid femur,[3] part of an assemblage of fossils representing 28 individuals assigned as either *H. heidelbergensis* or early Neanderthals. The fossils were recovered in the early 1990s from Sima de los Huesos ("the Pit of Bones") in northern Spain.

Since almost all evolutionary biologists believe the Neanderthal lineage split into Neanderthals and Denisovans, anthropologists predicted the mtDNA isolated from the femur would show Neanderthal characteristics. Instead, it appears as if the hominids represented by the femur were a sister group to the Denisovans and, thus, more closely related to these baffling hominids than to Neanderthals, but Spain is a long distance from Siberia, home of the first known Denisovan fossils. In other words, the DNA sequences and the fossils tell different stories regarding the last common ancestor of humans and Neanderthals.[4]

The authors of the research suggest ways to accommodate the unexpected result, but, all things considered, the scenarios lack certainty. Their best explanation invokes an appeal to interbreeding between the Sima de los Huesos hominids and an unknown hominid the researchers hope will be soon identified. Clearly, there is more work to be done. But failure to identify humanity and Neanderthal's common ancestor raises eyebrows.

Biological Differences

Earlier studies (see chapter 12) described anatomical and developmental differences between Neanderthals and humans. Some of the developmental distinctives included Neanderthals' more-rapid craniofacial growth and the microanatomical features of teeth indicating Neanderthals matured much more rapidly than humans.

Since 2005, paleoanthropologists have affirmed and extended the insights of these initial studies.[5] Differences continue to mount, especially in regard to brain comparisons.

Brain shape

The 33,000-year-old remains of a Neanderthal infant reveal that these hominids were larger and more robust during infancy than humans.[6] Virtual endocasts (brain casts) of human brains show that our brains change shape, from more elongated to more globular, as we mature from infancy. However, statistical comparisons with virtual endocasts of Neanderthals indicate their brains did not undergo globularization.[7]

These studies affirm the notion that humans and Neanderthals are distinct species. Such differences in brain development are confirmed by recent comparisons of the Neanderthal and human genomes, which have uncovered dissimilarities in the genes associated with brain development. The developmental contrasts also point to cognitive differences between human beings and Neanderthals.

Brain organization

Size matters, but so does the layout. In 2013, Oxford University researchers published a report on differences between Neanderthal and human brain organization.[8] Neanderthals possessed nearly the same brain size as humans (see chapter 12). (They also had a greater body mass and, consequently, a smaller encephalization quotient compared to modern humans.) However, Neanderthal brain structure—such as the shape of the parietal lobe—varied from that of humans and even slight dissimilarities in brain organization will affect cognitive function.

The same group of Oxford researchers identified other differences. They measured the eye socket size of 32 humans and 12 Neanderthal skulls. (The skulls came from Europe and the Near East and dated between 27,000 and 75,000 years old.) The team used socket size as a proxy for eye size. A tight relationship exists between primate eye size and the cortical primary and downstream visual areas of the brain. Neanderthals possessed larger eye sockets than modern humans, meaning that a greater portion of their brain area was devoted to vision.

Additionally, the team noted the Neanderthals' larger body size required a greater area of their brain be devoted to body maintenance and control, leaving a much smaller brain portion available for other processes and activities. Based on these two observations, the Oxford researchers concluded that a limited volume of this hominid's brain was used for forming social networks.

Among primates, scientists discovered a relationship between brain volume and bonded group size. They reason that an individual primate in a bonded group must keep track of other individuals in the group, which requires brain activity. The greater amount of brain area available, the bigger the social network in which the individual can take part.

It is no surprise that social networks employed by humans are larger and more elaborate than those of Neanderthals. Smaller networks would have limited Neanderthals' ability to trade for resources outside the region they occupied, restricted their foraging range, and reduced their capacity to retain newly learned innovations.

Old Genes Tell the Story

Comparisons made at the time *Who Was Adam?* was first published between Neanderthal mtDNA sequences and corresponding human DNA indicate that Neanderthals did not directly evolve into humans (of European descent) as multiregionalism predicts (see chapter 12). Over the last decade, advances in ancient DNA analysis have been legion.

Mitochondrial DNA breakthroughs

Since 2005, paleoanthropologists have isolated mtDNA fragments from about 15 other Neanderthals (a total of about 20 specimens have yielded mtDNA). Until recently the available techniques allowed researchers to amplify and sequence only relatively large amounts of ancient DNA. New DNA sequencing technology has expanded the possibilities for the characterization of ancient DNA to nuclear DNA sequences.

In 2008, an international team of collaborators applied this cutting-edge technology for the first time to sequence the entire Neanderthal mtDNA genome.[9] Soon after, geneticists generated the entire sequence for *five* Neanderthals. The specimens spanned the geographical range and much of the time Neanderthals existed (38,000 to 70,000 years ago).[10]

This research confirms that Neanderthal mtDNA falls outside the range of human variation. In fact, the new, more comprehensive understanding of the entire mitochondrial genome indicates a greater genetic difference between humans and Neanderthals than do the smaller mtDNA fragments. The analysis also reveals Neanderthals had a genetic diversity close to one-third that of humans. It likely means Neanderthals had a relatively small population size, which could explain why these hominids went extinct. The lower genetic variability also has implications regarding the likelihood of human-Neanderthal interbreeding. (See chapter 21.)

A genetic coup: nuclear DNA sequencing
As insightful as Neanderthal mtDNA has been, researchers wanted information about this hominid's *nuclear* genome. Mitochondrial DNA provides limited (though important) information about the relationship between humans and Neanderthals. Compared to the human nuclear genome (which is 3.2 billion base pairs, or genetic letters, in size), the mitochondrial genome (16,500 base pairs) is relatively small; thus, it harbors much less genetic information than the nuclear genome. Additionally, information harbored by the mitochondrial genome is confined to proteins that play a role in the functioning of mitochondria.

Comparisons of the nuclear genomes would produce the best and most complete understanding of the relationship between humans and Neanderthals. Nuclear genomes' larger size provides more opportunities to compare genetic differences and similarities between the two species. (Mitochondrial DNA is a small, single chromosome passed from mother to child. Nuclear genomes consist of 46 chromosomes, 23 inherited from each parent.) Also, nuclear genomes possess genetic information that describes an organism's complete biology.

In August 2006, as part of the commemoration of the 150th anniversary of the discovery of the first Neanderthal fossil, scientists from Germany and the United States announced plans to complete a draft of the Neanderthal nuclear genome (hereafter, simply the Neanderthal genome) within two years.

Researchers were confident they could accomplish this goal because of successful preliminary studies. In those earlier efforts, two independent research teams generated sequences of nuclear DNA from Neanderthal remains that were 65,000 base pairs and 1 million base pairs in length, respectively, using the same techniques that allowed researchers to produce the complete mitochondrial genome sequence for the five Neanderthals.[11]

In 2010, researchers reported on the breakthrough: the first-ever analysis of the Neanderthal genome.[12] The scientific community finally had access to a Neanderthal genetic mine—albeit a low-quality rough draft sequence.

Composition of the genome

This genome represented a composite sequence generated from DNA fragments isolated from three Neanderthal specimens all recovered from the Vindija Cave (Croatia) and dating between 38,000 and 44,000 years old. The researchers sequenced about 4 billion base pairs, giving them 1.3-fold coverage of the Neanderthal genome. (When geneticists sequence the entire genome one time, they refer to it as 1-fold coverage. When they sequence a genome five times, for example, they refer to this as 5-fold coverage. Because mistakes can happen during the sequencing process, the more times the genome is sequenced, the better the quality of the sequence data.) Investigators were able to assemble sequences for roughly two-thirds of the Neanderthal genome, with one-third intractable.

Brief Genetic Comparison

Researchers compared the rough draft Neanderthal genome with those of a chimpanzee and of five humans. This comparison indicates—as does the Neanderthal mtDNA—that these hominids are distinct from, and did not directly evolve into, humans.

Their analysis also uncovered what appear to be important genetic differences between a number of human genes and the corresponding chimp and Neanderthals genes. These genes are involved in determining skull morphology, rib cage structure, skin and hair features, metabolism, and cognitive development. It is possible these genetic disparities help account for some of the key anatomical and behavioral differences between humans and Neanderthals, in accord with RTB model predictions.

Better DNA Yields More Differences

By the end of 2013, sequencing technology progressed to the point that researchers were able to produce a high-quality genome sequence (with 52-fold coverage!) of a female known as the "Altai Neanderthal."[13] The DNA was extracted from a finger bone recovered in the same cave—located in the Altai Mountains of Siberia—as the Denisovan remains (see "Meet the Denisovans" on pages 299–300). The layer yielding the finger bone was dated at 50,000 years in age. The research team also reported a low-coverage sequence (0.5-fold coverage) of the nuclear genome for another Neanderthal specimen from the Caucasus (Eurasia).

Overall, the sequence data again affirm that Neanderthals and humans are distinct species and that Neanderthals did not directly evolve into humans. Comparisons of the three Neanderthal genomes with those of humans also identified a number of differences related to genes that play a role in brain development, including those associated with neuronal stem cell maintenance and proliferation during cortex development.

Researchers also gained insight into the Altai Neanderthal's family history. This understanding has far-reaching implications regarding Neanderthal population structure and dynamics. Regions of the Neanderthal's chromosome pairs (one pair comes from the mother, one from the father) display long stretches in which the sequences are identical (called homozygosity). Such a feature means that this Neanderthal's parents were closely related, likely being half-siblings from the same mother. By analyzing the heterozygosity (differences in the DNA sequence of chromosome pairs), the team concluded that the Altai Mountain Neanderthal population must have been small and decreased over time.

Small Populations, Inbreeding

In still another study (early 2014), geneticists sequenced 17,367 protein-coding genes from two additional Neanderthals from Spain and Croatia, dating at 49,000 and 44,000 years in age, respectively. The sequences were good-to-exceptional in quality, with 12.5-fold coverage for the Spanish specimen and 42.0-fold coverage for the Croatian.[14] The team compared these gene sequences and those from the Altai Neanderthal to the corresponding human genes. Differences appear between human and Neanderthal genes involved in determining skeletal morphology and skin pigmentation. Also, low heterozygosity and long stretches of homozygosity appeared in the three Neanderthal sequences. This means that the population structure for the Altai Neanderthal was not unusual. Indeed, all Neanderthals lived in small, isolated populations characterized by extensive inbreeding.

Methylation Maps

In spring 2014, another team of researchers advanced ancient DNA analysis even further when they reported DNA methylation "maps" of the Neanderthal and Denisovan genomes. (DNA methylation, which refers to biochemical reactions that attach methyl chemical groups to DNA, regulates gene expression.)[15] Methylated DNA degrades differently from nonmethylated DNA.

Geneticists took advantage of this difference to determine methylation sites in Neanderthals and Denisovans genomes by examining degradation patterns in the ancient DNA. Methylation maps give scientists insights into the all-important gene expression patterns of these ancient hominids and allow them to be compared to humans. The team detected about 2,000 regions in these genomes that displayed dissimilarities in methylation patterns. Regions that were methylated differently and which allowed for Neanderthal-human comparisons included those involved in brain development, neurological and psychiatric disorders, and immune and cardiovascular systems.

Light Skin, Red Hair?

Additional research efforts have probed the Neanderthal genome for *variants* of genes with the hope of understanding this hominid's physical appearance. One study examined the gene that encodes the *melanocortin 1 receptor (MC1R)*.[16] This protein regulates pigment production in humans and other vertebrates. Variations in the structure of this protein can result in pale skin and red hair in humans.

Scientists isolated and amplified a small piece of DNA containing a portion of *MC1R* gene from two Neanderthal specimens, one from Spain and one from Italy. They compared the Neanderthal gene to the same gene from 3,700 humans. The Neanderthal variants of the gene would have given them light skin and hair color like many European people, but the Neanderthal *MC1R* was distinct from human genes. Thus, researchers concluded that light skin and hair pigmentation must have emerged independently in humans and Neanderthals. This makes sense because lighter skin pigmentation in the northern latitudes (where both species lived) is advantageous for the synthesis of vitamin D. (See pages 361–363).

Adaptation to Cold

As humans and hominids migrated northward, they would need to adapt to cold climates. To understand how, investigators studied the genetic basis for cold adaptation in Neanderthals (and Denisovans), focusing on genes that play a role in the metabolic pathways of brown adipose tissue.[17] This fat tissue helps regulate body temperature by breaking down fat and turning nearly all the available chemical energy into heat. (Such activity is an important contributor to what is called nonshivering thermogenesis.)

The researchers examined the variation in 28 genes involved in metabolic pathways associated with nonshivering thermogenesis for Neanderthals and Denisovans and for people around the world. Cold adaptation in Neanderthals, Denisovans, and humans involved the same gene *leptin receptor* (*LEPR*), but the specific differences in the *LEPR* gene observed for humans were distinct from those observed for the two archaic hominids. This genetic difference means that cold adaptation arose independently in humans and Neanderthals.

A Difference in Taste

Researchers also took interest in whether Neanderthals possessed the receptor protein encoded by the *TAS2R38* gene. A specific variant of this gene allows individuals who possess it to taste bitter substances (as measured by their response to the compound phenylthiocarbamide). Taste perception of this compound is associated with the human ability to detect toxic compounds found in certain plants and it serves as a mechanism that prevents poisoning.

It turns out that a Neanderthal specimen recovered from El Sidrón (Spain) possessed the variant of *TAS2R38* that would have enabled it to taste bitter plant materials.[18] Again, this finding makes sense because of the obvious advantage for Neanderthals (and humans) to be able to detect toxic compounds in certain plants.

All of this powerful insight about biology and lifestyle was gained through recent technological advances in Neanderthal genome sequencing. Certainly researchers will continue to probe the Neanderthal genome to learn the answers to additional intriguing questions about the appearance and behavior of these creatures.

Another mysterious hominid—was it a Neanderthal or was it not?—leaped from history and landed at the nexus of scientific inquiry in 2008. Without advances in genome sequencing, the headline-grabbing creature would not even have been known.

Meet the Denisovans

Sometimes truth is stranger than fiction. This is particularly true for paleoanthropology. The scarcity of fossils makes it difficult for scientists to know how many species of hominids existed. So, it is ironic that paleoanthropologists discovered a new hominid species, not from a fossil find, but from sequencing and analysis of ancient DNA.

In 2008, fossil hunters found a number of bones in a cave site in the Altai Mountains of Russian Siberia. Among these fossils were two molars and a finger bone fragment (the distal phalanx of the fifth digit). The specimens were recovered from a layer that dates between 30,000 and 48,000 years in age. When researchers sequenced mtDNA isolated from the finger bone, they were shocked to discover that it did not match either human *or* Neanderthal DNA sequences. It belonged to a completely distinct hominid population, and perhaps species, dubbed the Denisovans after the cave—Denisova—that yielded the fossil remains.[19] Since then researchers have sequenced the entire Denisovan nuclear genome with a 30-fold coverage.[20]

Despite headlining in the scientific and popular news, the identity of the Denisovans is currently not known. It is a hominid in search of fossils (beyond the relatively uninformative finger bone and molars). Some people have suggested that the Denisovans could be the Red Deer Cave people (see page 287). Others have posited them to be *H. heidelbergensis*. Both ideas could be wrong. Researchers have speculated, based on the Denisovan genetic makeup, that these hominids had dark skin and brown hair and eyes. From an evolutionary standpoint, it looks like the Denisovans diverged from the lineage that led to modern humans about 800,000 years ago and then branched again from the lineage that led to Neanderthals about 650,000 years ago.

Comparison of the human and Denisovan genomes reveals a number of gene variants that are unique to modern humans; namely genes tied to brain function and nervous system development, including regions involved in language. Given that Denisovans are genetically distinct from modern humans, RTB's human origins model readily accommodates them. These mysterious hominids could rightly be considered a unique species that lacked humanity's cognitive abilities. A fossil site or two will help, but until then unanswered questions about their biology and appearance remain.

A whirlwind of discoveries in ancient DNA affirms the genetic distinctions between Neanderthals and modern humans predicted by RTB's model. This past decade has also provided a genetic basis that accounts for the *cognitive* differences between modern humans and Neanderthals, which is also in agreement with the RTB model.

But these insights are not as provocative as a different query: Did our species interbreed with Neanderthals or Denisovans? Access to the Neanderthal genome allows for wider, more overt testing of this fascinating question.

Chapter 21

That Messy Interbreeding Problem

No matter how sophisticated and thoughtful one might be, it is easy to get hooked on the intrigue of a soap opera. People love the drama of an on-again, off-again romance and a story line fraught with plot twists.

Scientists in recent years seem to be relishing their own soap opera of sorts, but not on television. This drama has been unfolding in the pages of scientific literature. Did humans and Neanderthals interbreed?

Though the very idea is morally repugnant from a Christian perspective, genetic evidence yields results without consideration of such sensitivities. What does the data show? The following discussion provides a historical retrospective on the question of human-Neanderthal interbreeding.

At the time *Who Was Adam?* was first published, the technology to sequence the Neanderthal genome did not exist. Without access to the Neanderthal genome, researchers began to study the human genome to look for features that could serve as markers for interbreeding between humans and other hominids. In 2006, geneticists from the University of Chicago (UChicago) created a stir when they announced detection of a version of the human brain size gene, *microcephalin* (*MCPH1*), which appeared to have come from Neanderthals. The geneticists alleged the gene was introduced into the human gene pool as a result of interbreeding between the two species.[1]

Does Brain Size Matter?
MCPH1 plays an important role in human brain size development. Mutations to this gene lead to microcephaly, a condition characterized by a severe reduction in brain volume. Some evolutionary biologists think that changes in this gene through time led to the emergence of the unusually large human brain size as hominids evolved into modern humans. This idea prompted the UChicago team to examine the origin of this gene from an evolutionary perspective.

First haplotype test

There are two categories of *MCPH1*, referred to as D and non-D haplotypes. The D haplotypes are found in over 70 percent of the world's population, the non-D types in the remaining 30 percent. Based on haplotype characterization, the researchers concluded that the D haplotypes originated in modern humans about 37,000 years ago and the non-D haplotypes about 1.1 million years ago in another hominid. The team estimated that two hominid species carrying the haplotypes diverged from one another about 1.7 million years ago.

Researchers speculated that the non-D haplotypes emerged uniquely in the lineage that led to modern humans and the D haplotypes originated in the Neanderthal lineage. Accordingly, at 37,000 years ago, when Neanderthals and humans coexisted in Europe, interbreeding introduced the D haplotypes into the human gene pool. The D haplotypes then spread rapidly among human people groups until they reached a frequency of about 70 percent.

Second haplotype test

A follow-up study, however, refuted the scenario when scientists performed a *direct* analysis of the nuclear DNA sequences (where more information stands to be gained) of the El Sidrón Neanderthal genome and found no evidence for the D haplotype of the *MCPH1* gene.[2]

Does Methodology Matter?

Two implications follow from this result. First, other investigators have made similar claims of interbreeding between African people groups and archaic hominids based on anomalies (or divergent features based on age or mutational patterns) in the genomes sampled from African populations.[3] In these instances, it is assumed that the older, unusual genetic locations were introduced into the human gene pool (called introgression) as a result of interbreeding between humans and *Homo erectus* or some other hominid. Yet failure to detect the D haplotype for *MCPH1* in Neanderthals casts doubt on the validity of the methodologies and interpretative approaches used to conclude that humans and hominids interbred based on unusual features in the human genome. As one research team aptly noted, "It is possible that unrecognized structural variants or other alignment errors could generate a spurious signature similar to introgression."[4]

Second, "unambiguous evidence of introgression is difficult to obtain in the absence of an archaic reference sequence."[5] In other words, what researchers needed to adequately address the question of interbreeding was the Neanderthal genome sequence.

Genomic Evidence for Interbreeding?

As discussed in the last chapter, the first such "reference sequence" was made available toward the end of 2006 when two independent teams sequenced 62,250 base pairs and 1 million base pairs, respectively, of the Neanderthal genome.[6] Though this was impressive science, only a small portion of the Neanderthal genome was available at that time and the sequences that were available were "rough drafts." (See chapter 20.)

Earlier analysis of mitochondrial DNA (mtDNA) failed to provide evidence for interbreeding between humans and Neanderthals, but preliminary results from the first Neanderthal nuclear DNA sequences were ambiguous.[7] One analysis found *no* evidence for interbreeding. Another study, however, noted *some* genetic signatures in the Neanderthal genome that could be taken as evidence for interbreeding.

A follow-up study involving a detailed comparison of Neanderthal DNA signatures with human DNA signatures from Africans and Europeans found no evidence for gene flow between humans and Neanderthals. Also, analysis of human and Neanderthal Y chromosome sequences failed to detect any evidence for interbreeding.[8] In still another study, investigators suggested the evidence for interbreeding was more than likely due to contamination of the Neanderthal samples with low levels of human DNA.[9]

Finally, a Full Draft Sequence

All controversy seemed resolved when the rough draft sequence of the Neanderthal genome—a veritable DNA map of 4 billion base pairs—was completed in 2010.[10] Examining the average genetic differences between Neanderthal and human genomes, the researchers noted that Neanderthals had more in common with non-African peoples than with African groups. Geneticists can account for this if there had been limited interbreeding between humans and Neanderthals in the eastern portion of the Middle East, roughly 45,000 to 80,000 years ago, as humans began to migrate around the world. Such limited encounters would explain why non-African populations display what appears to be a 1 to 4 percent genetic contribution from Neanderthals while African people groups have no contribution whatsoever. A follow-up study seemed to affirm this scenario by estimating that the interbreeding events between humans and Neanderthals took place between 47,000 and 65,000 years ago.[11]

Denisovan Encounters?

When the Denisovan genome is compared to representative human genomes, it has a much greater affinity to the genomes of Oceanic people groups than with other human populations.[12] Researchers take this result to indicate that after humans interbred with Neanderthals (in the Middle East), a subset making its way across Asia interbred with the Denisovans (Siberia), leaving behind signatures in the genomes of Oceanic people groups as they migrated into the South Pacific.

These putative signatures for interbreeding between modern humans and Neanderthals were detected anew in 2014, when researchers led by Kay Prüfer generated and analyzed the high-quality genome for the Altai Neanderthal.[13] The team demonstrated what appears to be a 1.5 to 2.1 percent Neanderthal contribution to genomes of non-African people. Results showed that this contribution bore a much stronger signature to Neanderthals from the Caucasus (Eurasia) than to Neanderthals from either Siberia (northern Asia) or Croatia (Europe).

Another conclusion from this research suggested interbreeding took place between the Denisovans and Asiatic and Oceanic people. While Prüfer's team failed to detect any Denisovan contributions in genomes of European people, they did find about a 0.2 percent contribution to the genomes of Asians and of Native Americans (who were thought to have migrated from Asia). They noted a stronger Denisovan contribution, 5 percent, to the genomes of Oceanic people. Finally, Prüfer's team also detected apparent interbreeding between Neanderthals and the Denisovans; they even suspected the Denisovans interbred with an unnamed hominid.

What a soap opera! At this point, genetic evidence reveals a sordid past. Does it get messier?

Tianyuan Man

Possible additional evidence for human-Neanderthal interbreeding comes from analysis of mtDNA and nuclear DNA recovered from a human tibia that dates to about 40,000 years ago.[14] The tibia and other remains were found in the Tianyuan Cave near Beijing. Researchers from China and Germany generated the Tianyuan individual's entire mitochondrial genome from 4.4 million fragments of ancient DNA, representing a 35.6-fold coverage.

As expected given humanity's migration patterns, the mtDNA clustered with those sequences taken from Native American, Korean, Taiwanese, central Asian, and Oceanic people groups. The researchers were also able to piece together the DNA sequence for chromosome 21, with about a 1.75-fold coverage. This sequence clustered most closely to Asian people groups and had the least affinity to African people groups—again, as expected.

The investigators also looked for any indication of interbreeding between the people represented by the Tianyuan man and Neanderthals and Denisovans. They found no evidence for encounters with the Denisovans, but did see Neanderthal signatures in the Tianyuan genome. Thus, it appears that as humans migrated out of Africa, some of them encountered Neanderthals, interbred with them, and then continued on through Asia and Oceania. Genetic evidence of that scandalous travel log survives in the tibia of the Tianyaun man.

Three More Encounters

In fall of 2014, two studies investigated ancient genomes recovered from anatomically modern human remains. In one study, researchers isolated ancient DNA from a 36,000-year-old arm bone.[15] The bone was recovered from an area of Russia that borders Eastern Europe and Western Asia. Though researchers possessed only a low-quality genome, they were able to detect Neanderthal signatures in it. Of most significance was the observation that this genome possessed much longer stretches of Neanderthal DNA than those of contemporary Europeans.

The other study yielded similar results. These investigators isolated ancient DNA from a 45,000-year-old human femur.[16] Their work yielded a genome with 42-fold coverage, an exceptionally high-quality sequence. Here again, researchers detected Neanderthal signatures much longer than those found in contemporary Europeans. Based on the length of the Neanderthal DNA in the ancient genome, the team estimated that interbreeding took place between 50,000 and 60,000 years ago.

A third discovery, reported in 2015, of a 55,000-year-old modern human skull in Manot Cave (Israel) increased the likelihood that interbreeding took place.[17] This discovery placed modern humans and Neanderthals in the Levant (countries bordering the Eastern Mediterranean) at the same time, corresponding to the time anthropologists think the interbreeding events took place.

Are We Part Neanderthal?

Neanderthal DNA might be more pervasive throughout human populations than previously thought.[18] According to two independent research teams, the genome of any one individual possesses around 2 percent Neanderthal DNA, but across the human population up to 20 percent of the genome appears composed of Neanderthal sequences. So, Neanderthal DNA amounts in human genomes vary from individual to individual and Neanderthal sequences are peppered throughout human DNA. Additionally, each individual possesses different Neanderthal DNA sequences. In fact, one research team concluded that they could reconstruct nearly 40 percent of the Neanderthal genome from the genomes of about 660 Eurasian people.

Before continuing with this salacious soap opera, a question arises: Why does *nuclear* DNA reveal evidence for interbreeding, but *mitochondrial* DNA does not? Molecular biologist Svante Pääbo, a scientist at ground zero for much of the work in ancient DNA studies of hominids, offers an explanation.[19] He suggests the sheer size difference between the nuclear (nearly 3.2 billion base pairs) and mitochondrial (16,500 base pairs) genomes provides more opportunities to detect interbreeding in the nuclear genome, particularly if the signal for interbreeding is weak.

Shopping for Genes

If humans and Neanderthals (and Denisovans) interbred, then researchers should detect actual genetic markers from these hominids within the human genome. Along these lines, an international team of scientists claimed they detected *human leukocyte antigen (HLA)* genes in the human genome that look like they originated in Neanderthals and Denisovans and were introduced via interbreeding into the Eurasian and Oceanic gene pool.[20] *HLA* genes play a role in the immune system's operation and would, presumably, have provided an advantage to humans as they migrated out of Africa and encountered new pathogens (disease agents) in Europe and Asia. Neanderthals and Denisovans would already have had the genes in place to fight off these pathogens because they had lived in Europe and Asia for millennia. It is important to note that these variants of the *HLA* genes occur in some African people groups as well. Thus, the researchers who discovered these genes in the Neanderthal and Denisovan genomes assumed that the hominid *HLA* genes were introduced into African genomes when people of Eurasian descent reproduced with Africans.

But another explanation also makes sense. It could be that these *HLA* genes already existed in the human gene pool before humans began migrating. In that case, the shared genes could be understood as reflecting shared design features.

In 2014, an independent team of researchers from Germany identified variants of the HLA class II receptors in Europeans that had counterparts in the Neanderthal genome.[21] These variants are rare in the genomes of African people groups. Again, the results were interpreted as evidence for human-Neanderthal interbreeding, with the rare variants later introduced into African populations by Europeans. But shortly after publication, a separate research team argued that the so-called Neanderthal contribution was an artifact of ancient population structures, not of interbreeding.[22]

Shared UV protection?

In 2014, a research team reported evidence that interbreeding with Neanderthals introduced genes that play a role in the cellular response to UV radiation into Asian genomes.[23] It appears that these genes have experienced positive selection, presumably because they offer the advantage of protecting these people from UV radiation's harmful effects.

The team noted an unusual distribution of these genes among different population groups. For example, they detected UV-protective "Neanderthal" genes in 49 percent of Japanese and 66 percent of South Chinese people. On the other hand, these genes occurred with low frequency among European people groups. Researchers argued that the versions of the genes imparting UV protection were lost after humans left Africa and then reintroduced when Asians interbred with Neanderthals. However, this scenario does not square with the model for why only non-African people groups possess a Neanderthal signature; namely, the primary interbreeding events took place in the Middle East, not in Asia, as modern humans were leaving Africa.

Getting under the skin

Skin pigmentation offers another area of insight into humanity's licentious past. It is unclear whether Neanderthals contributed genes for light skin pigmentation to humans as the latter entered Europe. Some evolutionary biologists have argued that light skin and hair pigmentation emerged independently in humans and Neanderthals. Lighter skin pigmentation in the northern latitudes is advantageous for the synthesis of vitamin D. Both humans and Neanderthals have variants of the *melanocortin 1 receptor* (*MC1R*) gene that favors lighter skin and hair. Yet these two variants are distinct from one another. Thus, it does not appear that Neanderthals introduced the genes for light skin into the human genome. (See "Light Skin, Red Hair?" on page 298.)

Two other studies, however, suggested that light skin in Europeans indeed came from Neanderthals.[24] In these two studies researchers detected "Neanderthal" genes that relate to keratin biochemistry and biology in the human genome. Keratin is the protein found in skin, nails, and hair. *BNC2*, one of the genes that codes for keratin, is involved in skin pigmentation. On this basis, both research teams suggest Neanderthals contributed to the light skin and hair prevalent among Europeans.

Another pair of studies raised further questions about interbreeding's contribution to light skin and hair. One of the studies dates the variants of a collection of genes (*KITLG*, *TYRP1*, *SLC24A5*, and *SLC45A2*) that also play a role in light skin in Europeans to 11,000 to 19,000 years ago—well after humans made their way to Europe and after Neanderthals had gone extinct.[25] In the other study, researchers isolated ancient DNA from 7,000-year-old human remains recovered near León, Spain. Genome analysis indicates this individual had dark skin.[26] Thus, light skin was not uniformly present in Europe, even as recent as 7,000 years ago.

Clearly, light skin pigmentation is important: it improves fitness for people living in northern latitudes. In fact, it is so vital for survival that this trait emerged independently in humans and Neanderthals. Given its importance, it is surprising that clear-cut evidence does not exist for Neanderthals contributing this trait to the human gene pool.

One explanation advanced to account for Neanderthals' failure to contribute genes for light skin to Europeans has to do with the location of the interbreeding.[27] Presumably, Neanderthals and humans interbred in the Middle East, not in Europe. Given the latitude, light skin pigmentation would not be advantageous. In fact, it would compromise fitness. According to this explanation, the Neanderthals that interbred with humans would not have had fair skin but relatively dark pigmentation.

Breakdown on fat
In another study, researchers discovered that Europeans—but not Asians—have high levels of "Neanderthal" genes that play a role in the breakdown of fat.[28] These genes appear to have been introduced under positive selection, imparting some type of advantage.

Clues from Tibet
Neanderthals are not the only hominid to putatively introduce beneficial genes into the human genome. A recent study shows that Tibetans, who live at elevations of 15,000 feet and higher, share the same version of *EPAS1* with Denisovans. Presumably, Denisovans contributed this gene to Tibetans via interbreeding. *EPAS1* helps boost the production of hemoglobin, the protein that carries

Was It All Good?

If Neanderthals did make genetic contributions to humans, it would be reasonable to assume that not all contributions were beneficial. Some evolutionary biologists believe Neanderthals passed along genes that adversely impact human health. For example, researchers have found Neanderthal genes in the human genome that are implicated in Type 2 diabetes, Crohn's disease, lupus, and even smoking addiction.[29] Perhaps humans can lay blame for some common contemporary maladies on sordid past encounters.

oxygen in the blood.[30] The increased level of hemoglobin helps Tibetans adapt to low oxygen levels at high altitudes. No other human population possesses their version of *EPAS1*.

But the story is more complicated than that. Tibetans possess a unique version of *EGLN1* not found in any other people group.[31] This gene prevents the overproduction of red blood cells under low-oxygen conditions. (Overproduction makes the blood too thick to flow efficiently through veins and arteries, which can lead to heart failure.) It turns out the Tibetan version of *EGLN1* emerged only 8,000 years ago—much later than humans are thought to have interbred with Denisovans. So, Tibetans' ability to live at high altitudes might not have come from Denisovans.

At this point in time, most anthropologists believe Neanderthals and Denisovans contributed to the genomes of Eurasian and Oceanic people groups, respectively. Human-hominid interbreeding is regarded as near scientific orthodoxy and the case for it is strong. Still, is there reason to be skeptical about this distasteful scenario?

Reproductive Barriers
Research shows strong reproductive barriers must have existed between humans and Neanderthals due either to the low fitness of Neanderthal-human hybrids or to strong avoidance between the two groups.[32] The same research also shows that the Neanderthal contribution to European genomes is genetically distinct from the contribution to Asian genomes. If so, then this study doesn't square with the idea that interbreeding took place in the Middle East.

Small Neanderthal Populations
Neanderthal population sizes as estimated from the genetic diversity of

mtDNA sequences and the homozygosity of the Neanderthal genome also raise questions about the likelihood of human-Neanderthal encounters.[33] Estimates based on the mtDNA data indicate that the effective population size of Neanderthals across Europe and Asia might have been as low as 3,500 breeding individuals.

Using a different approach (that estimates genetic diversity by comparing the genetic contribution from the mother and father), researchers studied the Altai and El Sidrón Neanderthal genomes and the high-quality Denisovan genome and also concluded that these hominids must have had a relatively small population size, forming isolated, insular communities characterized by inbreeding. The low population densities of these two hominids greatly reduce the likelihood that migrating humans would have encountered these creatures.

Small Human Populations on the Move

The population dynamics of the human migration out of Africa further reduces the possibility for interbreeding. Geneticists and paleoanthropologists have noted that genetic diversity and morphological variation decreases the farther a particular people group is removed from Africa.[34] This pattern indicates that when humans left Africa, only a small number of individuals began the migration. As the migration continued, the frontline of migrants (first into the Middle East, then elsewhere) consisted of a relatively small number of individuals. That number became increasingly smaller as humans first entered Europe and Asia. If human, Neanderthal, and Denisovan numbers were all low, interactions between them would have been rare at best.

If interbreeding did take place, it is expected that the trend toward decreasing genetic and anatomical diversity would be interrupted by *increased* diversity at the points where contact between humans and other hominids took place.[35] It does not look as though such a diversity boost has happened.

Although a few questions remain, a decade of scientific advances strongly indicates that humans interbred with Neanderthals and Denisovans.

Did Two Become One?

And what if it did happen? If humans interbred with other hominids would it invalidate the Reasons to Believe (RTB) human origins model that predicts humans and Neanderthals (and the Denisovans) were biologically and behaviorally distinct?

Not necessarily. Just because humans and Neanderthals interbred, does not mean they must be the same species. Mammals in the same family have been known to interbreed to produce viable hybrids. For example, lions and tigers can produce "ligers" and dolphins and whales can produce "wholphins."

No scientist doubts that Neanderthals and humans are distinct species. According to paleoanthropologist Ian Tattersall, "The difference in skull structure between *Homo neanderthalensis* and *Homo sapiens* is far greater than...the one between lions and tigers."[36] The anatomical, genetic, and developmental differences between humans and Neanderthals (and, presumably, the Denisovans) justify viewing them as distinct biological entities. Along these lines, it is important to note that researchers believe the resulting human-Neanderthal hybrids lacked fecundity.[37] Geneticist David Reich noted that humans and Neanderthals "'were at the edge of biological compatibility.'"[38]

Some people maintain that interbreeding provides prima facie evidence humans and Neanderthals must have shared a common ancestor and that both lineages emerged from a self-contained interbreeding population. However, from a Christian perspective, it is still possible to view humans and Neanderthals as distinct products of God's creative activity. On this view, an ability to interbreed reflects common design, not common descent. (See pages 366–370).

Interbreeding Signals Human Depravity

From a biblical standpoint, and given humanity's depraved post-fall nature, it should not be surprising that humans interbred with Neanderthals. Genesis 6:5 states that prior to the flood "The LORD saw how great the wickedness of the human race had become on the earth, and that every inclination of the thoughts of the human heart was only evil all the time." Leviticus 18:23 condemns and forbids bestiality. Given humanity's propensity for intercourse with animals, it is not shocking that humans would choose to interbreed with creatures like Neanderthals, who closely resemble humans. Also, it is interesting to note that Genesis 6:1–42 describes the Nephilim as the hybrid offspring of interbreeding between the sons of God and the daughters of men.

Still, if humans and Neanderthals interbred, it raises several tricky theological issues such as whether the human-Neanderthal hybrids had a soul. Such worthwhile considerations lie beyond the scope of this primarily scientific book, but RTB scholars continue to wrestle through the philosophical and theological implications. However, taking into account strong evidence for human-hominid interbreeding, such data do not invalidate the RTB human origins model. They do raise points of concern, but RTB's model can accommodate evidence for such degenerate behavior.

Trying to cover up sexual sins of the past is a messy business, but what about other indicators of Neanderthal-human similarity? What does wider, more overt testing suggest about possible intelligent behavior in Neanderthals? The next chapter updates the evidence.

Chapter 22

Did Neanderthals Have the Smarts?

Did Neanderthals bury their dead? Did they cook, use medicine, and make art? Could they speak?

Over the last ten years, there has been perhaps no more exciting facet of physical anthropology than the study of Neanderthal's cognitive ability—and no area in which paleoanthropologists disagree more. Some argue that Neanderthals were cognitively inferior to humans; others maintain that Neanderthals displayed sophisticated behavior on par with humans.

Reasons to Believe's (RTB) model predicts that hominids, including Neanderthals, should be behaviorally distinct from humans. According to our model, hominids were not made in God's image (Genesis 1:26–27). Thus, when hominids are compared to humans, RTB expects hominids to lack sophistication in cognitive capacity, behavior, "technology," and "culture."

What has a decade of investigation shown? A first stop in the quest for scientific comparison entails a visit to ancient graveyards.

Were Caves Graves?

Many anthropologists hold the idea that Neanderthals buried their dead as unassailable. Others challenge this dogma. The dispute emanates from the fact that many of the purported Neanderthal gravesites were discovered at a time when the standards for excavation and recording site information were not as robust as they are today.

For example, in 1961, archeologists unearthed a three-year-old child in Roc de Marsal (a cave in France) and interpreted the discovery as a deliberate Neanderthal burial. The gravesite became widely considered as an unequivocal example of an intentional entombment, but in 2011 an international team of investigators took a second look at the site.[1]

Their careful reexamination indicates the "gravesite" was actually a natural depression in the cave floor and the child's remains appear to have slid into this natural cavity. When archeologists first unearthed the specimen, they discovered associated animal bones and stone artifacts and assumed these materials were added to the grave as part of the burial ritual. They did not consider the abundance of animal and lithic (stony) remains richly distributed throughout the cave. Their proximity to the child appears coincidental. According to the second research team, "Realistically, it would be impossible to dig anywhere within these deposits without encountering concentrated lithics and faunal remains."[2]

The new interpretation of the Roc de Marsal site might help throw dirt on the idea of Neanderthal burials, but there's more. Over a century ago, archeologists working in La Ferrassie Cave (France), one of the most important Neanderthal burial sites, recovered several specimens that looked as though they were buried deliberately, but appearances did not hold up under scientific scrutiny. Reanalysis of the site in 2012 suggested these findings were natural burials, not purposeful ones.[3]

Nevertheless, a follow-up study of another burial location presented possible evidence for the authenticity of Neanderthal burial sites.[4] So, the back-and-forth continues. What can be stated confidently is that questions surrounding Neanderthal burials are far from unassailable.

What Constitutes Sophisticated Behavior?

In the past ten years, growing numbers of anthropologists have taken the position that Neanderthals displayed sophisticated behavior. Numerous recent archeological finds have been interpreted to support this view.[5] Space does not allow discussion of all these discoveries but a few representative examples will illustrate the point.

Did Neanderthals cook?

In 2011, Smithsonian paleoanthropologists published a paper wherein they concluded that Neanderthals not only ate plant matter but also *cooked* the plants before consuming them.[6] This finding presumably indicated that Neanderthals' diet was far more diverse than previously thought and implied Neanderthals were capable of fairly sophisticated behavior, stemming from advanced cognitive ability like that possessed by humans.

The researchers studied tartar surrounding Neanderthal teeth recovered from the Shanidar (Iraq) and Spy (Belgium) caves. The team isolated starch grains from the tartar and determined from the grains' morphological structure that the starches came from grasses, dates, legumes, roots, and other plant materials. The grains also showed damage consistent with heating. Because these specimens came from two locales, the investigators concluded that cooking plant matter (which releases more nutrients from the foodstuff) was widespread among Neanderthals. The implication was that these creatures could effectively exploit resources in their environment and utilize sophisticated gleaning and food preparation practices.

Later in 2011, archeologists Matthew Collins and Les Copeland reevaluated the data and pointed out the same type of damage occurs to the starch grains as they age.[7] So, Neanderthals might have eaten but not necessarily cooked plants. The residue on the teeth could simply be the result of passing time. It seems the Smithsonian paleoanthropologists overlooked the most obvious explanation for the starch grain morphologies. Moreover, to our knowledge, archeologists have not recovered any grinding implements, such as would be used to prep the plant matter for cooking, from any Neanderthal site. There remains no compelling evidence that Neanderthals cooked vegetable matter.

Did Neanderthals use medicinal plants?

In 2012, researchers from Spain and the United States analyzed the tartar of 13 Neanderthals (between 47,000 and 51,000 years in age) from El Sidrón Cave (Spain).[8] Detailed characterization of trace compounds extracted from the tartar revealed plants as important to the Neanderthal diet. These compounds also indicated that Neanderthals consumed bitter-tasting plants with anti-inflammatory properties (but no nutritional value). It appears Neanderthals might have deliberately consumed plants for medicinal purposes.

On the surface, this finding makes it seem that Neanderthals possessed advanced cognitive abilities, but many animals consume plants for medicinal purposes.[9] For example, chimpanzees will eat certain leaves to induce vomiting to help rid their digestive system of parasites. Zoopharmacognosy renders Neanderthal use of medicinal plants much less significant (see chapter 23).

Did Neanderthals make art?

Accurately dating cave art is challenging. Traditionally, archeologists would either: (1) date the remains associated with the cave art and try to establish a correlation; or (2) attempt to date the cave paintings directly via carbon-14 measurements of the pigments and charcoal used to make them. Both approaches have limitations. For example, carbon-14 dating is not reliable for samples much older than 40,000 years. And, obviously, dating nearby artifacts is not the same as dating the art itself.

In 2012, researchers from the United Kingdom and Spain developed and employed a new technique to date the art found on the walls in 11 caves located in northwestern Spain.[10] The team chose to analyze the calcite deposits underneath and on top of the cave paintings. When calcite forms it contains trace amounts of uranium-238, which decays into thorium-230. Detecting low quantities of these isotopes usually required extremely large samples. By using accelerator mass spectrometry, the research team discovered they could get by with 10-milligram samples.

By dating calcite from 50 samples, they deduced minimum and maximum ages for the cave paintings. Most of the samples dated to about 25,000 years old (or younger). Three samples were significantly older: A club-shaped symbol dated to 31,000 years old, hand stencils dated to 37,000 years old, and a red disk dated to 41,000 years old.

At the time the team's work was published, most anthropologists believed humans entered Europe about 40,000 years ago, prompting the researchers to suggest that Neanderthals created some of the cave art. They claimed "because the 40.8-ky [thousand-year] date for the disk is a minimum age, it cannot be ruled out that the earliest paintings were symbolic expressions of Neandertals, which were present at Cantabrian Spain until at least 42 ka [thousand years ago]."[11]

This interpretation is problematic. The latest evidence (published in 2014) indicated that Neanderthals had disappeared from Europe and Iberia by 40,000+ years ago.[12] How, then, could they be the creators of the red disk? And plainly speaking, there is no conclusive evidence whatsoever that Neanderthals engaged in artistic expression. So, why should the red disk be interpreted as the work of these hominids? Abundant evidence indicates that humans produced art, and all other art in the 11 cave sites is attributed to humans. Why would researchers not reasonably conclude that the red disk is, too, the work of human artists? Perhaps these results show that humans migrated to Europe and, specifically, northwestern Spain earlier than thought. In fact, there are studies that suggest human presence in Europe as early as 43,000 to 45,000 years ago.[13]

In fall of 2014, researchers from Spain interpreted hatch marks discovered in the bedrock of Gorham's Cave (Gibraltar) as Neanderthal art.[14] The markings are more than 39,000 years old; the layer immediately above the bedrock dates between 30,000 and 38,000 years old and contains Neanderthal-produced artifacts. Thus, the team to concluded Neanderthals made the markings.

However, it is debatable if the hatch marks are markers for symbolism and, hence, artistic expression. It appears they were made intentionally and they do display a geometric patterning—but the "artist's" intent is unclear. Did he or she intend to communicate anything with these marks? Could the marks' geometric quality be coincidental? Not to be trite, but my English bulldog has scratched the legs of our furniture and, occasionally, the scratch marks do have a geometric character to them. Though Archie scratched the furniture on purpose, it would be difficult to argue that he was engaged in artistic expression. Could the markings on the bedrock be interpreted the same way?

For the sake of argument, let's assume the engravings are evidence for symbolism. Can these cut marks rightly be attributed to the work of Neanderthals? Probably not because, as previously noted, the latest dating of Neanderthal remains indicates that these hominids went extinct in Iberia well before 40,000 years ago. If so, then there is no way they could have produced 39,000-year-old hatch marks.

It makes more sense to attribute these "motifs" (if they are artistic at all) to humans. The archeological record indicates that humans have been engaged in symbolism for at least 80,000 years and, arguably, since they first appeared on Earth about 130,000 years ago (see chapter 18). Also, the latest data indicates that modern humans made their way into Europe earlier than thought, closer to 44,000 years ago—not 40,000 years ago, which had been the traditional understanding. An earlier arrival of the first modern humans in Europe would have given them plenty of time to produce the hatch marks in Gorham's Cave.

Were Neanderthals capable of symbolism?

Over the last decade, some paleoanthropologists have interpreted various archeological finds as evidence that Neanderthals possessed symbolic thought—a quality RTB scholars link to the image of God and predict should be unique to humans.

Eagle toes. In 2012, scientists from Canada and France reported on finds from two sites in France (one dating to 90,000 years ago and the other between 40,000 and 60,000 years ago) that appear to show deliberate markings on the toe bones of golden and white-tailed eagles.[15] It appears the markings were made with stone tools. The scientists attributed them to Neanderthals. They argued that because these birds were rare in that environment and the toes useless as a food source, the markings demonstrate symbolic intent. Raptor remains have been recovered from other Neanderthal sites. Clearly, Neanderthals prized these birds.

Claiming these finds evince Neanderthal symbolism seems a stretch. It is interesting that *only* the remains at these two French locations show supposedly deliberate markings. Raptor toe remains from other locales do not. Neanderthals rarely consumed eagles, but there are sites containing remains of a leftover meal of raptors. In these instances, the remains show markings on skeletal parts with food value. This explanation might be mundane, but could it be that the Neanderthals simply scraped the eagle toes in their attempts to glean every bit of food from the carcasses?

Red ocher. Perhaps the discovery of ocher (iron ore used as pigment) at several Neanderthal sites provides more compelling evidence for symbolism. The first humans used red ocher produced from the mineral hematite as a medicine, food preservative, insect repellent, and hide tanner. They also used it for body painting and cave art. Paleoanthropologists view these last two applications as reflecting symbolism. Therefore, recovering red ocher at Neanderthal sites at least opens up the possibility for symbolism among these hominids—but it does not demand this interpretation.

Most red ocher found in archeological sites dates between 40,000 and 60,000 years old. But, in 2012, a research team from the Netherlands identified red ocher from a local site that dates to between 200,000 and 250,000 years old.[16] The red ocher appears to be nonlocal in origin. Perhaps somebody transported it there. However, this discovery only indicates that Neanderthals *used* red ocher and does not support the notion that they exercised symbolic thought. As the authors noted, "In our view, there is no reason to assume that the mere presence of iron oxide at an archeological site, whether Neandertal or modern human, implies symbolic behavior."[17]

Painted pendants. In 2010 and 2013, two independent research teams reported finding pigmented marine shells at Neanderthal sites. At a site in Iberia, one of the teams found marine shells next to red and yellow colorants (pigments inside a marine shell) and one shell painted orange.[18] Using carbon-14 dating methods, the researchers dated the artifacts to be about 50,000 years old. The other team found negligible remains of a marine shell with red pigment in micropits on its surface in a cave in northern Italy.[19] They concluded the shell was part of a pendant. Carbon-14 dating placed the shell between 45,000 and 47,000 years old.

These finds are impressive, but it might be premature to count them as evidence for Neanderthal symbolism. Given that evidence for Neanderthal symbolism is generally absent, it is reasonable to attribute these artifacts to humans. In both cases, the remains date close to the time when humans entered Europe. Again, there is a growing consensus that Neanderthals went extinct earlier than thought and the dates for these two finds are close to the time that some anthropologists think Neanderthals disappeared.

The popular interpretation of these salient discoveries challenges RTB's prediction that Neanderthals were cognitively inferior to humans. Yet these interpretations are controversial and the archeological finds do not necessarily support the idea of symbolic thought and advanced cognition in Neanderthals. Reasonable, alternate explanations exist. As anthropologists Ian Tattersall and Jeffrey Schwartz pointed out, "All claimed evidence for symbolic activities among Neanderthals is highly debatable...Currently, there is little compelling reason to conclude that *Homo neanderthalensis* was a symbolic creature in the same sense as modern *Homo sapiens*."[20]

Did *Homo erectus* Make Art?

If the case for Neanderthal art is not compelling, how about that of *H. erectus*? Not long ago, this question would have been considered absurd. Yet late in fall of 2014, researchers from the Netherlands reported on the discovery of engravings on a marine shell that dates to 540,000 years ago.[21] They attributed these markings to *H. erectus*.

This shell was part of a collection unearthed by Eugène Dubois in the 1890s. Dubois collected shells in Indonesia, near where he discovered the first *H. erectus* remains (a skull cap). He recovered nearly 200 articulated shells, valves, and shell fragments.

These shells, which encompass 11 freshwater mussel species, are housed in a museum in Leiden, Netherlands. Recently, researchers discovered perforations in many of the collection's shells. All the perforations are located just above the mussel's anterior abductor muscle. It appears *H. erectus* used a sharp instrument, such as a shark tooth, to puncture the shell in order to damage the muscle used to keep the valves closed. Once the anterior abductor was compromised, it would have been easy to open up the mussel and gain access to the fleshy part of the organism.

This is impressive behavior—but it is on par with wild chimpanzee activities (see chapter 23). Therefore, this finding is not troubling for the biblical view of human uniqueness. What is of potential concern is the discovery of engravings on one of the marine shells. These engravings consist of geometric patterns that appear to have been made intentionally using a sharp object (such as a shark tooth). Sediment within the shell dates to 540,000 years in age. On this basis, there is no way to attribute the patterns to humans. It truly appears *H. erectus* made the markings.

Do these markings constitute art? Or is the geometric character of the patterns happenstance? The rarity of such markings supports the latter interpretation. Out of nearly 200 shells and shell fragments, only one displays any markings at all. If these markings reflect some sort of inherent artistic ability, why are they unique to a single shell? In fact, to scientists' knowledge, no other erectine archeological site—anywhere in the world—shows any evidence for symbolism or even *proto*-symbolism.

Evidence against Neanderthal Symbolism
Other scientific studies demonstrate that Neanderthals lacked humanlike cognitive sophistication. It is impractical to discuss all of these studies here, but two will illustrate the point.

Division of labor
In anthropology, division of labor refers to the different activities assigned to males and females in societies. They view specialization between males and females (and between juveniles and adults) as a defining feature of humans. This behavior promotes robust economies and allows people to survive, even thrive, in diverse environments.

Evolutionary biologists have long sought to account for division of labor. When did this behavior emerge? Did our hominid predecessors display this behavior?

A 2006 study examined human and Neanderthal archeological records to determine the origin of division of labor. Anthropologists Steven Kuhn and Mary Stiner concluded that division of labor among Neanderthals was relatively limited.[22] It seems Neanderthal activity was focused on pursuing large terrestrial game; so, their foraging practices were restricted to species easily collected. The implication is that all Neanderthals, whether male or female, adult or juvenile, must have all been involved in hunting large game.

In sharp contrast the first humans foraged a wide range of creatures, those easy to collect and those requiring some level of ingenuity. Humans hunted a smattering of animals. They fished and made use of plants. They produced a wide variety of tools and manufactured clothing. This assortment of behaviors indicates a division of labor among the earliest humans.

Behavioral differences of this extent yield important implications. First, because Neanderthals hunted only large game animals, they occupied the top trophic levels in the ecosystem. This placement limited their population sizes to small numbers and made them susceptible to extinction. (Neanderthal genomes indicate they formed small insular population groups. See chapter 20.) In fact, Kuhn and Stiner speculated that Neanderthals' failure to divide labor ultimately led to the species' demise.

Second, the first humans' hunting and foraging practices placed them in lower trophic levels, allowing them to achieve much larger and intrinsically more robust population sizes. Division of labor among the first humans allowed them to occupy diverse, novel, and harsh environments and made them ideally suited to migrate rapidly from their point of origin to fill the earth.

Châtelperronian culture might not have existed

Some paleoanthropologists have argued that about 40,000 years ago—the time of humanity's arrival in Europe and right before Neanderthals' disappearance—Neanderthals evolved the capacity for modern behavior and, with it, symbolic thought. (See pages 200–201.) Archeological finds in the Grotte du Renne (a French cave) provide the chief evidence for this claim. Both Neanderthals and humans occupied this cave at various times between 28,000 and 45,000 years ago. The site consists of 15 archeological layers. Of greatest interest to paleoanthropologists is a layer containing Neanderthal teeth and artifacts such as personal ornaments, rings, pierced animal teeth, and ivory pendants—remains viewed as evidence for symbolic thought and typically connected to humans.

When *Who Was Adam?* was originally published, we argued that one way to explain the association of Neanderthal remains and sophisticated artifacts is the mixing of cave layers. In such a scenario, Neanderthal remains accidentally wound up in the same layer as body ornaments, rings, and pendants.

A 2010 study of Grotte du Renne affirmed our explanation.[23] Researchers carefully applied radiocarbon dating to the cave layers, expecting that deeper layers would measure progressively older than the upper layers. However, they discovered that the layers' dates displayed no pattern, indicating that the cave layers were mixed, perhaps by the last occupants, and raising questions as to whether Neanderthals indeed possessed the capacity for symbolic thought.

Did Neanderthals Speak?

In Neanderthal studies, perhaps no topic generates more controversy than the debate over whether these hominids could speak. At the time of this book's first publication (2005), the controversy centered around the hyoid bone and the hypoglossal canal (see chapter 12). Analysis of these anatomical features was inconclusive at that time (and still is). The structure of the hyoid bone and the hypoglossal canal neither rules out nor supports Neanderthal language capabilities.

Anthropologists interested in this question have now turned to the Neanderthal genome in the hopes that it will offer insight into the issue.

Language Gene?
Toward the end of 2007, scientists from the Max Planck Institute at Leipzig, Germany, announced the isolation of *FOXP2*, the so-called language gene, from a Neanderthal specimen recently recovered in Spain.[24] Some people took this discovery as evidence that Neanderthals had language ability like that of humans.

Prior to this news, in 2001, a research team from the United Kingdom reported that mutations in *FOXP2* cause severe language disorders. It was concluded that the FOXP2 protein plays a vital role in controlling the development of brain and facial structures that support human language capacity (see chapter 12).

Among mammals, humans possess a unique variant of *FOXP2* and it seems this variant's distinctiveness is key for our language capability. Using molecular clock analysis, researchers determined that, from an evolutionary perspective, the human variant of *FOXP2* arose about 200,000 years ago.[25] Subsequent work placed the origin of human *FOXP2* at about 100,000 years ago.[26] From an evolutionary standpoint, 100,000 years is well after the human and Neanderthal split from a common ancestor (about 500,000 to 750,000 years ago). Neanderthals should not possess a humanlike *FOXP2* gene and, therefore, language capability.

It was surprising, then, that the Max Planck team isolated the human variant of *FOXP2* from a Neanderthal specimen. However, the team recovered only a portion of *FOXP2* from the El Sidrón Neanderthal. Isolation of that portion of the gene is indistinguishable from the human version. In 2014, analysis of the high-quality Altai Neanderthal genome revealed that Neanderthals' *FOXP2* is distinct from the one found in humans.[27]

Language Involves More Than One Gene
Does the presence of *FOXP2* in the Neanderthal genome imply that these hominids possessed language? Not necessarily. This gene cannot be the only one responsible for human language. It is most likely that language derives from the activity of a complex network of gene interactions that dynamically vary through the course of human development. *FOXP2* represents only *one* of

these genes. If any gene involved in human language ability becomes defective, a breakdown in verbal communication occurs. *FOXP2* can be likened to a part of an automobile engine. If that part is defective, the engine will not run properly, if at all—yet the operation of that particular part does not explain how the whole engine works.

Researchers have yet to catalog all the genes involved in human language ability, let alone how the genes interact to generate language capacity. Defects in *FOXP2* do provide important insight into human language development and abilities, but this understanding is limited. It would be a mistake to assume that because Neanderthals had *FOXP2*, they could speak, too. As Tattersall pointed out, "It is evident that the notion of a single gene 'for' language (even a regulating gene, like FOXP2) is an illusion, albeit an attractive one. What the Neanderthals possessed was a necessary condition for language, but it wasn't sufficient."[28]

At this point, scientific evidence offers no reason to believe that Neanderthals had language ability, though the idea is not impossible. As far as anyone can tell, only humans had (and have) the capacity for speech and language. As such, they stand alone in advanced cognitive ability and symbolic thought.

The Origin of Language

When it comes to the origin of language, uncertainty extends beyond whether or not Neanderthals had the capacity to communicate complex, abstract ideas. Evolutionary biologists struggle to account for the origin of language from within the evolutionary paradigm.[29]

According to Tattersall and linguist Noam Chomsky, one of the factors confounding an evolutionary explanation for language stems from an improper understanding of what language is—and what it is not. They argue that language doesn't equate to the ability to communicate—animals can communicate, but they don't posses language—nor is language the same as speech. Instead, the authors assert that language is a cognitive process that starts with neural activity that affects vocalization. Language is possible, even when humans lack the capacity for vocalization (and hearing). For example, deaf people can only communicate by signing. Still they have the same language capacity as all humans because the neural apparatus required for language is in place.

Tattersall and Chomsky argue that too often evolutionary biologists focus on vocalization when trying to explain the evolution of language. But, as they point out, the emergence of this capability doesn't coincide with the origin of language. It is true that vocalization is a necessary condition for language, but it is not a sufficient condition.

So, how can researchers study the origin of language? Tattersall and Chomsky maintain that the archeological record is the best way to characterize the origin of language, with symbolism being the closest proxy.

Symbolism appears to be unique to modern humans. As previously discussed, there is no compelling reason to think that Neanderthals displayed symbolism. This feature makes its first appearance in the archeological record close to the time that modern humans appear on the scene (see chapter 18). There is unequivocal evidence for symbolism at 80,000 years ago, and other indicators that symbolism might have appeared around 150,000 years ago, coincident with the origin of humanity. Presumably, language had its genesis the same time that modern humans did.

The fact that every human being has the identical language capacity compels Tattersall and Chomsky to argue that language originated suddenly. Their argument gains added support from the exponential growth of technology since the time that modern humans first appeared on Earth. This rapid growth must have been facilitated by language. It's noteworthy that Neanderthal technology did not experience a similar pattern of growth. In fact, it remained largely static from the time Neanderthals first appeared (around 250,000 to 200,000 years ago) to the time they went extinct (around 40,000 years ago.) This implies that these hominids lacked language capacity.

According to Tattersall and Chomsky,

> By this reckoning, the language faculty is an extremely recent acquisition in our lineage, and it was acquired not in the context of slow, gradual modification of preexisting systems under natural selection but in a single, rapid, emergent event that built upon those prior systems but was not predicted by them...The relatively sudden origin of language poses difficulties that may be called "Darwin's problem."[30]

Linguists from the University of São Paulo (in Brazil) and the Massachusetts Institute of Technology add support to this new scenario by arguing that when language first appeared, it was not simplistic, but intrinsically complex.[31] In other words, there was no proto-language that evolved into the complex language displayed by all people groups. Instead, language was complex at its outset. According to one of the authors, "The hierarchical complexity found in present-day language is likely to have been present in human language since its emergence."[32]

The rapid emergence of complex language poses a problem for the theory of evolution, but it fits nicely with a biblical understanding of humanity's origin. If human beings were uniquely made in God's image through the Creator's direct action, then it would be reasonable to think that complex language would appear suddenly and be uniquely associated with modern humans.

Anthropologists are not interested only in hominid cognitive abilities. They focus attention on great ape behavior, too. They believe great apes shed light on the origin of human cognition. So what does the behavior of the great apes show? The next chapter takes up this question.

Chapter 23

Comparing Chimp and Hominid Behaviors

YouTube can distract anyone, but its plethora of animal videos is the most beguiling. Most people are enraptured when they see a gorilla caring for a kitten or a chimp learning American Sign Language. Such humanlike traits entertain and fascinate us. They make us wonder if we might be related to these creatures. Does this captivating behavior shed light on human origins? What does great ape behavior tell us about sophisticated human capabilities?

In attempts to understand the origin of advanced cognitive behavior and symbolic thought, scientists often compare hominid activities to human behavior. The tendency, then, is to regard the hominid behavior as progressing inexorably toward that of humans. Humans make tools; so hominid tool use must represent a transitional state. Humans bury their dead; so Neanderthal burials must be a prelude to the ritualistic burials we perform. Humans hunt; so habiline and erectine scavenging practices and Neanderthal hunting practices must presage the sophisticated hunter-gatherer activities of humanity.

But full understanding of hominid behavior requires that scientists also compare their activities to great ape (primates such as orangutans, gorillas, and chimpanzees) behavior because, from an evolutionary perspective, humans share a common ancestor with great apes. Over the last decade, primatologists have logged remarkable observations of wild and captive primates, thereby providing an unprecedented opportunity to make appropriate comparisons. These recent observations reveal that the great apes are more amazing than anyone imagined, as the following chimpanzee studies illustrate.

Chimps Use Caves for Shelter
In 2007, a team of anthropologists from Iowa State University discovered that chimpanzees seek shelter in caves.[1] Jill Pruetz and her group collected chimp feces and hair samples from caves in Senegal and uncovered evidence of

feeding in these locales. Occasionally, the researchers observed chimps entering and leaving caves. Correlating temperature measurements and cave usage suggests chimps dwell in caves temporarily to avoid extreme heat.

Chimps Carefully Construct Beds

Field observations indicate chimps expend much time and energy selecting a sleeping spot and constructing their treetop beds. These apes bunk as far from the main trunk as possible—with an escape route to neighboring trees. They also carefully select branches made of the stiffest possible material with the greatest bending strength.

It is well known that great apes construct sleeping platforms daily. Researchers have observed these creatures choosing certain tree species as a place to build their beds. Until a 2014 study, there was no clear indication why one tree species was chosen over others.[2] At the Toro-Semliki Wildlife Reserve in Uganda, primatologists observed that chimps preferred to bed down in the Ugandan ironwood. This tree makes up only about 10 percent of the trees in the sample area, yet almost 75 percent of nests are made in these trees. To solve the mystery, primatologists studied the mechanical properties of 325 branches taken from the seven most commonly used nesting trees.

They learned that, of the trees available to chimps in this area, ironwood branches are the stiffest, have the greatest bending strength, and have the smallest leaf surface area. This allows chimps to construct concave beds using a basket weave technique that produces the greatest number of interlocking points to prevent falls, as well as provide comfort and insulation and perhaps even ward off pests. The team concluded that chimpanzees seem to understand mechanical and other properties of the nesting branches and employ a sophisticated technique to weave stable, durable nest structures.

Chimps Hunt with Spears

Another study by Pruetz's team reported, in 2007, that chimpanzees hunt bush babies (small nocturnal primates) using wooden spears deliberately manufactured from tree branches.[3] The spear-production process involves several steps:

1. Selecting an appropriate branch
2. Stripping away smaller side branches and leaves
3. Removing bark from the branch
4. Using incisors to sharpen the ends to a point

Wild chimps were observed jabbing spears into tree openings, where the arboreal bush babies sleep in the daytime, to kill their prey. This behavior was observed for males, females, and juveniles and marks the first time an animal has been seen using a tool to hunt a vertebrate.

Chimps Make Stone Tools

Another 2007 study documented the range of chimp tool usage observed in the Republic of Congo from 1999 to 2006.[4] Chimps from this location typically use tools to puncture, pound, and extract ants and termites from their nests and they usually manufacture tools from materials in their immediate vicinity. Those materials include leaves, twigs, sticks, and branches. Manufacturing processes include anywhere from one to four steps that include removing extraneous parts from the raw material and shaping and cutting it with their hands and mouths. This research demonstrated that chimpanzee tool usage is much more diverse than primatologists previously conceived.

Not only that, but chimpanzees also manufacture *stone* tools to crack open nuts. In 2007, a team of paleontologists uncovered chimp-produced stone tools that date to 4,300 years old.[5] Analysis of the tools seemed to indicate that chimps transported stones some distance for later use and sought out raw materials with optimal properties.

Comparing hominid and chimpanzee toolkits

These recently recognized chimp behaviors are reminiscent of activities attributed to hominids such as *Homo habilis* and *Homo erectus*. Many believe *H. habilis* was the first hominid to use "tools." As discussed in chapter 2, paleoanthropologists refer to *H. habilis* "technology" as Mode I (or Oldowan) technology. Mode I tools appeared around 2.5 million years ago and consisted of rock flakes chipped away from a stone core using a hammer stone. Mode I technology persisted for at least 1 million years in the archeological record with no perceptible change.

H. erectus used Mode II (or Acheulean) "technology." Though more sophisticated than Mode I, Mode II technology, which appeared around 1.5 million years ago, was still quite crude. Mode II involved shaping stones (bifaces) into a variety of forms: (1) tear-drop shapes (hand axes); (2) flat, sharp edges (cleavers); and (3) triangular shapes (picks). Once this technology appeared in the archeological record it remained static for nearly 1 million years. Anthropologists believe the bifaces were used to butcher animal remains; however, much debate centers on whether *H. erectus* was a hunter or scavenger.

It appears that chimps behave in ways similar to the first *Homo* species. Paleoanthropologist Julio Mercader and his coauthors described the commonalities:

> The full implications of this line of work require a reevaluation of the terms under which we can make meaningful comparisons of Oldowan and Chimpanzee cultures. The behavioral variables documented at Noulo [archeological site in Côte d'Ivoire] indicate that chimpanzees and hominins share cultural attributes, including the transport of stones across the landscape for a projected use elsewhere; the optimal combination of raw material, size, and weight criteria to perform a predicted activity; the re-occupation of focal points (the accumulation and concentration of both stone and botanical debris is artificially created by behavior); creation of activity areas; the use of locally available resources; and the curation and selection of specific types of stones that are most optimal for specific technological activities.[6]

Implications of implements

Most people consider tool use a quality unique to humans. So, hominid tool use is often taken as evidence that these creatures were gradually acquiring human characteristics as they evolved from an apelike creature. It is assumed the ancestral species had limited, if any, tool-making capabilities. However, the newly recognized chimpanzee behavior—which supposedly descended from the same ancestral creature as humans and hominids—suggests that this interpretation of the archeological record might be incorrect. It does not appear that the behavior of *H. habilis* and *H. erectus* departed much from the creatures preceding them in the fossil record. Their tool-making "skills" might represent not much more than microevolutionary advances.

Chimpanzees shelter in caves, construct their beds carefully, hunt with spears, and make tools from a variety of materials, including stones. Still, these primates are unquestionably and profoundly inferior to humans in terms of cognitive abilities, capacity for rational and symbolic thought, language use, and musical and artistic expression. The growing consensus among primatologists is that human behavior differs from great ape behavior in *kind*, not just *degree*. Primate behaviorist Thomas Suddendorf summarizes the recent comparisons of human and great ape behavior:

We reflect on and argue about our present situation, our history, and our destiny. We envision wonderful, harmonious worlds as easily as we do dreadful tyrannies. Our powers are used for good as they are for bad, and we incessantly debate which is which. Our minds have spawned civilizations and technologies that have changed the face of the Earth, while our closest living animal relatives sit unobtrusively in their remaining forests. There appears to be a tremendous gap between human and animal minds.[7]

Although the habilines and erectines made and used tools and engaged in hunting and scavenging activity, it does not necessarily follow that they were "becoming human." It could simply be that they engaged in animal-like, albeit impressive, behavior similar to chimp activities today.

Chimpanzee Response to Death
If any area of life seems unmistakably human, it is our response to death. And yet, one of the most fascinating chimpanzee discoveries in recent years concerns *their* response to death. Primatologists have learned that wild and captive chimpanzees respond to death in ways similar to humans.

Researchers studying a small community of chimpanzees in the forests near Bossou in the Republic of Guinea observed two instances over the course of five years in which chimpanzee infants died from a respiratory infection.[8] In both cases, the mothers carried their infants' lifeless bodies for days (19 days and 68 days, respectively) after death. The mothers exhibited extensive care of the dead infants—grooming them, sharing day and night nests with them, etc. Clearly, a close connection exists between mother and infant chimpanzees.

Another dramatic and poignant case involved the response of a chimpanzee community in captivity to the death of an elderly female called Pansy.[9] When it became apparent that Pansy was on the verge of death, the zookeepers decided to video record the death process and the reaction of the community to her passing. Just prior to Pansy's death, members of the community provided pre-death care that went beyond the routine grooming they normally extended to each other. When Pansy died, her daughter stayed by her body in an all-night vigil. A male chimp became aggressive, at one point striking Pansy's body, either out of frustration or in a futile attempt to revive her. Other members carefully examined her body to make sure she was dead.

After zookeepers removed the corpse, community members avoided the place of death, presumably out of fear. The surviving chimpanzees remained subdued for several weeks—grooming at a lower than normal frequency and not eating as much food as usual.

Based on these two studies, the scientific community has underestimated chimpanzee awareness of death. More similarities appear between chimp and human responses to death than previously imagined. Evolutionists view the similarity as evidence that the human-chimp common ancestor possessed such capacities. As the two lineages separated, humans gradually attached ritualistic practices and religious beliefs to the death experience.

At least on the surface this insight appears to support the evolutionary framework. However, the results of these studies readily fit within the scope of the Reasons to Believe (RTB) creation model. It is easy to anthropomorphize creatures like chimpanzees, gorillas, and Old World monkeys—attributing to them human qualities they do not genuinely possess. Even though chimps react to death in ways that superficially resemble the human response, it does not necessarily mean that they have the same kind or degree of awareness of death that humans do. For example, the chimpanzee's response to death did not involve ritualistic or religious behavior.

Still, it is evident that chimpanzees grieve the loss of community members and have some fear of dying. This sense of loss and fear need not be understood in evolutionary terms. It could be viewed from a biblical vantage point. As Hugh Ross discusses in *Hidden Treasures in the Book of Job*, birds and mammals are "soulish" creatures created with the capacity for emotion.[10] All such creatures grieve the death of a companion with whom they have formed a strong emotional bond.

Unlike humans, great apes do not possess the image of God (Genesis 1:26–27), but they do possess emotional and intellectual capacities. We would argue that God endowed some animals with soulishness as a way to form bonds with each other and with human beings so that humans could use these creatures to establish civilizations and provide fulfillment. In this context, the chimpanzee response to death reflects their soulishness, not a deep evolutionary connection to human beings.

Chimpanzee awareness of death and Neanderthal burials

The chimp response to death provides a context for understanding the Neanderthal response to death gleaned from archeology. According to anthropologists, human funerals and burials (mortuary rituals) reflect symbolic thought, ritual behavior, and a desire to protect and preserve human remains. Archeology shows the earliest humans had some sense of an afterlife.

However, some believe such symbolic activity is not unique to humans.

They maintain that Neanderthals also possessed this capability and cite the recovery of Neanderthal remains in what appear to be gravesites to support this view. New insights about chimpanzee awareness of death help shed light on Neanderthal behavior. It could be argued that Neanderthals' nonritualistic burial practices likely resembled apes observed behavior rather than human behavior.

Behavior is one thing, but what about genes? Do they buttress or erode the case for common ancestry? The next chapter applies ten years of wider, more overt testing to this question.

Trying on the Genes

Popular-level science sources are fond of trotting out the 99 percent genetic similarity between humans and chimps as evidence of a shared evolutionary history. But what exactly does this claim mean? As geneticists learn more and more about genomes, has the 99 percent similarity remained a significant means of comparing humans and chimps?

Chimp Genome Sequenced

One of the most significant advances in genetics over the past decade has been the sequencing of chimpanzee, bonobo, gorilla, and orangutan genomes. In late 2005, the Chimpanzee Sequencing and Analysis Consortium published a rough-draft sequence of the chimp genome and performed an extensive comparison with the human genome.[1] About 98 percent of the chimp genome was considered of high quality and proved to be consistent with results of earlier studies (see chapter 13). Substitutions produced only a 1.23 percent difference between the chimp and human genomes, which amounted to about 35 million base pairs. But when the consortium included indels (insertions and deletions of bases) in the comparison, they uncovered another 1.5 percent difference, corresponding to 5 million additional changes. So rather than 99 percent, the actual genetic similarity is about 97 percent.

Gorilla and Bonobo Genomes Sequenced

In 2012, two independent research teams sequenced the genomes of the bonobo and gorilla. The bonobo group found a 98.7 percent genetic similarity with humans and a 99.6 percent similarity with chimpanzees.[2] The gorilla team found that the human genome shares greater similarity with about 30 percent of the gorilla genome than it does with corresponding regions in the chimp genome.[3] Within the genomes' protein-coding region alone, the team found that

22 percent of gorilla DNA sequences aligned much more closely to the human genome than did the chimpanzee sequences.

This result is unanticipated because gorillas and humans are believed to have parted evolutionary ways 8 to 9 million years ago, whereas the humans and chimps supposedly diverged 5 to 6 million years ago. Evolutionary biologists consider chimpanzees more closely related than gorillas to humans. Yet depending on the genome region sampled, evolutionary trees built from human, chimp, and gorilla genomes display incongruence.

Evolutionary biologists try to account for these incongruous results by appealing to the effects of incomplete lineage sorting and gene flow between populations. But these explanations raise questions. For example, current evolutionary theory claims significant time elapsed between the gorilla divergence and the chimp divergence from humanity's evolution. It would seem, then, that the primate gene pool became homogenized within the ancestral population, thus wiping out the effects of incomplete lineage sorting and gene flow between populations. If incomplete lineage sorting and gene flow can't adequately account for the incongruent evolutionary trees, then this result would stand as a failed prediction of evolutionary theory.

Gene Similarities and the Reasons to Believe Model
Though many people take the high degree of human-ape genetic similarity as evidence for shared evolutionary history, it is not problematic for Reasons to Believe's (RTB) human origins model. As discussed in chapter 13, our model *predicts* such similarities. We view them as reflecting shared *designs*, rather than shared descent (see chapter 27).

Explaining Genetic Differences
As discussed in chapter 13, the hoopla surrounding human-chimp genetic similarities is largely irrelevant. Many biologists do not think that a simple comparison of DNA sequences is especially meaningful. Ten years ago, the emerging consensus regarded gene regulation (or gene expression) as the basis for the biological differences and cognitive gap between humans and chimps.

Meaningful genetic differences do exist between humans and chimpanzees, but have little to do with the set of genes found in the genomes or the close correspondence of the DNA sequences. Instead, the most biologically meaningful comparisons focus on *how the genes are used*—in other words, the patterns of gene expression. In the first edition of *Who Was Adam?*, we described a number of studies indicating that the most profound instances of gene expression differences were found in human and chimpanzee brain tissues. In the decade since then, researchers have continued to affirm gene expression differences.[4]

What is alternate splicing?
There are other types of meaningful genetic differences. In 2007, University of Toronto (UToronto) medical researchers compared human and chimp alternate splicing patterns for the first time ever.[5] In cells, protein production begins when the cell's machinery makes a copy of the appropriate genetic information by assembling messenger RNA (mRNA). Once assembled, mRNA migrates from the nucleus into the cytoplasm and, upon reaching the ribosome, directs protein synthesis.

In humans and chimps, mRNA undergoes extensive modification before heading to the ribosome. These final modifications involve so-called splicing reactions. In eukaryotes (all organisms except bacteria and archaea), a gene consists of sequences that code for part of the protein (exons) interrupted by sequences that don't code for anything (introns). After the gene is copied, the intron sequences are excised from the mRNA and the exons spliced together. An RNA-protein complex called a spliceosome mediates this process.

The spliceosome can splice a single mRNA several ways to produce a range of functional proteins. This is known as alternate splicing. Variation is possible because the spliceosome does not necessarily use all the splice sites. Structuring genes to contain introns interspersed between exons serves as an elegant strategy that allows a single gene to simultaneously house the information to produce a range of proteins.

How alternate splicing patterns account for differences
The UToronto team discovered high similarity among a significant proportion of alternate splicing reactions in humans, chimps, and mice. From an evolutionary perspective, this means splicing reactions have not evolved over a span of 80–90 million years. This makes sense because splicing is a precise process. Some splicing mistakes result in human diseases. Medical disorders such as atherosclerosis (plaque buildup in arteries), cardiomyopathy (abnormal heart muscle), and myotonic dystrophy (multisystemic inherited disease) result because splicing errors fatally distort or destroy the information, temporarily stored in mRNA, needed to assemble protein chains at ribosomes. And improperly produced proteins cannot carry out their functional role in the cell.

In spite of alternate splicing patterns' apparent resistance to evolution, the UToronto researchers also noted that six to eight percent of the genes examined in their study displayed differences between human and chimp alternate splicing patterns. Furthermore, it appears that these differences evolved rapidly. Alternate splicing differences were observed for both brain and heart tissues and involve genes that take part in diverse functions. These results suggest that such differences may account for some of the biological and behavioral differences between humans and chimps.

Some researchers have approached such gene expression studies with caution. The chief point of concern is that the comparisons have relied primarily on preserved tissues taken post mortem. These samples do not reflect the behavior of *live* tissues and cells nor do they provide access to differences in gene expression that likely take place during the course of embryonic development.

It's All about Gene Expression

To remedy this problem, scientists from the Salk Institute for Biological Studies and the University of California, San Diego (UCSD), prepared induced pluripotent stem cells (iPSCs) from chimpanzee and bonobo fibroblasts (a type of skin cell) and compared their gene expression activity with human iPSCs.[6] It has been found that iPSCs behave just like embryonic stem cells in that they can be coaxed to form a wide range of different adult cell types. These cells allow researchers a window into the gene expression differences from the earliest stages of embryological development and provide them with a gene expression profile for each of the different cell types in the human body.

The Salk and UCSD investigators discovered no significant differences among humans, chimps, and bonobos for about 11,500 protein-coding genes. They also found 1,375 genes in human iPSCs with increased levels of expression and 1,050 different genes in chimpanzee and bonobo iPSCs with increased activity. In human iPSCs, two of the genes with the greatest expression increase play a role in suppressing the movement of LINE-1 (L1) retrotransposons. Chimp and bonobo genomes, being without such means of suppression, possessed more copies of L1 sequence elements.

L1 DNA plays a role in X-chromosome inactivation and influences monoallelic (single allele) gene expression. L1 DNA can also lead to the inactivation of genes and even disrupt genome integrity as it is copied and moved around. It is reasonable to think that these mobile pieces of DNA can account for some of the biological differences among humans and great apes.

A decade of wider, more overt testing has shown that genomic sequencing of the great apes affirms a high degree of genetic similarity between humans and the great apes—but it also adds to the growing recognition that gene expression is the key to understanding humanity's biological and behavioral uniqueness. Despite the oft-touted genetic similarity, humans manifest significant genetic differences in the form of gene expression, in a way that accords with the RTB human origins model.

Another meaningful genomic comparison lies in analysis of an evolutionary favorite: the junk DNA argument. Has it been strengthened or weakened by scientific advance?

Chapter 25

Is It Time to Scrap Junk DNA?

The ability to make predictions about what is *yet to be discovered* is the true test of a model's viability. Some skeptics accuse the Reasons to Believe (RTB) model of making predictions after the fact to fit what scientists have already discovered. They are not impressed that most of our predictions (which logically follow based on the model's tenets) can be evaluated based on past discoveries. So the question persists, does the RTB model make predictions about *future* discoveries? Yes, it does.

Junk DNA Prediction

When the human genome was first sequenced and analyzed in the early 2000s, researchers found that it harbored only about 20,000 genes. The common narrative held that around 99 percent of human nuclear DNA is functionless, merely a leftover vestige of our evolutionary history. Yet several years before the 2005 publication of *Who Was Adam?*, we predicted that so-called junk DNA (genetic sequences that do not code for proteins) would turn out to have function. We incorporated this prediction into our human origins model.

In chapter 14, we highlight the work of several research groups who identified function for individual noncoding DNA sequences, including duplicated and processed pseudogenes (such as *Makorin-1-p1* and *PGAM3*, respectively), specific LINE, SINE, and LTR segments, and particular endogenous retroviruses. We took these initial findings as an indication that junk DNA was not functionless after all. We proposed that the shared junk DNA found in humans and great apes constitutes useful genomic features fashioned by the Creator.

Still, in 2005, it was impossible to conclude with certainty that most, if not all, junk DNA was functional and our proposal did not address the existence of junk DNA classes without any known function, such as unitary pseudogenes. The widespread presence of these DNA elements counted against our hypothesis that junk DNA had utility and, thus, represented God's handiwork. At the time, we acknowledged our model's deficiency, but nevertheless we predicted that geneticists would eventually discover function in these elements, as had been the case for other types of junk DNA. This counts as a prediction about future scientific discoveries.

Evolutionists readily agreed that *some* junk DNA sequences possess function, but they did not think such an admission undermined the case for common descent. They remained confident that the vast majority of junk DNA still lacked function. They proposed a small number of junk DNA segments could acquire function via a process called neofunctionalization. Through neofunctionalization, evolutionary mechanisms would occasionally co-opt junk DNA as raw material with which to evolve new functions within genomes. Through this process, biological innovation occurs.

However, the evolutionary assumptions about junk DNA have not held up. Over the last decade the case for the universal functionality of junk DNA has become compelling and challenges the neofunctionalization explanation. It is beyond the scope of this book to list the numerous studies that ascribe function to junk DNA, but a handful of important examples should demonstrate junk DNA's functionality.

Enter the ENCODE Project

Shortly after the final draft of the human genome was completed, the National Institutes of Health (NIH) launched the ENCyclopedia Of DNA Elements (EN-CODE) Project—a multimillion-dollar international effort to catalogue all of the human genome's functional sequences. Initial results of the ENCODE Project were reported in 2007.[1] This early stage involved a detailed search for every functional element contained in a 1 percent sample of the human genome. The cursory glimpse indicated that a significant proportion of junk DNA sequences play key roles in regulating gene expression.

The success of ENCODE's pilot phase justified the second stage of the project. This phase cost nearly $130 million, involved some 450 researchers from around the world, and required over 1,650 experiments. They examined the gene expression in nearly 150 different types of human cells. Project investigators carefully and specifically chose tests to detect biochemical activity (transcription, binding of transcription factors, histone binding, sites where modified histones bind, methylation, and three-dimensional interactions between enhancers and genes) with well-established function related to gene regulation and gene expression.

Based on its second phase, the ENCODE Project Consortium reported that a staggering 80 percent of the human genome consists of functional elements.[2] And with the third phase of the project now underway, that number could increase.

Alu Sequences

Unique to primates, *Alu* sequences are a subclass of SINE (short interspersed elements; see chapter 14). The human genome contains over 1 million *Alu* elements, making up about 11 percent of the genetic material. Humans and chimps share large numbers of *Alu* sequences in common. Identical (or nearly identical) sequences occur in corresponding locations in both genomes.

In the last few years, molecular biologists have determined that many *Alu* sequences influence gene expression.[3] *Alu* sequences serve as the site for transcription factor binding and promote the degradation of mRNA molecules.[4] (Transcription factors are proteins that bind to specific DNA sequences and then control the rate of transcription—thus influencing gene expression.) Researchers have also discovered that *Alu* sequences play a role in nucleosome placement (see "Chromosomes" on page 208) by helping establish and maintain chromosomes' higher order structure.[5]

Alu sequences and gene expression

In the classification of DNA sequences, transposons (or transposable elements) are pieces of DNA that can move around the genome. *Alu* sequences, like all SINE DNA elements, belong to a subgroup of transposons known as retrotransposons, which can make copies of themselves. When they do, the copies take up residence in new locations in the genome.

In 2013, scientists from Canada published an early attempt to quantify the extent to which transposable elements impact gene regulation.[6] Using ENCODE Project data, the team determined that of the genomic regions accessible to the cell's machinery for gene expression, 44 percent are transposable elements (which amounts to about 730,000 sequence elements). And of this 44 percent, transcription factor binding sites represent a large proportion. It is believed that the binding of these special proteins to accessible regions initiates gene expression. In other words, transposable elements seem to play a comprehensive role in regulating human gene expression.

When only a few examples of transposon function had been reported, neofunctionalization seemed a reasonable explanation for capabilities such as transcription factor binding and toggling gene expression. However, the

344 Who Was Adam? / Part III

Canada team uncovered pervasive transposon function that makes it difficult to argue that this feature resulted from neofunctionalization. It makes better sense to think of it as God's intentional design.

Functional Pseudogenes

Pervasiveness of function is not limited to transposons. For decades, evolutionary biologists assumed pseudogenes lack function based solely on the fact that pseudogenes appear to be the remains of once-functional genes. Ten years ago the few known examples of processed pseudogenes that coded for functional proteins were attributed to neofunctionalization, but now research teams have recognized large-scale function for pseudogenes.

In 2014, researchers from Sweden reported the development and application of a new method for identifying and determining which genes encode for proteins.[7] They discovered a number of previously unidentified genes in human and mouse genomes. About 35 percent of the newly identified genes are pseudogenes that the cell's machinery uses to produce proteins—a completely unexpected result. As one of the researchers noted, "Our study challenges the old theory that pseudogenes don't code for proteins."[8]

The extent to which pseudogenes encode for useful protein products remains unknown at this point. Still, this study opens up the possibility that a significant fraction (a third or more) is translated. If so, it is difficult to attribute the wide-scale function to neofunctionalization.

Duplicated Pseudogenes and Gene Regulation

To fully appreciate the roles junk DNA plays in gene expression and regulation, some background information is necessary. Gene expression refers to the process employed by the cell's machinery to read the information harbored in DNA and use it to make proteins. Some genes are expressed throughout the cell cycle. These "housekeeping genes" specify the production of proteins required for biochemical activities that operate continually inside the cell. Other genes are expressed only when the proteins they specify are needed. When not required, these genes are "turned off."

However, gene expression involves more than simply turning genes on and off. It also entails regulating the amount of proteins produced. Some genes are expressed at high levels and others at low levels. Traditionally, scientists believed gene regulation primarily involved controlling the frequency and amount of messenger RNA (mRNA) produced during transcription. They believed mRNA was produced continually for housekeeping genes and produced only when needed for genes that specify situational proteins. Thus, more mRNA was produced for highly expressed genes but less for genes expressed at low levels.

However, *preventing* protein production can be as important as promoting it. Recent discoveries indicate that an elaborate mechanism that dictates the amount of proteins produced involves the selective degradation of mRNA transcripts before they make it to the ribosome for protein production. Selective degradation of mRNA functions in a complementary manner to the transcriptional control of gene expression.

In 2005, researchers gained the first indication of duplicated pseudogenes' involvement in gene regulation. As discussed in chapter 14, researchers learned that both the *Makorin-1* gene and *Makorin-1-p1* pseudogene have to be present in the genome in order to produce the protein encoded by *Makorin-1*. The pseudogene's mRNA prevents the breakdown of the *Makorin-1* mRNA, thus allowing it to be translated at the ribosome.

Five years later another research team reported a similar result for the *PTEN* and *PTENP1* gene-pseudogene pair. *PTEN* codes for a protein that suppresses tumors. When *PTEN* is functionally impaired it leads to the onset of several different types of cancer. The researchers learned that cancer also results if mutations occur in *PTEN*'s corresponding pseudogene, *PTENP1*. This finding means *PTENP1* must be functional.[9]

What is *PTENP1* doing? To answer that question, it is important to know that cells harbor various distinct microRNA (miRNA) species, a type of molecule that flags mRNA for destruction by binding to an mRNA molecule at specific sites in an area called the 3' untranslated region. (These binding locations are called miRNA response elements.) Researchers discovered that miRNA can down-regulate *PTEN* expression. The tiny molecules bind to mRNA produced from *PTEN* and then direct the breakdown of the mRNA to prevent the PTEN protein from carrying out its cellular role. Left unchecked, the miRNA molecules would direct the breakdown of most of the *PTEN* mRNA, thus suppressing the activity of *PTEN* gene products and leading to the onset of cancer.

However, the similarity between *PTEN* and *PTENP1* allows *PTENP1* mRNA to act as a decoy, binding to miRNA molecules, which then breakdown *PTENP1*'s mRNA, instead of *PTEN*'s. From a design perspective, this explains why pseudogenes and their corresponding "intact" genes share close structural similarity. Gene-pseudogene pairs make regulation of gene expression possible.

As part of the same study, scientists uncovered similar relationships for a number of gene-pseudogene pairs, including *KRAS* and *KRASP1*, which are also implicated in the onset of certain cancers. They suggested that such decoy mechanisms were widespread. Research published a year later bore out their expectation. This work showed that functional pseudogenes are *not* a rarity. Molecular biologists from China demonstrated that a large number of functional pseudogenes exist in the genome of *Trypanosoma brucei*, a parasitic protist that causes sleeping sickness in humans.[10] This organism's genome consists of about 9,000 genes and 900 pseudogenes. It seems nearly all of the pseudogenes pair to an intact gene and regulate its expression.

Such patterns indicate that the occurrence of functional pseudogenes is widespread among all eukaryotic organisms because, from an evolutionary standpoint, protists anchor the evolutionary tree that led to plants, fungi, and animals. Therefore, if functional pseudogenes are present in protists, they must be present in all eukaryotic organisms.

Bottom line

A widespread occurrence of functional pseudogenes and the likely universal distribution of functional pseudogene decoys among eukaryotic organisms undermine the case for biological evolution. It is one thing to say that pseudogenes *occasionally* acquired function via undirected natural processes, but it is quite another to say that this happened over and over again, until virtually every pseudogene in the genome possessed function. Pseudogenes, therefore, can legitimately be viewed as the work of the Creator who intentionally introduced these features into genomes for a specific purpose.

Network Decoys at Work

Insights into duplicated pseudogenes' capability of regulating gene expression via a decoy mechanism prompted Pier Pandolfi and collaborators from Harvard University to propose the competitive endogenous RNA (ceRNA) hypothesis in 2011.[11] Pandolfi and his team noted that duplicated pseudogenes and their intact counterparts are not the only genetic material that shares miRNA response elements. A number of other genes share the same set of miRNA response elements and, consequently, will bind to the same set of miRNAs. These genes, in effect, are part of a network that, when transcribed, will influence the expression of all the network members. This relationship means that *all* the mRNA transcripts in the network can function as decoys, binding miRNAs and allowing the other member genes of the network to be expressed.

One important consequence of this hypothesis is that mRNA has dual functions inside the cell: (1) it encodes information needed to make proteins;

and (2) it plays a role in regulating the expression of other transcripts in its network. This insight and the ceRNA hypothesis help the RTB model make sense of the unitary pseudogenes in the human genome.

Regulatory Role for Unitary Pseudogenes

One troubling feature of the initial RTB human origins model was that no function could be legitimately ascribed to *unitary* pseudogenes. In the absence of any clearly defined function, common ancestry was the only reasonable way to interpret the presence of the identical (or nearly identical) unitary pseudogenes in corresponding locations in human and great apes genomes.

In 2012, research from Oxford University eased RTB scholars' concerns when it was demonstrated that unitary pseudogenes can influence gene regulation in a manner related to the decoy mechanism central to duplicated pseudogene function.

The ceRNA hypothesis describes unitary pseudogene function. The Oxford researchers supplied one of the first tests of the ceRNA hypothesis by examining unitary pseudogenes' potential regulatory roles in rodents.[12] Rodent unitary pseudogenes have counterparts in the human genome, except the human versions are intact genes. The team studied 48 unitary pseudogenes, demonstrating that 65 percent of them are transcribed even though they do not produce functional proteins. In fact, the tissue profiles for the expression of these transcripts in rodents are comparable to those found in the corresponding human tissues.

The Oxford team determined that unitary pseudogenes can take part in distinct regulatory networks of genes defined by shared miRNA response elements. They also learned that the gene expressions in the networks correlate with each other, meaning that the transcripts in the networks all function as molecular decoys for one another and that unitary pseudogenes are vital components of the networks. When a unitary pseudogene is not transcribed, it causes the expression of other genes in the network to be down regulated, leading to decreased protein production. When a unitary pseudogene is transcribed, the other genes in the network are up regulated and protein production increases.

Junk No More

It is remarkable that in the last decade biochemists and molecular biologists have come to recognize that all three classes of pseudogenes are functional. Processed pseudogenes code for functional proteins. Unitary and duplicated pseudogenes carry out a function in gene regulatory networks along with intact genes by serving as molecular decoys, binding miRNAs and permitting the translation of intact genes.

This important new insight means that shared pseudogenes in the genomes of humans and the great apes do not demand an evolutionary interpretation (shared ancestry). Instead, from a creation standpoint, one could maintain that the unitary and duplicated pseudogenes shared among the genomes of humans and the great apes reflect common design.

Scientific advance has radically altered our view of the human genome. No longer can scientists consider it an evolutionary junkyard. It is an elegant system that displays sophistication in its architecture and operation far beyond what most evolutionary biologists ever imagined. In a press release, NIH's National Human Genome Institute director Eric Green stated, "During the early debates about the Human Genome Project, researchers had predicted that only a few percent of the human genome sequence encoded proteins, the workhorses of the cell, and the rest was junk. We now know that this conclusion was wrong."[13] Wider testing has led to the right conclusion.

Is it time to scrap junk DNA arguments? A decade of scientific advances has vindicated RTB's model by identifying function. Still, evolutionary biologists will point out that our model has not really addressed the big obstacle. Outside of the miRNA binding region, the pseudogenes share identical mutations in a manner consistent with common descent. We take up this challenge in chapter 27, where we present the RTB genomics model. But before that, we respond to several other criticisms of the RTB model.

Chapter 26

Criticisms of RTB's Human Origins Model

Since 2005, the Reasons to Believe (RTB) human origins model has received a fair share of criticism. Here we respond to the most salient critiques and, in the next chapter, address frequently asked questions. While it is not possible to respond to all the critiques, we have attempted to respond to those that have the biggest impact on the validity of our model.

1. Humanity Arose from a Population, Not a Primordial Pair

In chapter 4, we argue that "mitochondrial Eve" was the biblical Eve and "Y-chromosomal Adam" was the biblical Adam. This conclusion has been the focal point of significant criticism. Most in the scientific community argue that humanity arose from a population of *several thousand*, not *two* individuals. They reject the notion that humanity came from an Adam and Eve. Instead they argue that many Eves and Adams existed—mitochondrial Eve and Y-chromosomal Adam were the lucky ones whose lineages just happened to survive while their contemporaries' mitochondrial and Y-chromosomal lines were lost over time.

When other genetic markers are used to characterize humanity's origin, they, too, trace back to a single ancestral sequence that can be interpreted as corresponding to a single individual. Evolutionary biologists argue, however, that these Eves and Adams were not the same individuals as mitochondrial Eve and Y-chromosomal Adam. They rationalize this claim based on the nature of the mechanism driving evolutionary change and, more substantially, on estimates of the human ancestral population sizes based on genetic diversity.[1] Yet, despite the scientific community's near-consensus on this issue, we maintain that our interpretation—that humanity originated from a primordial pair—has scientific legitimacy.

Assumptions

As discussed in chapter 9, most members of the scientific community assume that biological evolution is a fact. That is, it is a *given* that the evolutionary paradigm provides sufficient explanation for life's origin, history, and diversity. Most biologists *begin* their study of human origins with the assumption that humanity evolved from a preexisting lineage of hominids. And if humans evolved, then, by definition, our origin must have started with a population, not two individuals because, according to the tenets of neo-Darwinism, evolutionary transformations are a population-level, not individual-level, phenomenon.

As a result of this presupposition, when studies in molecular anthropology trace the origin of all humanity back to single ancestral sequences for mitochondrial DNA (mtDNA) and Y-chromosomal DNA, it is assumed that mitochondrial Eve and Y-chromosomal Adam must have been members of a population, not two individuals. One could argue that, to some degree, evolutionary biologists' insistence that humanity emanated from a population results in a theory-laden conclusion.

Modeling studies

For many scientists, the genetic diversity observed among human population groups powerfully supports the argument that humanity began as a population. Mathematical models make it possible to estimate the effective population size of any ancestral group from the genetic diversity of present-day populations, if the mutation rate is known. All of these studies indicate that humans stemmed from a small population on the order of a few hundred to a few thousand.[2] (See chapter 4.)

Skeptics also point to other methods for modeling the ancestral population size that depend on processes, other than mutations, to generate genetic diversity, such as linkage disequilibrium.[3] Studies employing these techniques also seem to indicate that humanity arose from populations of a few thousand individuals. Given the seriousness of this challenge to our model, we are unwilling to accept the results of the population-size measurements uncritically. Instead, we raise legitimate questions about the results of these modeling studies.

For example, we contend that the population sizes generated by these methods are merely estimates, not hard and fast values. We hold this view because, though sophisticated, the mathematical models are highly idealized, generating differing estimates based on a number of factors. Consider two studies discussed in chapter 4. One, reported in 2003 by a Russian and American research team, examined DNA sequence elements called short tandem repeats at 377 locations in the human genome for 1,056 individuals that represented 52 population groups. On the basis of this analysis, the team concluded that humanity originated from a single point of origin (apparently Africa), from a small population (~2,000 or less) between 71,000 and 142,000 years ago.[4] Although this conclusion was in line with that of an earlier study of short tandem repeats, the population-size estimate from the earlier study was about 500 individuals.[5] The reason for the difference (of 500 vs. 2,000) was due, in part, to differing sample sizes and number of locations in the human genome that were studied.

Additionally, we maintain that the methods used to generate these population-size estimates have not been adequately validated. Generally speaking, method validation requires that samples of a known value be analyzed with the method in question. If this analysis produces the expected result, it engenders confidence in the methodology. If not, then the methodology is suspect.

The work that most closely provides validation of population-size estimates comes from conservation biology. Three studies—involving Mouflon sheep, Przewalski's horses, and gray whales—show that when the original population size was known, genetic diversity measured generations later was much greater than expected based on the models.[6] As a case in point, consider the sheep study.

We all, like sheep

In 2007, a research team reported on the genetic diversity of wild Mouflon sheep located on Île Haute, an island of the Kerguelen sub-Antarctic archipelago in the southern Indian Ocean.[7] This sheep population provided researchers with an unprecedented opportunity to study the effects of population dynamics on genetic diversity in small populations.

In 1957, two yearlings, one male and one female, were taken from a captive population in France and introduced to Île Haute. By the early 1970s, the population had grown to 100 individuals and peaked at 700 sheep in 1977. Since that time the population has fluctuated in a cyclical manner between 250 and 700 members. Given that the population began with only two individuals (the founder effect), experienced cyclical changes in size, and was isolated on an island, the researchers expected very low genetic diversity (measured as heterozygosity).

Using mathematical models, the heterozygosity of a population can be computed at any time from the heterozygosity of the ancestral population (which was known for the original Mouflon pair) and the original population size. The researchers discovered that when they measured this quantity directly for the sheep on the island, the diversity exceeded model predictions by up to a factor of 4. It seems the models underestimated the genetic diversity of the actual population. Researchers speculated that selection drives the increase in genetic diversity, which boosts the population's survivability.

Consequently, if these same models were used to estimate the effective sizes of humanity's ancestral population from the measured genetic diversity at any point in time, they would have *overestimated* the original population size to be much larger than two individuals. To be fair, the sheep study does not necessarily invalidate the more sophisticated models used to characterize humanity's initial population size, but it gives some pause for thought.

Recent bird and mammal studies, however, raise questions as to whether the mathematical underpinning of these models is even correct.[8] In fact, the author of one study stated, "Analyses of mitochondrial DNA (mtDNA) have challenged the concept that genetic diversity within populations is governed by effective population size and mutation rate...variation in the rate of mutation rather than in population size is the main explanation for variations in mtDNA diversity observed among bird species."[9] While this conclusion is specific to the genetic diversity of mtDNA, again, it does cause us hesitancy in accepting the initial population-size estimates for humanity.

Sampling regional DNA
In light of these concerns, researchers from the United Kingdom and New Zealand acknowledged the problem associated with using mtDNA data to estimate population sizes.[10] In response, they attempted to show that variations in mtDNA *were* predictive of human population sizes. They hoped that the difficulties associated with population-size estimates in mammals and birds would not apply to modern humans. Toward this end, they developed a sophisticated estimation method using mtDNA sequence data and illustrated the use of the method by analyzing 357 regions of human mtDNA collected from 3,000 individuals. Their sample represented eight geographical regions.

To validate their method, the researchers compared their population-size estimates with those determined from present-era census data. For some regions of the world, their estimates and census estimates agreed—but for other regions, they did not. Given this result and the fact that the researchers used only one calibration point, it is difficult to claim that mtDNA variation provides a rigorous measure of population size. Even so, it might provide a relative measure. When the research group plotted population-size estimates through-out time and across geography, they generated profiles that made sense in light of human migration patterns. Again, this result indicates that mtDNA varia-tion in humans can give reasonable and *relative* estimates of population sizes, but not *absolute* values.

Have the original numbers been overestimated?
So, did humanity originate from a single pair? Based on mathematical model-ing, the scientific community's consensus says no. Even though population-size estimates indicate that humanity emanated from several hundred to several thousand individuals, we maintain that these numbers overestimate the actual original population size. Given the limited method validation and population-size models' performances when applied to conservation biology, we are not willing to abandon our conviction that mitochondrial Eve and Y-chromosomal Adam correspond to the biblical Eve and Adam. Keep in mind that humanity can trace its origin to a single ancestral mtDNA sequence (which, again, we interpret as a single individual).

Finally, it is also important to note that human origination from a small population *is* still consistent with the existence of a historical Adam and Eve who gave rise to all of humanity. The Bible teaches that Adam and Eve pro-duced many sons and daughters (Genesis 5:4). It could be that the population-size estimates are reporting on the population structure of humans sometime *after* Adam and Eve's creation when the population would have been on the order of a few thousand.

2. Humanity Arose from Multiple Locations, Not a Single Place
Scientific data clearly indicates that humanity's origin locates to Africa (or, at least, to populations currently living in Africa). African populations are the most genetically diverse and compose the earliest branches of all human gene trees. Additionally, all of the genetic haplotypes outside of Africa are subsumed by African haplotypes.

When *Who Was Adam?* was first published, all scientific reports indicated an east African origin for humanity. However, more recent studies have mud-dled the precise origin location.[11] Earlier studies had used a limited number of African populations, but the latest work has striven to incorporate the com-plex structure of African subpopulations into the analysis of human genetic variability. Based on these studies, mtDNA gene trees place humanity's origin in the southern and eastern part of Africa, Y-chromosomal DNA variation places it in north central Africa, and studies using nuclear DNA se-quences place it in southwestern Africa.

Evolutionary biologists argue these disparate results indicate that human-ity arose from several populations that coalesced over time into modern hu-mans. It is presumed that mtDNA, Y-chromosomal DNA, and nuclear DNA represent different genetic loci, each with their own history. These results line up with the notion that the various genetic markers trace an origin to many Eves and Adams. A multiple-population, multiple-location origin of humanity presents an obvious problem for our biblical model.

As explained in chapter 4, when anthropologists use genetic data to locate humanity's origin (and spread), they assume that the contemporary location of population groups represents their location throughout human history. This assumption remains open to question, particularly because numerous groups have migrated as many as thousands of miles throughout their history. Con-sequently, the results from molecular anthropology provide a crude (at best) guess as to the location of humanity's origin.

Other methodological concerns abound. Recent studies attempting to ac-count for the substructure of African populations were conducted indepen-dently using different African subpopulations, different DNA sequence sizes, different modeling techniques, and so on. The lack of uniformity in this new research could account for the disparate results. Genetic drift also raises prob-lems, particularly for mtDNA and Y-chromosomal genetic markers when pop-ulation sizes are small.

Moreover, scientists must reconcile humanity's passage through a recent genetic bottleneck (interpreted from the limited genetic diversity of humanity around the world) with our origin from distinct populations in widely separat-ed regions of Africa that coalesced before the bottleneck. These ideas cannot be simultaneously correct. The results that point to the fractured origin location do not necessarily mean that humanity arose from multiple populations resid-ing in different locales. It could merely be an artifact of experimental design.

3.   Human Chromosome 2 Shows Solid Evidence for Evolution

In the last decade, considerable scientific attention has focused on human chro-mosome 2. Proponents of the evolutionary paradigm assert that the structure of human chromosome 2 stands as axiomatic evidence that humans evolved from a shared ancestor with chimpanzees and bonobos. On the surface, this claim seems compelling. Is it possible to accommodate the structure of human chromosome 2 within the framework of the RTB model?

As noted in chapter 13, the most noticeable difference between human and chimp chromosomes is the quantity: 46 for humans and 48 for chimpanzees. Evolutionary biologists suggest that within human evolution history, two chromosomes (which correspond to chimp chromosomes 2A and 2B) fused and generated what is now human chromosome 2.

Evidence for fusion comes from the close similarity of the banding patterns for human chromosome 2 and chimp chromosomes 2A and 2B, when the latter two are oriented end-on-end. The presence within human chromosome 2 of two centromeres (one functional, the other inactive) and an internal telomere sequence support the fusion hypothesis.[12] The location of the two centromeres and internal telomere sequences correspond to the expected locations if, indeed, human chromosome 2 arose as a fusion event.[13]

Evolutionary biologists claim the fusion took place in the human lineage sometime after it separated from the evolutionary lineage that led to chimpanzees and bonobos. The high-quality sequence data for both the Neanderthal and Denisovan genomes, which indicates that these two hominids possessed a fused chromosome 2 as well, bolstered this claim. Thus, the apparent fusion of the two chimpanzee chromosomes is taken as evidence for common descent and a shared ancestry for humans and chimps.

Doubts about the cause of fusion
It is clear that chromosome fusion occurred. Yet, there is reason to challenge the evolutionary explanation. When chromosomes break, "sticky ends" result, which readily combine with other chromosomes that have also broken apart. Yet, while it is not unusual for chromosomes to fuse, they will almost never fuse with intact chromosomes because of telomeres. These structures, in addition to providing stability, are designed to *prevent* chromosomes from undergoing fusion with chromosome fragments.

For human chromosome 2 to arise, it would have required either telomere-telomere fusion (a highly unlikely event) or fusion of an intact chromosome at its telomere with a sticky end generated when another chromosome fractured near its telomere. This type of fusion can happen, but it is a rare occurrence. Fusion would also need to occur in one of the gametes (sperm and egg cells), thereby changing the number of chromosomes. When the sperm fertilizes the egg, if the chromosome numbers do not match, fertilization almost always results in either: (1) a nonviable zygote or embryo; (2) a viable offspring that suffers from a diseased state; or (3) a viable offspring that is infertile. Though possible, it is extremely rare for the offspring to be viable and fertile.

Evidence of genetic engineering
The highly unlikely nature of these events could be taken as evidence for the Creator's role in engineering or designing the fusion. The Bible's description of animal and human creation suggests a large degree of genetic similarity (which would include similarity of chromosomes) is to be expected between humans, hominids, and chimpanzees (and the other apes). We propose that the apparent fusion of two chimp chromosomes to produce human chromosome 2 offers a hint as to how the Creator worked. Perhaps God used a preexisting template that He reshaped to create the physical makeup of the hominids and human beings. And perhaps part of the reshaping activity involved fusing together two chromosomes to make human chromosome 2. After all, genetic engineers—who are made in God's image—are capable of altering organisms by manipulating genetic material. Might not the Creator do the same? Could not God be thought of as a divine genetic engineer? If valid, we predict that in the future geneticists will find that the fused chromosome has functional importance.

4. RTB Misrepresents Hominid Brain Sizes
Critics claim that we have incorrectly interpreted changes in hominid brain size throughout the fossil record (see chapter 10) to fit the predictions of our model. Does this misrepresentation-of-data charge stand?

In our earlier work we argued that the data does not show a gradual, continuous increase in hominid brain size with time; rather, it reveals stasis followed by punctuated increases in brain size. We maintained that brain size increases do not occur within a species over time, but only when a new species appears. Our plot (see figure 10.2) shows discontinuous brain size increases over time as new hominid species appear, with the greatest change occurring upon the arrival of modern humans. We pointed out that this pattern matches the prediction our model makes about the expected features of the hominid fossil record.

To illustrate this trend, we plotted the encephalization quotient (EQ) as a function of time for four hominid representatives (all australopithecines, *Homo habilis*, *Homo erectus*, and modern humans). We chose to focus on these hominids for two reasons. In most evolutionary models for human evolution, they represent key transitional forms. Also, we have the best and most abundant estimates of EQ for these hominids. We omitted a number of hominid species from the graph for clarity's sake. A cluttered, uninformative plot would have resulted if we included EQ data for hominids species for which there were only a limited number of brain size measurements. It should also be noted that we modeled our presentation of the brain size data after plots presented in Roger Lewin and Robert Foley's textbook on human evolution.[14] Instead of plotting individual data points, we graphed the average value for the EQ, with the understanding that brain size values will deviate from the average, representing the range of biological variation.

It has been pointed out to us, both publicly and privately, that by not including other hominid brain size values in the figure and by plotting average values and not individual data points, we artificially made it seem like there is a discontinuity in brain size values over time, when in fact there is a gradual increase. While we did not intend to misrepresent the hominid brain size data and the changes in brain size throughout time, the complaint has merit. We should have included EQ data for other hominids such as Neanderthals. (As discussed in chapter 12, Neanderthals have a brain size slightly larger than that of modern humans.) If we had included Neanderthal EQ data, it would not have changed our conclusion: namely, that brain size (or more appropriately EQ) undergoes saltational changes through time.

Having pointed this out, it is true, however, that plots of raw hominid brain size data do show a continuous increase over time.[15] Nevertheless, we think that plotting the raw data as individual points does not yield appropriate insight into the mode and tempo of brain size changes. These types of plots do not take into account body mass and, hence, EQs, which are a better measure of intelligence than the raw cranial capacity. Unfortunately, body mass data is not always available for many hominid remains, and when it is, it is not necessarily reliable. (The reliability of brain size measurements is also questionable for some fossil specimens, as well.) This problem limits the analysis of brain size changes over time and explains why anthropologists plot brain size, instead of EQs, as a function of time. But again, when they do so, it obscures—what we think to be—the real pattern in the data.

We also think it is important to include information about the hominid species in the plots of brain size (or EQ) over time, recognizing that each hominid species is a distinct entity. We also maintain that average values for brain size (or EQ) are preferred compared to the raw data. The hominid fossil record is incomplete and scientists must work with a limited number of brain size values for each hominid species. Given the natural range of biological variability, it can be easy to misconstrue an aberrantly high or low value for cranial capacity at the beginning or end of the hominid's existence in the fossil record as a change in brain size when it is merely due to biological variation. By plotting average brain size values and only including hominids with abundant brain size (EQ) data, the likelihood of interpreting deviant measurements as a trend is avoided.

All this being said, we stand by the rationale that undergirds our graph, but acknowledge it is incomplete. It presents a simplistic view of the natural history of hominid brain size, but one that allows what we believe to be a real trend in the data to be readily pictured.

What has become apparent to us is how easy it is to unintentionally mislead in this arena. It is possible to demonstrate either gradual change or discontinuities over time, depending on how one chooses to present the data. And there are good reasons to choose either approach. In light of this criticism, we urge the reader to proceed with caution, recognizing that we have been criticized for misrepresenting the brain size data, though, again, that was not our intention.

5. Agriculture Emerged Well after Humans Arrived
This critique concerns a discrepancy in the timing of agriculture's emergence. The most prevalent view has wide-scale agricultural practices emerging in the Neolithic Revolution less than 12,000 years ago—well after humanity's origin and global spread.[16] Agriculture first became prominent in the Fertile Crescent about 10,000 years ago.

Here's the tension. RTB's human origins model predicts that some type of farming and animal husbandry existed at (or close to) the time humanity first appeared. Genesis 4:1–4 explains that Adam and Eve's sons, Cain and Abel, "worked the soil" and "kept flocks," respectively. The RTB model also maintains that farming and animal husbandry spread from the Middle East to different locations around the world as a consequence of human migrations.

But if modern humans first appeared 100,000 to 150,000 years ago, then doesn't the origin of agriculture over 80,000 years (under the best of circumstances) *later* contradict the RTB model? Not necessarily. Archeological and genetic evidence traces the origin of *large-scale, specialized* domestication of plants and animals. It is quite possible that the first humans engaged in *small-scale, mixed* farming and animal husbandry well before 12,000 years ago at levels that escape scientific detection. Although the first humans lived as hunter-gatherers, they may have supplemented this lifestyle by harvesting wild plants and taming wild animals on small scales.

Evidence for early agriculture
The latest understanding of agriculture's origin supports our assertion. Studies of Ohalo II, an archeological site in Israel, indicate that humans engaged in proto-farming practices nearly 12,000 years before the Neolithic Revolution. Field evidence suggests that the domestication of plants was a gradual process, occurring over the course of several thousand years. Humans cultivated wild plants for thousands of years before the plants showed the anatomical changes associated with large-scale domestication. Once domesticated plants were developed, they were planted in mixed fields along with wild versions of the crop.[17]

Archeologists have unearthed the remains of six grass huts, a hearth, and graves at Ohalo II. Over 40 radiocarbon measurements date the site to about 23,500 years ago. The site also contains well-preserved plant remains in its water-logged sediments. Archeologists discovered wild grasses, including wheat and barley, among the plant remains. Size analysis indicates that the Ohalo II humans were preferentially harvesting grasses that had larger seeds. Researchers also uncovered starch grains derived from the wild grasses that were associated with stone grinding implements. Some were even charred, indicating that the occupants of the site had ground the seeds to make flour and to bake dough in the hearth.

It is possible that humans developed proto-agricultural practices as far back as 45,000 years ago. Stone grinding implements have been discovered at sites in northern Africa, Europe, and southwest Asia. Because plant remains have not survived at these sites, it is not known whether the implements were used to process wild grass seeds. (These grinding stones could have been used to prepare pigments from ocher, for example.) The discovery at Ohalo II, however, makes it much more likely that grinding implements at other sites were also used to process grass seeds.

Possible flour production
Adding to the finds at the Ohalo II site is a survey of archeological sites in Italy, Russia, and the Czech Republic that uncovers evidence for the processing of plant matter and maybe even evidence for the production of flour about 30,000 years ago.[18] Researchers recovered grindstones and pestles from these sites that were coated with starch grains derived from grasses, cattails, and moonworts (a fern with roots rich in starch). They believe it is reasonable to conclude that the ground-up starch was used as flour and cooked because that is the only way for the starch to provide sufficient calories.

This recent evidence indicates that the first humans did not follow a meat-dominated diet. Instead they made use of *both* meat and processed vegetable matter. A varied diet would have given these ancient humans greater independence over their environment.

Widespread, simultaneous appearance of agriculture

Scientific evidence also indicates that plant and animal domestication occurred independently around the world about 10 separate times.[19] The first large-scale domestication of plants occurred about 13,000 years ago in the Fertile Crescent, followed by similar activities in Southeast Asia (8,000 years ago) and New Guinea (7,000 years ago). A more recent breakthrough uncovered evidence for large-scale plant domestication in South America as far back as 10,000 years ago, only a few thousand years after the first humans made their way into the Americas.[20]

Such independent, multiple origins of large-scale agriculture support the notion that the first humans engaged in farming and animal husbandry well before 12,000 years ago. It seems highly unlikely that human beings would have independently, simultaneously acquired knowledge of plant and animal domestication that many times. It appears that humans took with them a well-developed understanding of farming and animal husbandry when they migrated to different regions of the world. It's significant to note that human migrations began about 50,000 to 60,000 years ago.

While these fresh insights do not rescue the RTB human origins model completely from the challenges stemming from the Neolithic Revolution, they do make it much more likely that humans engaged in some form of proto-farming prior to agriculture's wide-scale emergence. We anticipate that future discoveries will continue to push *back* the date for proto-agricultural practices, closer to the time that modern humans arose.

6.   There Are No 900-Year-Old Human Fossils

Do Christians really believe humans like Methuselah lived to be 900 years old? For many skeptics the long life spans recorded in Genesis chapters 5 and 11 seem absurd. If anything, anthropological evidence seems to indicate that humans who lived just thousands of years ago had *shorter* life spans than we do today.

Chapter 7 reviews advances in the biochemistry of aging and astronomical insights into changes in Earth's radiation environment that make such long life spans scientifically plausible. These advances, however, raise a fundamental question: If the biblical account is correct, then why are there no fossils of 900-year-old humans?

Recent research offers a possible explanation. Anatomists from Japan have developed a new method to determine the age of humans at the time of their death based on analysis of the ilium (one of the bones of the pelvis).[21] This novel approach bears similarity to methods currently used by forensic scientists to determine age at the time of death.[22] As humans age, characteristic changes take place in their skeletal features. Carefully correlating these changes with age allows scientists to estimate an age-at-death from skeletal remains. This new technique, and others like it, critically depends on the individuals comprising the reference sample. Researchers demonstrated that the age-at-death measured for an individual will depend on the known age and sex distribution of the human subjects used to build the calibration curve. The measured age can be skewed high or low if there is not a balanced representation of ages and sexes in the reference samples.

Age determination of human remains in the fossil record, of necessity, is based on calibrations derived from contemporary humans. But this process would not apply to humans who aged differently, and more slowly, prior to the flood. Therefore, the failure to detect 900-year-old humans in the fossil record does not necessarily mean that humans did not live that long. Instead, it may reflect, at least in part, use of the wrong calibration of chronological age and skeletal changes.

Also, long life spans recorded in the Bible may only apply to a few people. In the era before Noah's flood, murder was rampant. It is quite possible average life spans might have been shorter than today.[23]

Robust scientific models must respond to critiques. How has RTB's model fared in light of the six criticisms? Were they adequately addressed? Sometimes such wider, more overt testing opens up areas not previously considered. Is RTB's model incomplete? That prospect forms the basis for the next chapter.

Chapter 27

Three New Questions to Address

Since its unveiling in 2005, the Reasons to Believe (RTB) human origins model has met several recurring questions for which our original theory did not account. Good questions go beyond idle curiosity. They deserve a robust response and stand as a clear signal that the RTB model is incomplete. Because these questions concern areas central to human origins, we will use them as motivation to expand the scope and explanatory power of our model.

1. Where Did the Races Come From?

No matter the audience or venue, people want to know how RTB scholars explain the origin of the races. Scripture does not provide explicit descriptions of the rise of racial diversity, but it does imply that diversity arose rapidly when God scattered people following the Tower of Babel event (Genesis 11). On this basis, one RTB model prediction holds that racial differences can appear quickly.

For many people, the rub is that the biblical account does not seem to square with the scientific explanation for racial diversity, which anthropologists now refer to as regional differences. For decades, extending back to the work of famed anthropologist Carleton Coon, the scientific consensus has maintained that regional differences required about 2 million years to arise through evolutionary processes. This idea is closely aligned with multiregionalism, an evolutionary human origins model that proposes humanity arose 2 million years ago in a primitive form (see chapter 2). Primitive humans migrated from Africa into Europe and Asia and, once in these regions, independently evolved toward the modern type. Regional differences then resulted from these separate evolutionary trajectories that required a long time to manifest.

Yet, in the last ten years or so, genetic variability studies have undermined multiregionalism. The data indicate that modern humans appeared recently, about 100,000 to 150,000 years ago, and only migrated to Europe, Asia, and the Americas within the last 50,000 to 60,000 years. This means the evolutionary view faces the same problem as the biblical view: How to account for the rapid emergence of regional differences over a few thousand years, not 2 million. According to Christopher Stringer, an evolutionary anthropologist and a leading proponent of the out-of-Africa model, "One of the most difficult aspects for some people to accept, if we evolved very recently in Africa, is why we all look so different."[1]

This conundrum has resulted in a focused effort for all models to explain the origin of racial diversity. Ten years of research has shown that regional differences—driven by microevolutionary processes such as natural and sexual selection, genetic drift, and the serial founder effect—can arise rapidly for migrating humans.[2]

First humans resembled Africans
Scientific data indicates that the first humans looked very much like African people groups today. Heavy (dark) skin pigmentation offered protection against the harmful effects of UV radiation in hot, southern latitudes and prevented the loss of folic acid. One of the drawbacks of heavy skin pigmentation, however, is that it slows down the rate of vitamin D synthesis in the skin. (The last step in the metabolic route for vitamin D synthesis requires exposure to UV radiation.) As humans made their way into northern latitudes, a lightening of the skin allowed for more efficient vitamin D synthesis.

Near the equator, elongated bodies and broad, flat noses are an advantage because they dissipate body heat more efficiently. In colder, northern latitudes, shorter limbs and a more barrel-shaped body help retain heat and narrow noses help to warm air before it reaches the lungs.

In addition, many of the qualities that account for regional differences among humans are "signaling traits" that play a role in mate preference. These include facial features and the color of eyes, hair, and skin. As human populations separated and became isolated, it is reasonable to think that different facial features and eye, hair, and skin color became desirable in disparate populations, forming the basis for mate selection. Those traits deemed more desirable would have increased in local populations over time while other signaling traits disappeared, leading to regional differences in appearance.

Genes on the move
Perhaps the greatest contributors to the rapid rise of racial diversity are genetic

drift and the serial founder effect. When populations become isolated from one another by chance events alone, each will accrue biological differences over time. The effects of genetic drift become more pronounced for small populations. Anthropologists believe the population sizes of the first migrating humans around the world were small.

Chance events drive the serial founder effect as well. When a small subgroup breaks away from the main population (which undoubtedly happened when humans first migrated around the world), the gene frequencies (and hence, the physical appearance) in the breakaway group will be much different from that of the parent population. This difference results from a well-understood statistical effect related to sampling. As the small breakaway population begins to expand, their idiosyncratic gene frequencies will define the growing population as a whole. As a consequence of the founder effect, the breakaway population will look quite different from the parent population in just a few generations.

When humans began to migrate around the world, the founder effect would have occurred over and over again, in a serial fashion, for those people at the edge of the human migratory wave. (Sometimes population geneticists refer to the serial founder effect at the edge of the migratory wave as surfing.) The net result of the serial founder effect would have been to establish regional, racial differences in humans in short order.

The bottom line
The latest scientific work into the origin of racial diversity indicates that regional differences in humans can arise quickly through well-understood microevolutionary processes, which supports both the biblical account of human prehistory and the RTB human origins model.

2.   How Does the RTB Model Account for the Origin of Human Diseases?
Did God create bacteria to infect humans and cause diseases? Are these microbes part of God's good creation? These types of questions highlight the need to augment our creation model to formally include an explanation for the origin of human diseases.

Microorganisms are part of God's good design
Microbes have a bad reputation, but they actually play a key role in ecosystems and in maintaining human health. As a case in point, viruses help cycle nutrients in the oceans by infecting and destroying other microorganisms, resulting

in the release of nutrients into the ecosystem.[3] In medicine, viruses are used in biomedical applications.[4] For example, the properties that make viruses infectious are the same characteristics that make them useful for gene therapy. In this sense, viruses can be understood as part of God's providential care for humanity.

Microbial parasites control animal population numbers and, thus, help maintain ecosystem stability.[5] Throughout Earth's history, bacteria transformed the planet's atmosphere and oceans to make advanced life possible. Bacterial action also created metal deposits that now serve as key resources for civilization and technology.

And, believe it or not, bacteria also play an important role in maintaining human health. Scientists can characterize the entire microbial flora associated with the human body. It turns out that there are over 100 trillion bacterial cells on each person's exterior and interior surfaces. Compare that to about 10 trillion cells composing the human body. Estimates indicate that over 1,000 bacterial species exist in the human gut, a few hundred in the mouth, and about one hundred species on the human skin. Meanwhile, there are only about 100 pathogenic bacterial species. In fact, over 99 percent of the genes associated with the human organism come from surface bacteria.[6] One might say, biologically speaking, that we are only one percent human.

A recent study demonstrated that skin-surface bacteria prevent excessive inflammation when injury occurs.[7] In other research, scientists learned that gut bacteria help harvest energy from food. Changes (improper balance) in the gut flora are associated with obesity.[8] Researchers also think lack of exposure to bacteria during early childhood is responsible for the increase in autoimmune disorders such as asthma and could lead to increased risk of cardiovascular disease in later life.[9] (This idea is referred to as the hygiene hypothesis.)

Microorganisms can evolve

RTB's human origins model stands in contradistinction to the evolutionary paradigm. We believe life's origin and history cannot be fully explained apart from the direct involvement of the Creator. This does not mean, however, that our model stands in opposition to *all* forms of biological evolution. It is clear that species can vary (or adapt) over time and there is evidence that a species can give rise to a closely related sister species. Science has produced an abundance of evidence that microorganisms (like viruses, bacteria, and single-celled eukaryotes) evolve.

Microbial evolution is not surprising. Microorganism population sizes are enormous and, furthermore, these life-forms can gather pieces of DNA from their surroundings and incorporate them into their genomes.

Microorganism evolution and the origin of human disease
While RTB scholars maintain that God created microbes for a variety of reasons (including as parasites that infect animals and other life-forms), God did *not* create corresponding human pathogens when He made human beings. We would assert, however, that He *did* create beneficial microbes that would form mutualistic symbiotic associations with humans by populating their exterior and interior surfaces.

Because microorganisms can evolve, our model predicts that a small fraction of the human microbiome became pathogenic over time as a consequence of mutations occurring within the context of the large population sizes. Once pathogens emerged, they could transfer their toxin-producing genes to other microbes through horizontal (or lateral) gene transfer, creating new disease-causing strains. A recent example of this process explains the emergence of the deadly *Escherichia coli* strain, O157:H7. Most strains of *E. coli* (found in the human gut) are harmless. O157:H7 appears to have originated when toxin-encoding genes were transferred to a benign strain of *E. coli* from the microbe *Shigella*, a human pathogen.

Microbes that infect animals are another source of human pathogens. Again, mutations allow these microbes to jump from animal hosts to humans. Host hopping occurs frequently with viruses. For example, HIV appears to have originated from SIV, a virus that infects chimpanzees, and SARS might have hopped from a civet (cat-like mammal) host to humans. Incidentally, host hopping can work in the other direction as well. Researchers have observed that a strain of *Staphylococcus aureus* in poultry originated in a human host.[10]

Scientists have used genetic diversity patterns in human pathogens, such as *Helicobacter pylori* (the bacterium that causes ulcers and stomach cancer), to trace the origin of human parasites and their spread around the world. (See pages 74–77). The timing and location of many pathogens' origin closely coincides with the timing and location for humanity's origin. And the pattern of human pathogens' spread around the world follows the migration routes people took as they populated the planet.

In sum, RTB's model still maintains that microbes as originally created are part of God's *good* creation.

3. Do Genetic Similarities between Humans and Apes Support Common Descent?

Ten years ago researchers had only recently generated a high-quality sequence for the human genome. Since 2005, the scientific community has sequenced the genomes of Neanderthals and the enigmatic Denisovans. Researchers have also determined the genome sequences for all of the great apes (chimpanzees, bonobos, gorillas, and orangutans) and the macaques. This vast amount of sequence data provides an unprecedented opportunity to perform genome-wide comparisons among primates.

These comparisons consistently identify shared features in corresponding locations in the genomes of humans, Neanderthals, Denisovans, and the great apes. Most scientists interpret these shared features as compelling evidence of common descent. Researchers consider these shared features—many of which are thought to be nonfunctional—as "molecular fossils" that provide insight into humanity's evolutionary history. It is akin to the way that the hominid fossil record provides clues about human evolution. It is thought that these shared features arose in the common ancestor and were retained after evolutionary lineages diverged. For many people these molecular fossils represent perhaps the most significant challenge to the traditional biblical view of human origins.

For many scientists, the molecular fossils make sense only in the context of the evolutionary paradigm. But as discussed in chapter 14, RTB's model predicts, based on Genesis 2:7 and 2:19, that anatomical, physiological, genetic, and biochemical similarities will exist among humans, hominids, and apes. In light of this prediction, the RTB model interprets the shared features as reflections of common *design*, not common descent.

However, given that modern genomics has produced a vast amount of DNA sequence data and the capacity to perform myriad detailed sequence comparisons, merely asserting that shared features reflect common design seems overly simplistic and unsatisfying. The genomics era requires a more sophisticated creation model that can make sense of the similarities and differences among primate genomes.

Sir Richard Owen and the biological archetype
Thus motivated, we appeal to history. Interpreting shared biological features from a design framework has historical precedence. Before Charles Darwin, distinguished biologist Sir Richard Owen interpreted homologous structures (and, consequently, related organisms) as manifestations of an archetype.[11]

Sixteen years before *The Origin of Species* was published, Owen delivered a discourse entitled *On the Nature of Limbs*, on February 9, 1849, at the meeting of the Royal Institution of Great Britain (RI). This presentation stands as a classic analysis of the shared features of vertebrate limbs. In this study (and elsewhere), Owen proposed an interpretation of homologous features that did not rely on the notion of common ancestry. Instead Owen explained shared anatomical features using the idea of an archetype.[12]

The theoretical framework Owen presents demonstrates that it is possible to understand features like homology (similar structure) apart from the evolutionary paradigm. Owen's ideas have far-reaching implications. They provide the historical context for a contemporary design model that can account for anatomical, physiological, biochemical, and genetic similarities—so often touted as the most compelling evidence for common ancestry—among organisms.

Owen's description of the vertebrate archetype provided a theoretical framework to interpret anatomical and physiological similarities shared among organisms. Owen saw these mutual features as manifestations of a common blueprint. He defined the archetype thus, "'that ideal original or fundamental pattern on which a natural group of animals or systems of organs has been constructed, and to modifications of which the various forms of such animals or organs may be referred.'"[13]

Form or function?

Although the human hand, the bat's wing, the horse's hoof, and a whale's flipper all perform distinct functions, Owen recognized that these structures share the same basic design. He and other like-minded biologists explained vestigial structures, like the pelvis and hind limb bones found in whales and snakes, as resulting from the archetype. They regarded these structures as necessary to the architectural design of the organism.

In Owen's day, the great debate among biologists related to whether function or form provided the theoretical framework for understanding biological structures. While many scientists in Britain at that time favored a teleological (designed, or functional) view, Owen preferred the transcendental view popular on the European continent. This view favored form over function.

Still, Owen's goal was to come up with a theoretical framework that united both approaches. To his mind, the archetype represented teleology of a higher order. In his presentation to RI, Owen stated, "The satisfaction felt by the rightly constituted mind must ever be great in recognizing the fitness of parts for their appropriate functions; but when this fitness is gained, as in the great-toe

of the foot of man and the ostrich, by a structure which at the same time be-
tokens harmonious concord with a common type, the prescient operations of
the One Cause of all organization becomes strikingly manifested to our limited
intelligence."[14]

Archetype vs. ancestor

Owen's and others' conception of function and form were strongly theistic in
orientation. According to Owen, the archetype points to "some: archetypal ex-
emplar on which it has pleased the Creator to frame certain of his living creatures."[15]

When Darwin proposed his theory of biological evolution, he made use
of the vertebrate archetype in support of his theory. Instead of the archetype
serving as a blueprint in the mind of the "One Cause," Darwin argued that homologous structures were physically instantiated. In doing so, Darwin replaced
the archetype with the common ancestor. Homology became evidence for biological evolution and common descent. However, prior to Darwin's theory,
teleological meaning for biological systems was the prevailing scientific view.
If nothing else, the work of Owen and his contemporaries demonstrates that
there are alternate scientifically robust models that make sense of biology.

Common descent or common design?

In light of Owen's ideas, shared genomic features can be interpreted as either
evidence for common descent *or* common design. Consequently, the shared
features in the genomes of humans and apes point exclusively to common descent *only* if certain assumptions are true: (1) the genomes' shared structures
and sequences are nonfunctional junk; (2) the events that created the shared
features are rare, random, and nonrepeatable; and/or (3) common descent is
the only mechanism (vertical gene transfer) that can generate shared features
in genomes.

Recent studies challenge these assumptions. For example, evolutionary
biologists claim that synteny (the ordering of genes along a chromosome) reflects the degree of evolutionary relatedness,[16] but there are examples where
this relationship does not hold.[17] Plus, other studies have shown that genes'
locations along the length of the chromosome have functional significance and
therefore could represent intentional design.[18]

As pointed out in chapter 14, as well as in chapter 25, molecular biologists
and molecular geneticists have discovered that essentially every class of so-
called junk DNA, including unitary pseudogenes, has function. Thus, shared

features in human and ape genomes could be understood as common design.

Scientists have also learned that many of the processes that alter genomic structures and DNA sequences are not necessarily rare and random. For example, biochemists have long known that mutations occur in hotspots and that transitions happen more often than transversions. Recent work also indicates that transposon insertion and intron insertion occur at hotspots and gene loss is repeatable.[19] In yet another study, researchers discovered that retroviruses insert into genomes at hotspots as well.[20]

Additional studies reveal that horizontal gene transfer can mimic common descent. This phenomenon is not confined to bacteria and archaea, but has been observed in higher plants and animals as well, via a vector-mediated pathway or organelle capture.[21]

These breakthroughs show that even if genomic features are nonfunctional, they need not be taken as evidence for common descent. We can just as easily explain them as arising independently via reproducible mechanisms. Such advances put the case for common design on equal footing with common descent, thereby paving the way for RTB to propose a creation model for comparative genomics.

Comparative genomics

Undergirding RTB's model is the assumption that the Creator is responsible for life's origin and history. We believe God created genomes via direct intervention, but, once created, genomes are subjected to physical, chemical, and biochemical events that can induce changes in their structure. The genomics revolution is new, thus RTB's coverage of this topic is a work in progress. Nevertheless, the following tenets form the basis for our genomics model:

- *Genomes are created.* Some shared features reflect common function and/or common archetype. Meanwhile, some genomic features are unique and reflect special designs that impart biological uniqueness.
- *Once created, genomes experience mutations and natural selection, sexual selection, and genetic drift.* Some mutations are random, rare, and nonreproducible while others are nonrandom, repeatable, and occur at hotspots.
- *Genomes continually accrue mutations over time that are, in turn, subject to selection.* As a corollary, the genomes of organisms created before humans will have experienced more mutational events.

With these principles in mind, the RTB genomics model explains the simi-larities among organisms' genomes in one of two ways:

- They reflect the work of God who deliberately designed similar ge-nomic features according to a common function or a common blue-print.
- They reflect the outworking of physical, chemical, or biochemical pro-cesses that occur frequently, are nonrandom, and are reproducible. These processes cause the independent origin of the same features in the genomes of different organisms.

More work on this aspect of RTB's human origins model is needed, and future scientific advances will shed more light on its viability. RTB scholars welcome the challenge.

Have the three new questions been adequately addressed? Does ten years of wider, more overt testing erode or bolster confidence in our model's ability to accommodate new information? If these questions are not settled in any reader's mind, the final chapter could serve as a scorecard of sorts to show where the RTB model stands.

Chapter 28

Where Does the RTB Model Stand?

W hen the first edition of *Who Was Adam?* was published in 2005, it was difficult, if not impossible, to imagine what the following decade of scientific exploration would bring. In anthropology the last ten years of discoveries have been unprecedented. The number of new hominid species unearthed boggles the mind. Some of these advances have revolutionized the way anthropologists study the question of human origins. It borders on science fiction to realize there is now an actual subdiscipline in anthropology dedicated to studying the genetics of Neanderthals and other hominids.

This rapid succession of discoveries has put the Reasons to Believe (RTB) human origins model on alert. At times, it seemed like the model faced tests on a weekly basis. The following summary of affirmations and challenges shows how our model has fared.

Where Science Has Affirmed the RTB Model

Hominid fossils

RTB's model effectively accounted for significant hominid fossil discoveries reported over the last decade. The hominid fossil record is often regarded as evidence for human evolution, but more often than not, new fossil finds have brought greater confusion and uncertainty to evolutionary explanations for human origins. Hominids that were thought to delineate the pathway from an ancestral primate to modern humans have either: (1) been relegated to a side branch; (2) had their status in human evolution questioned; or (3) been rendered nonexistent.

A decade of discoveries has highlighted the disconcerting fact that paleoanthropologists cannot map out the evolutionary route to humans. To consider human evolution anything more than a hypothesis seems unwarranted, but we go a step further. We maintain that the bedlam associated with attempts to interpret hominid fossils from an evolutionary view justifies skepticism and supports RTB's biblical creation view.

Neanderthal biological differences
New insights into Neanderthal biology and genetics support RTB's creation model by showing biological differences between humans and Neanderthals. Additional evidence demonstrates that the shape and organization of the Neanderthal brain were different from those of the human brain. So was the process of brain development. Comparative studies of Neanderthal and human dental microanatomy also highlight developmental differences. Humans spend much more time in adolescence than did Neanderthals. Studies of the Neanderthal genome also indicate key differences in genes associated with neural development.

Neanderthal cognitive differences
These same studies also suggest cognitive and, hence, behavioral differences in line with the predictions of our model. However, assessing Neanderthal behavior from the archeological record has not been straightforward. Some insights affirm Neanderthals' cognitive inferiority compared to humans while other discoveries seem to favor advanced cognitive ability on par with humans. If valid, this latter interpretation presents a problem for the RTB model, but it should be noted that archeological finds cited as evidence for symbolism in Neanderthals are not universally accepted among anthropologists. As we point out, these controversial claims have alternate explanations.

Ape behavior as a proxy for hominid behavior
New insights into primate behavior demonstrate that apes, whether captive or wild, are capable of remarkable behavior. Even so, it is clear they are not in the same behavioral category as humans. However, the ape behavior *is* comparable to what we know about the behaviors of *Homo habilis*, *Homo erectus*, and, to some degree, Neanderthals.

Fresh studies of chimpanzee behavior distance the hominids from humans. Just because the habilines and erectines made and used tools and engaged in hunting and scavenging activity does not necessarily mean they were "becoming human." Rather, their behavior seems to have been animal-like, particularly when compared to chimpanzee activities. This is in accord with the RTB model.

Ape genome comparisons
During the past ten years, researchers have determined the sequences for all of the great ape genomes and made comparisons with the human genome. RTB's human origins model predicts biological similarity (which implies genetic similarity) between humans and other creatures, including apes. As such, our model readily accommodates the results of whole-genome comparisons.

Gene expression
Many biologists consider simple DNA sequence comparisons meaningless. The most biologically significant comparisons involve gene expression patterns. In 2005, researchers had already noted key differences in gene expression patterns for humans and chimpanzees, particularly for comparisons of brain tissue. The RTB human origins model readily accommodated these observations. Over the past decade, a number of studies have identified *additional* differences between human and chimpanzee gene expression and gene splicing patterns. Undoubtedly, these differences help account for the biological and behavioral differences between the two primates. Again, the RTB model makes sense of this insight.

Junk DNA
Another advance in genetics and a tour de force for RTB's model involves the sea change in perception about junk DNA. The ENCODE Project has radically altered scientists' view of the human genome. It is not an evolutionary junkyard, but an elegant system that displays sophistication in its architecture and operation, far beyond what most evolutionary biologists ever imagined.

Functional unitary pseudogenes
Scientists have discovered that unitary pseudogenes can play a role in regulating gene expression as part of the competitive endogenous RNA hypothesis. This advance stands as a fulfilled prediction for the RTB human origins model. In 2005, we predicted that scientists would eventually discover that unitary pseudogenes are functional. They have done so.

Shared designs
Advances in genomics have also afforded evolutionary biologists the opportunity to make fine-structure comparisons of the human genome with those of the Neanderthals, Denisovans, and the great apes. These comparisons have revealed innumerable shared features in these genomes. Biologists interpret these shared features—veritable molecular fossils—as compelling evidence that

humans and apes share an evolutionary history. But RTB's model, employing scientific precedent in Sir Richard Owen's ideas, interprets shared features as a reflection of God's intent by repurposing common designs. Genetic evidence often cited as common descent can be justifiably claimed as common design.

Accounting for racial diversity

We have expanded the RTB human origins model to include the prediction that racial diversity arose quickly as humans migrated around the world. As it turns out, recent work demonstrates that the genesis of racial diversity does not require that populations be genetically isolated for millions of years. Regional differences driven by natural and sexual selection, genetic drift, and the serial founder effect can arise rapidly for migrating humans.

Where Science Has Challenged Our Model

Timing of humanity's origin

In 2005, we predicted that God created human beings between 10,000 and 100,000 years ago. The latest results from molecular anthropology place humanity's origin between 100,000 and 150,000 years ago. We were wrong. However, the new dates line up with estimates of humanity's origin from the fossil record (between 100,000 and 200,000 years ago). Though these dates are older than those reported in the first edition of *Who Was Adam?*, we argue that they still harmonize with Scripture. After carefully reconsidering our interpretation of the genealogies in Genesis 5 and 11, we now take the position that the biblical text implies that Adam and Eve were created while an ice age, probably the most recent one, was in effect.[1]

Bottleneck at the flood

In 2005, we took the position that humanity's female lineage should trace back to an earlier date than the male lineage. At that time, we suggested the discrepancy between the dates for "mitochondrial Eve" and "Y-chromosomal Adam" could be explained by genetic bottleneck following Noah's flood. In fact, we took this inconsistency as fulfillment of a key prediction of the RTB human origins model.

Unfortunately, the latest results from molecular anthropology no longer allow us to make this claim. We were wrong again. A number of recent studies indicate that mitochondrial Eve and Y-chromosomal Adam lived at the same time and were part of the same population. (However, we take a good deal of comfort in the evidence for concurrent dates for Adam and Eve.)

Also, even though the most recent dates fail to support the flood, it does not mean there is a lack of evidence for the flood. For example, the pattern and timing of human migration (discussed in chapter 8) comport well with the biblical account of humanity's forced spread around the world (Genesis 11), an event that took place after the flood.

Human-Neanderthal interbreeding

Regarding Neanderthals, we took the position that modern humans and Neanderthals did *not* interbreed. However, comparative analyses of the high-quality genomes of Neanderthals, Denisovans, and humans show evidence for interbreeding among all three. The most compelling evidence stems from detection of Neanderthal and Denisovan genes in the human genome. Still, there are some questions that remain. Small population sizes of migrating modern humans and Neanderthal groups make it unlikely that encounters took place.

The admission that humans interbred with other hominids does *not* invalidate the RTB human origins model. Interbreeding does not mean humans and Neanderthals belong to the same species. Nor does it mean that they shared a common ancestor. We argue that the ability to interbreed is a manifestation of shared design, not common descent.

From a theological standpoint, interbreeding, though repugnant, is not terribly surprising. The Bible and history testify to humanity's depraved nature following the fall. In fact, one could reasonably propose a human origins creation model derived from the biblical text that predicts humans would have at least *attempted* to interbreed with hominids when they encountered them.

Uncomfortable theological issues arise, such as whether the human-Neanderthal hybrids would have had a spirit. The RTB model can accommodate interbreeding between humans and Neanderthals—just not seamlessly.

The emergence of symbolic thought

A key feature of the RTB human origins model centers on the idea that human beings are *uniquely made in God's image* (Genesis 1:26–27). This view leads to two key predictions: (1) human beings should display unique behaviors compared to other creatures (including the hominids); and (2) these behaviors should appear suddenly, coinciding with the appearance of humans.

A decade ago anthropologists maintained that human behavior appeared suddenly about 40,000 years ago in an event described as the sociocultural "big bang." Evidence for this dramatic event came from the archeological record in Europe. It was believed humans migrated to Europe already possessing the capacity for symbolism.

However, the most recent dates for mitochondrial Eve and Y-chromosomal Adam (between 100,000 and 150,000 years ago), create a potential problem for RTB's model. It appears that a discrepancy (of possibly up to 100,000 years) exists between when humans first appeared (based on genetic and fossil data) and when symbolic capability first emerged. We explain in chapter 18 how scientific advances go a long way toward addressing this quandary for our human origins model, but we acknowledge some discomfort.

Humanity's original population size
One of the most significant challenges leveled against RTB's human origins model relates to humanity's original population size. Critics of our model assert that human genetic diversity is far too great to be accounted for by an initial pair of humans. They argue that mathematical modeling points to original population sizes of several thousand, not two. We counter that this challenge might be premature because studies in conservation biology demonstrate that these mathematical models perform poorly at predicting genetic diversity when the initial population size is known. In fact, other studies question whether the relationships used to model initial population sizes are even valid. As it stands now, we believe—though almost all geneticists disagree—the RTB model can withstand this challenge.

A Final Test?
In 2005, our goal was to present a scientifically testable, biblically derived model for human origins that would help demonstrate that creation *can* be science. But more importantly, we wanted to demonstrate that a traditional biblical view of human origins possesses scientific credibility. Outstanding questions remain and we have more work to do. It is certain that our model will be subjected to "more wider and more overt" tests in the years ahead.

One question we hope has been resolved concerns the title of the book. When you ask, who was Adam?, we trust that his identity has been established as an image-bearer of his divine Creator. Even more so, we hope the question, who was Adam's creator?, will lead to a fulfilling quest of lifelong discovery of that Creator's identity and His purpose for creating all human beings.

Notes

Introduction: Who Am I?

1. Charles Darwin, *The Descent of Man, and Selection in Relation to Sex*, 2nd ed., Great Minds Series (1874; repr., Amherst, NY: Prometheus Books, 1998).
2. Brian J. Alters and Sandra M. Alters, *Defending Evolution in the Classroom: A Guide to the Creation/Evolution Controversy* (Boston: Jones and Bartlett, 2001), 156.
3. Ibid., 123.
4. Hugh Ross, *The Creator and the Cosmos: How the Greatest Scientific Discoveries of the Century Reveal God*, 3rd ed. (Colorado Springs: NavPress, 2001); Fazale Rana and Hugh Ross, *Origins of Life: Biblical and Evolutionary Models Face Off* (Colorado Springs: NavPress, 2004); Hugh Ross, *A Matter of Days: Resolving a Creation Controversy*, 2nd exp. ed., (Covina, CA: RTB Press, 2015).

Chapter 1: The Differences between David and Darwin

1. Charles S. Cockell, *Impossible Extinction: Natural Catastrophes and the Supremacy of the Microbial World* (Cambridge: Cambridge University Press, 2003), 24.
2. Ibid., 25.
3. Dinah L. Moché, *Astronomy: A Self-Teaching Guide*, 4th ed. (New York: Wiley, 1993), 138–72.
4. A preliminary estimate based on the Hubble Ultra Deep Field shows that about 200 billion galaxies exist in the observable universe.
5. Moché, *Astronomy*, 52–155.
6. Psalm 8:3–4.
7. Peter C. Craigie, *Word Biblical Commentary*, ed. Bruce M. Metzger, John

D. W. Watts, and James W. Watts, vol. 19, *Psalms 1–50* (Waco, TX: Word, 1983), 108; Willem A. VanGemeren, "Psalms," in *The Expositor's Bible Commentary*, ed. Frank E. Gaebelein, vol. 5, *Psalms, Proverbs, Ecclesiastes, Song of Songs* (Grand Rapids, MI: Zondervan, 1991), 112.

8. Genesis 1:26–28.

9. Psalm 8:5–8.

10. Craigie, *Psalms 1–50*, 108–9; VanGemeren, "Psalms," 112–14.

11. Charles Darwin, *The Descent of Man, and Selection in Relation to Sex*, 2nd ed., Great Minds Series (1874; repr., Amherst, NY: Prometheus Books, 1998), 188.

12. Stephen Jay Gould, *Wonderful Life: The Burgess Shale and the Nature of History* (New York: Norton, 1989), 291.

13. Ibid., 51.

14. Ibid., 45–52.

15. Gabriel Yedid and Graham Bell, "Macroevolution Simulated with Autonomously Replicating Computer Programs," *Nature* 420 (2002): 810–12.

16. Darwin, *Descent of Man*, 5–26.

17. Ibid., 26–66, 172–213.

18. Ibid., 26–66.

19. Isaac Asimov, *Asimov's Chronology of Science and Discovery* (New York: Harper and Row, 1989), 353.

20. Ibid., 330–13.

21. Ibid., 395–96.

22. Ibid., 488–89.

23. Roger Lewin, *Principles of Human Evolution: A Core Textbook* (Malden, MA: Blackwell Science, 1998), 264–66.

24. Ibid., 269–73.

25. Asimov, *Asimov's Chronology*, 600–601.

26. Ibid., 648–49.

27. H. James Birx, introduction to *The Descent of Man*, by Charles Darwin, xix, xxiii.

28. Tim Friend, "Fossil Discovery Shakes Human Family Tree," *USA Today*, July 11, 2002, D05; Michael D. Lemonick and Andrea Dorfman with Simon Robinson, "One Giant Step for Mankind: Meet Your Newfound Ancestor, a Chimplike Forest Creature That Stood Up and Walked 5.8 Million Years Ago," *Time*, July 23, 2001, 54–61; Michael D. Lemonick and Andrea Dorfman, "Up from the Apes: Remarkable New Evidence Is

Filling in the Story of How We Became Human," *Time*, August 23, 1999, 50–58.

29. Darwin, *Descent of Man*, 643.

Chapter 2: Fossil Record Facts

1. Alexander Kohn, *False Prophets: Fraud and Error in Science and Medicine*, rev. ed. (Oxford, UK: Basil Blackwell, 1988), 133.
2. Ibid., 133–41.
3. Ibid., 140.
4. For a particularly egregious example, see Hank Hanegraaff, *The Face That Demonstrates the Farce of Evolution* (Nashville, TN: Word, 1998), 49–57; also see Ron Rhodes, *The 10 Things You Should Know about the Creation vs. Evolution Debate* (Eugene, OR: Harvest House, 2004), 79–89.
5. For some examples of this position, see Marvin L. Lubenow, *Bones of Contention: A Creationist Assessment of Human Fossils* (Grand Rapids, MI: Baker, 1992); Jack Cuozzo, *Buried Alive: The Startling Truth about Neanderthal Man* (Green Forest, AR: Master Books, 1998); Duane T. Gish, *Evolution: The Fossils Still Say No!* (El Cajon, CA: Institute for Creation Research, 1995), 209–331.
6. Robert Boyd and Joan B. Silk, *How Humans Evolved*, 3rd ed. (New York: Norton, 2003), 280–82.
7. Yohannes Haile-Selassie, Gen Suwa, and Tim D. White, "Late Miocene Teeth from Middle Awash, Ethiopia, and Early Hominid Dental Evolution," *Science* 303 (2004): 1503–5; David R. Begun, "The Earliest Hominins—Is Less More?," *Science* 303 (2004): 1478–80.
8. Boyd and Silk, *How Humans Evolved*, 282–302.
9. Roger Lewin, *Principles of Human Evolution: A Core Textbook* (Malden, MA: Blackwell Science, 1998), 248–53.
10. Brian G. Richmond and David S. Strait, "Evidence That Humans Evolved from a Knuckle-Walking Ancestor," *Nature* 404 (2000): 382–85; Mark Collard and Leslie C. Aiello, "Human Evolution: From Forelimbs to Two Legs," *Nature* 404 (2000): 339–40.
11. Boyd and Silk, *How Humans Evolved*, 282–302.
12. Ibid.
13. Ibid.
14. Ibid.
15. Ibid.
16. Ibid.

17. Ibid., 294–97.
18. Abesalom Vekua et al., "A New Skull of Early *Homo* from Dmanisi, Georgia," *Science* 297 (2002): 85–89.
19. Boyd and Silk, *How Humans Evolved*, 294–97.
20. Ibid., 315–38; Lewin, *Principles of Human Evolution*, 309–21.
21. Boyd and Silk, *How Humans Evolved*, 340–43.
22. Ibid., 343–47; Lewin, *Principles of Human Evolution*, 343–49.
23. Boyd and Silk, *How Humans Evolved*, 356–60.
24. Ibid., 360–67.
25. Lewin, *Principles of Human Evolution*, 386–89.
26. Ibid.
27. Ibid.
28. Fazale Rana, "The Unreliability of Hominid Phylogenetic Analysis Challenges the Human Evolutionary Paradigm," *Facts for Faith*, no. 3 (Q3 2000), 53–54.
29. Fazale R. Rana, "Toumai Man Offers Evolutionists No Hope," *Connections* 4, nos. 3 and 4 (2002), 6–7.
30. John Whitfield, "Oldest Member of Human Family Found," *Nature News* (2002): doi:10.1038/news020708-12.

Chapter 3: A Scientific Creation Model

1. J. P. Moreland and John Mark Reynolds, eds., *Three Views on Creation and Evolution* (Grand Rapids, MI: Zondervan, 1999); David G. Hagopian, ed., *The Genesis Debate: Three Views on the Days of Creation* (Mission Viejo CA: Crux Press, 2001).
2. Norman L. Geisler, foreword in *Genesis Debate*, 12.
3. Hugh Ross, *A Matter of Days: Resolving a Creation Controversy*, 2nd exp. ed., (Covina, CA: RTB Press, 2015); see also Don Stoner, *A New Look at an Old Earth: Resolving the Conflict between the Bible and Science* (Eugene, OR: Harvest House, 1997).
4. The early church fathers (second to fifth centuries) allowed for a diversity of views on the nature and duration of the Genesis creation days. Isaac Newton and Thomas Burnet (King William III's chaplain) explicitly taught the day-age interpretation of Genesis 1. For original source quotes and citations, see *Matter of Days* by Hugh Ross, 41–57.
5. R. Laird Harris, Gleason L. Archer Jr., and Bruce K. Waltke, eds., *Theological Wordbook of the Old Testament* (Chicago: Moody, 1980), 1:701–2; Harris, Archer, and Waltke, *Theological Wordbook*, 2:127.

6. Luke 3:23–38.
7. Genesis 2:8, 10–14, 22–23; 3:23; and 4:16, respectively.
8. Kenneth A. Mathews, *The New American Commentary*, vol. 1, *Genesis 1–11:26* (Nashville, TN: Broadman and Holman, 1996), 200–201.
9. Ibid., 208.
10. Hugh Ross, *The Genesis Question: Scientific Advances and the Accuracy of Genesis*, 2nd ed. (Colorado Springs: NavPress, 2001), 78–79.
11. K. A. Kitchen, *On the Reliability of the Old Testament* (Grand Rapids, MI: Eerdmans, 2003), 428–30.
12. Mathews, *Genesis 1–11:26*, 200–208; Gordon, J. Wenham, *Word Biblical Commentary*, ed. David A. Hubbard, Glenn W. Barker, and John D. W. Watts, vol. 1, *Genesis 1–15* (Waco, TX: Word, 1987), 60–67; Victor P. Hamilton, *The New International Commentary on the Old Testament*, ed. R. K. Harrison and Robert L. Hubbard Jr., vol. 1, *The Book of Genesis: Chapters 1–17* (Grand Rapids, MI; Eerdmans, 1990), 166–70; Derek Kidner, *Genesis: An Introduction and Commentary*, Tyndale Old Testament Commentaries, ed. D. J. Wiseman (Downers Grove, IL: InterVarsity, 1967), 61–65.
13. Ross, *Genesis Question*, 108–10.
14. William Henry Green, "Primeval Chronology," 1890, reprinted as appendix 2 in *Genesis One and the Origin of the Earth*, by Robert C. Newman and Herman J. Eckelmann Jr. (Hatfield, PA: Interdisciplinary Biblical Research Institute, 1977).
15. Genesis 5:1–2; Mathews, *Genesis 1–11:26*, 305–22.
16. Harris, Archer, and Waltke, *Theological Wordbook*, vol. 1, 5–6, 113–14; Mathews, *Genesis 1–11:26*, 302.
17. Harris, Archer, and Waltke, *Theological Wordbook*, 1:378–79.
18. Kitchen, *On the Reliability*, 440–41.
19. Green, "Primeval Chronology," 285–303.
20. Scott A. Elias et al., "Life and Times of the Bering Land Bridge," *Nature* 382 (1996): 60–63.
21. Genesis 7:13, 21.
22. Ross, *Genesis Question*, 110–12.
23. Psalm 8:4–9.
24. Genesis 1:26–27; 5:1–2.
25. Genesis 1:28–30.
26. Harris, Archer, and Waltke, *Theological Wordbook*, 2:701–2.
27. Ibid., 1:396.

28. Ibid., 1:127–28.
29. Genesis 2:7, 19.
30. Wenham, *Genesis 1–15*, 59–61.
31. Hamilton, *Book of Genesis*, 176.
32. Ross, *Genesis Question*, 139–71.
33. Genesis 1:28; 9:7.

Chapter 4: It's All in the Genes

1. Ann Gibbons, "One Scientist's Quest for the Origin of Our Species," *Science* 298 (2002): 1708–11.
2. Michel Brunet et al., "A New Hominid from the Upper Miocene of Chad, Central Africa," *Nature* 418 (2002): 145–51; Patrick Vignaud et al., "Geology and Palaeontology of the Upper Miocene Toros-Menalla Hominid Locality, Chad," *Nature* 418 (2002): 152–55; Bernard Wood, "Hominid Revelations from Chad," *Nature* 418 (2002): 133–35; Ann Gibbons, "First Member of Human Family Uncovered," *Science* 297 (2002): 171–72.
3. Harvey Lodish et al., *Molecular Cell Biology*, 4th ed. (New York: W. H. Freeman, 2000), 101–5.
4. Robert C. Bohinski, *Modern Concepts in Biochemistry*, 4th ed. (Boston: Allyn and Bacon, 1983), 86–87.
5. Roderic D. M. Page and Edward C. Holmes, *Molecular Evolution: A Phylogenetic Approach* (Malden, MA: Blackwell Science, 1998), 37–88; Wen-Hsiung Li, *Molecular Evolution* (Sunderland, MA: Sinauer Associates, 1997), 7–34.
6. Page and Holmes, *Molecular Evolution*, 63–65; Li, *Molecular Evolution*, 23–30.
7. Page and Holmes, *Molecular Evolution*, 251–61.
8. Ibid., 124–29; Li, *Molecular Evolution*, 243–45.
9. Page and Holmes, *Molecular Evolution*, 251–61; Li, *Molecular Evolution*, 215–35.
10. Robert Boyd and Joan B. Silk, *How Humans Evolved*, 3rd ed. (New York: Norton, 2003), 390–91.
11. Pascal Gagneux et al., "Mitochondrial Sequences Show Diverse Evolutionary Histories of African Hominoids," *Proceedings of the National Academy of Sciences, USA* 96 (1999): 5077–82; Henrik Kaessmann, Victor Wiebe, and Svante Pääbo, "Extensive Nuclear DNA Sequence Diversity among Chimpanzees," *Science* 286 (1999): 1159–62; B. Bower, "Chimps

Outdo People in Genetic Diversity," *Science News* 156 (1999): 295; Henrik
Kaessmann et al., "Great Ape DNA Sequences Reveal a Reduced Diversity
and an Expansion in Humans," *Nature Genetics* 27 (2001): 155–56; Anne
C. Stone et al., "High Levels of Y-Chromosome Nucleotide Diversity in
the Genus *Pan*," *Proceedings of the National Academy of Sciences, USA* 99
(2002): 43–48; Anne Fischer et al., "Evidence for a Complex Demographic
History of Chimpanzees," *Molecular Biology and Evolution* 21 (2004):
799–808.

12. Noah A. Rosenberg et al., "Genetic Structure of Human Populations,"
    Science 298 (2002): 2381–85; Mary-Claire King and Arno G. Motulsky,
    "Mapping Human History," *Science* 298 (2002): 2342–43.

13. Boyd and Silk, *How Humans Evolved*, 393.

14. Ibid., 392; for example, see John D. H. Stead and Alec J. Jeffreys,
    "Structural Analysis of Insulin Minisatellite Alleles Reveals Unusually
    Large Differences in Diversity between Africans and Non-Africans,"
    American Journal of Human Genetics 71 (2002): 1273–84; Ning Yu et al.,
    "Larger Genetic Differences within Africans Than between Africans and
    Eurasians," *Genetics* 161 (2002): 269–74.

15. Jennifer Couzin, "New Mapping Project Splits the Community," *Science*
    296 (2002): 1391–93.

16. Mark Stoneking, "Single Nucleotide Polymorphisms: From the
    Evolutionary Past…," *Nature* 409 (2001): 821–22.

17. Nila Patil et al., "Blocks of Limited Haplotype Diversity Revealed by
    High-Resolution Scanning of Human Chromosome 21," *Science* 294
    (2001): 1719–23; Pui-Yan Kwok, "Genetic Association by Whole-Genome
    Analysis?," *Science* 294 (2001): 1669–70.

18. Genesis 3:23–24.

19. Gabor Marth et al., "Sequence Variations in the Public Human Genome
    Data Reflect a Bottlenecked Population History," *Proceedings of the
    National Academy of Sciences, USA* 100 (2003): 376–81; Paola Sebastiani
    et al., "Minimal Haplotype Tagging," *Proceedings of the National Academy
    of Sciences, USA* 100 (2003): 9900–9905.

20. Immo E. Scheffler, *Mitochondria* (New York: Wiley, 1999), 326–27.

21. Wesley M. Brown, "Polymorphism in Mitochondrial DNA of Humans
    as Revealed by Restriction Endonuclease Analysis," *Proceedings of the
    National Academy of Sciences, USA* 77 (1980): 3605–9.

22. Rebecca L. Cann, Mark Stoneking, and Allan C. Wilson, "Mitochondrial
    DNA and Human Evolution," *Nature* 325 (1987): 31. For the story behind

the first mitochondrial DNA studies on human origins, see Michael H. Brown, *The Search for Eve: Have Scientists Found the Mother of Us All?* (New York: Harper and Row, 1990).

23. Scheffler, *Mitochondria*, 328.

24. Linda Vigilant et al., "African Populations and the Evolution of Human Mitochondrial DNA," *Science* 253 (1991): 1503–7.

25. For example, see Maryellen Ruvolo et al., "Mitochondrial COII Sequences and Modern Human Origins," *Molecular Biology and Evolution* 10 (1993): 1115–35; Stephen T. Sherry et al., "Mismatch Distributions of mtDNA Reveal Recent Human Population Expansions," *Human Biology* 66 (1994): 761–75; Satoshi Horai et al., "Recent African Origin of Modern Humans Revealed by Complete Sequences of Hominoid Mitochondrial DNAs," *Proceedings of the National Academy of Sciences, USA* 92 (1995): 532–36; Masami Hasegawa and Satohi Horai, "Time of the Deepest Root for Polymorphism in Human Mitochondrial DNA," *Journal of Molecular Evolution* 32 (1991): 37–42; Mark Stoneking et al., "New Approaches to Dating Suggest a Recent Age for the Human mtDNA Ancestor," *Philosophical Transactions of the Royal Society of London B* 337 (1992): 167–75.

26. Max Ingman et al., "Mitochondrial Genome Variation and the Origin of Modern Humans," *Nature* 408 (2000): 708–13; S. Blair Hedges, "Human Evolution: A Start for Population Genomics," *Nature* 408 (2000): 652–53.

27. Evelyn Strauss, "Can Mitochondrial Clocks Keep Time?," *Science* 283 (1999): 1435–38.

28. Ann Gibbons, "Calibrating the Mitochondrial Clock," *Science* 279 (1998): 28–29; Lois A. Tully et al., "A Sensitive Denaturing Gradient-Gel Electrophoresis Assay Reveals a High Frequency of Heteroplasmy in Hypervariable Region 1 of the Human mtDNA Central Region," *American Journal of Human Genetics* 67 (2000): 432–43.

29. Tully et al., "Sensitive Denaturing Gradient-Gel," 432–43.

30. Cassandra D. Calloway et al., "The Frequency of Heteroplasmy in the HVII Region of mtDNA Differs across Tissue Types and Increases with Age," *American Journal of Human Genetics* 66 (2000): 1384–97.

31. Gibbons, "Calibrating the Mitochondrial Clock," 28–29.

32. Dan Graur and William Martin, "Reading the Entrails of Chickens: Molecular Timescales of Evolution and the Illusion of Precision," *Trends in Genetics* 20 (2004): 80–86.

33. Gibbons, "Calibrating the Mitochondrial Clock," 28–29.

34. Hugh Ross and Sam Conner, "Eve's Secret to Growing Younger," *Facts and Faith* 12, no. 1 (1998), 1–2.
35. Erika Hagelberg, "Recombination or Mutation Rate Heterogeneity? Implications for Mitochondrial Eve," *Trends in Genetics* 19 (2003): 84–90; Yuichi Michikawa et al., "Aging-Dependent Large Accumulation of Point Mutations in the Human mtDNA Control Region for Replication," *Science* 286 (1999): 774–79.
36. Lucy Forster et al., "Natural Radioactivity and Human Mitochondrial DNA Mutations," *Proceedings of the National Academy of Sciences, USA* 99 (2002): 13950–54.
37. Dan Mishmar et al., "Natural Selection Shaped Regional mtDNA Variation in Humans," *Proceedings of the National Academy of Sciences, USA* 100 (2003): 171–76; Eduardo Ruiz-Pesini et al., "Effects of Purifying and Adaptive Selection on Regional Variation in Human mtDNA," *Science* 303 (2004): 223–26; J. L. Elson, D. M. Turnbull, and Neil Howell, "Comparative Genomics and the Evolution of Human Mitochondrial DNA: Assessing the Effects of Selection," *American Journal of Human Genetics* 74 (2004): 229–38.
38. For example, see Michael P. H. Stumpf and David B. Goldstein, "Genealogical and Evolutionary Inference with the Human Y Chromosome," *Science* 291 (2001): 1738–42.
39. Robert L. Dorit, H. Akashi, and W. Gilbert, "Absence of Polymorphism at the ZFY Locus on the Human Y Chromosome," *Science* 268 (1995): 1183–85; Svante Pääbo, "The Y Chromosome and the Origin of All of Us (Men)," *Science* 268 (1995): 1141–42.
40. Michael F. Hammer, "A Recent Common Ancestry for Human Y Chromosomes," *Nature* 378 (1995): 376–78.
41. For example, see Ann Gibbons, "Y Chromosome Shows That Adam Was an African," *Science* 278 (1997): 804–5; Mark Seielstad et al., "A View of Modern Human Origins from Y Chromosome Microsatellite Variation," *Genome Research* 9 (1999): 558–67; Ornella Semino et al., "Ethiopians and Khoisan Share the Deepest Clades of the Human Y-Chromosome Phylogeny," *American Journal of Human Genetics* 70 (2002): 265–68.
42. Jonathan K. Pritchard et al., "Population Growth of Human Y Chromosomes: A Study of Y Chromosome Microsatellites," *Molecular Biology and Evolution* 16 (1999): 1791–98; Russell Thomson et al., "Recent Common Ancestry of Human Y Chromosomes: Evidence from DNA Sequence Data," *Proceedings of the National Academy of Sciences, USA*

97 (2000): 7360–65; Peter A. Underhill et al., "Y Chromosome Sequence Variation and the History of Human Populations," *Nature Genetics* 26, (2000): 358–61.

43. L. Simon Whitfield et al., "Sequence Variation of the Human Y Chromosome," *Nature* 378 (1995): 379–80.

44. Elizabeth Pennisi, "Tracking the Sexes by Their Genes," *Science* 291 (2001): 1733–34; Carl Zimmer, "After You, Eve," *Natural History*, March 2001, 32–35.

45. Jason A. Wilder, Zahra Mobasher, and Michael F. Hammer, "Genetic Evidence for Unequal Effective Population Sizes of Human Females and Males," *Molecular Biology and Evolution* 21 (2004): 2047–57.

46. Agnar Helgason et al., "A Populationwide Coalescent Analysis of Icelandic Matrilineal and Patrilineal Genealogies: Evidence for a Faster Evolutionary Rate of mtDNA Lineages than Y Chromosomes," *American Journal of Human Genetics* 72, (2003): 1370–88.

47. J. S. Wainscoat et al., "Evolutionary Relationships of Human Populations from an Analysis of Nuclear DNA Polymorphisms," *Nature* 319 (1986): 491–93.

48. Jorune Balciuniene et al., "The Geographic Distribution of Monoamine Oxidase Haplotypes Supports a Bottleneck during the Dispersion of Modern Humans from Africa," *Journal of Molecular Evolution* 52 (2001): 157–63.

49. S. P. Wooding et al., "DNA Sequence Variation in a 3.7-kb Noncoding Sequence 5' of the *CYP1A2* Gene: Implications for Human Population History and Natural Selection," *American Journal of Human Genetics* 71 (2002): 528–42.

50. Hermelita Winter et al., "Human Type I Keratin Pseudogene φ *hHaA* Has Functional Orthologs in the Chimpanzee and Gorilla: Evidence for Recent Inactivation of the Human Gene after the *Pan-Homo* Divergence," *Human Genetics* 108 (2001): 37–42; Rosa Martínez-Arias et al., "Sequence Variability of a Human Pseudogene," *Genome Research* 11 (2001): 1071–85.

51. Catriona Macfarlane and Peter Simmonds, "Allelic Variation of HERV-K (HML-2) Endogenous Retroviral Elements in Human Populations," *Journal of Molecular Evolution* 59 (2004): 642–56.

52. Lev A. Zhivotovsky, Noah A. Rosenberg, and Marcus W. Feldman, "Features of Evolution and Expansion of Modern Humans, Inferred from Genomewide Microsatellite Markers," *American Journal of Human*

   Genetics 72 (2003): 1171–86.
53. Lev A. Zhivotovsky et al., "Human Population Expansion and
    Microsatellite Variation," *Molecular Biology and Evolution* 17 (2000):
    757–67.
54. Stead and Jeffreys, "Structural Analysis of Insulin," 1273–84.
55. W. Scott Watkins et al., "Patterns of Ancestral Human Diversity: An
    Analysis of *Alu*-Insertion and Restriction-Site Polymorphisms," *American
    Journal of Human Genetics* 68 (2001): 738–52; W. Scott Watkins et al.,
    "Genetic Variation among World Populations: Inferences from 100 *Alu*
    Insertion Polymorphisms," *Genome Research* 13 (2003): 1607–18.
56. Jack J. Pasternak, *An Introduction to Human Molecular Genetics:
    Mechanisms of Inherited Diseases* (Bethesda, MD: Fitzgerald Science,
    1998), 177–80.
57. S. A. Tishkoff et al., "Global Patterns of Linkage Disequilibrium at the
    CD4 Locus and Modern Human Origins," *Science* 271 (1996): 1380–87.
    For example, see David E. Reich et al., "Linkage Disequilibrium in the
    Human Genome," *Nature* 411 (2001): 199–204.
58. For example, see Reich et al., "Linkage Disequilibrium," 199–204.
59. Christine Lonjou et al., "Linkage Disequilibrium in Human Populations,"
    Proceedings of the National Academy of Sciences, USA 100 (2003): 6069–74.
60. Eric P. Hoberg et al., "Out of Africa: Origins of the *Taenia* Tapeworms in
    Humans," *Proceedings of the Royal Society of London B* 268 (2001): 781–87.
61. Jianbing Mu et al., "Chromosome-Wide SNPs Reveal an Ancient Origin
    for *Plasmodium falciparum*," *Nature* 418 (2002): 323–26.
62. Deirdre A. Joy et al., "Early Origin and Recent Expansion of *Plasmodium
    falciparum*," *Science* 300 (2003): 318–21.
63. Brian G. Spratt, "Stomachs out of Africa," *Science* 299 (2003): 1528–29.
64. Daniel Falush et al., "Traces of Human Migrations in *Helicobacter pylori*
    Populations," *Science* 299 (2003): 1582–85.
65. Angelo Pavesi, "African Origin of Polyomavirus JC and Implications for
    Prehistoric Human Migrations," *Journal of Molecular Evolution* 56 (2003):
    564–72.
66. Ralf Kittler, Manfred Kayser, and Mark Stoneking, "Molecular Evolution
    of *Pediculus humanus* and the Origin of Clothing," *Current Biology* 13
    (2003): 1414–17; J. Travis, "The Naked Truth? Lice Hint at a Recent
    Origin of Clothing," *Science News* 164 (2003): 118; John Whitfield, "Lice
    Genes Date First Human Clothes," *Nature News* (2003): http://www.
    nature.com/news/2003/030818/full/030818-7.html.

67. David L. Reed et al., "Genetic Analysis of Lice Supports Direct Contact between Modern and Archaic Humans," *PLoS Biology* 2 (2004): e340, doi:10.1371/journal.pbio.0020340.
68. Kevin Higgins and Michael Lynch, "Metapopulation Extinction Caused by Mutation Accumulation," *Proceedings of the National Academy of Sciences, USA* 98 (2001): 2928–33.
69. Alan R. Templeton et al., "Disrupting Evolutionary Processes: The Effect of Habitat Fragmentation on Collared Lizards in the Missouri Ozarks," *Proceedings of the National Academy of Sciences, USA* 98 (2001): 5426–32; Gonçalo Ferraz et al., "Rates of Species Loss from Amazonian Forest Fragments," *Proceedings of the National Academy of Sciences, USA* 100 (2003): 14069–73.
70. James V. Briskie and Myles Mackintosh, "Hatching Failure Increases with Severity of Population Bottlenecks in Birds," *Proceedings of the National Academy of Sciences, USA* 101 (2004): 558–61.

Chapter 5: Bones and Stones

1. Adam Sage and Helen Rumbelow, "Richest Prehistoric Cave Art Discovery Owned by British Couple," *Times-London*, July 10, 2001, http://www.rense.com/general11/brits.htm.
2. Roger Lewin, *Principles of Human Evolution: A Core Textbook* (Malden, MA: Blackwell Science, 1998), 384–442.
3. Christopher Stringer and Robin McKie, *African Exodus: The Origins of Modern Humanity* (New York: Henry Holt, 1996), 156; Li Jin and Bing Su, "Natives or Immigrants: Modern Human Origin in East Asia," *Nature Reviews: Genetics* 1 (2001): 126–33.
4. Stringer and McKie, *African Exodus*, 157–59.
5. C. John Collins, *Science and Faith: Friends or Foes?* (Wheaton, IL: Crossway, 2003), 124–27.
6. Millard J. Erickson, *Christian Theology*, 2nd ed. (Grand Rapids, MI: Baker, 1998), 517–36; Wayne Grudem, *Systematic Theology: An Introduction to Biblical Doctrine* (Grand Rapids, MI: Zondervan, 1994), 442–50.
7. For example, see Lewin, *Principles of Human Evolution*, 391–92.
8. Ian McDougall, Francis H. Brown, and John G. Fleagle, "Stratigraphic Placement and Age of Modern Humans from Kibish, Ethiopia," *Nature* 433 (2005): 733–36.
9. Lewin, *Principles of Human Evolution*, 391–92; Richard G. Klein with Blake Edgar, *The Dawn of Human Culture: A Bold New Theory on What*

Sparked the "Big Bang" of Human Consciousness (New York: Wiley, 2002), 223–29; Christopher Stringer, "Modern Human Origins: Progress and Prospects," *Philosophical Transactions of the Royal Society of London B* 357 (2002): 563–79.

10. Lewin, *Principles of Human Evolution*, 91–93.

11. Richard Roberts et al., "Optical and Radiocarbon Dating at Jinmium Rock Shelter in Northern Australia," *Nature* 393 (1998): 358–62.

12. Carl Wieland and Jonathan Sarfati, "Ethiopian 'Earliest Humans' Find: A Severe Blow to the Beliefs of Hugh Ross and Similar 'Progressive Creationist' Compromise Views," *Creation Ministries International*, June 12, 2003, http://creation.com/ethiopian-earliest-humans-find.

13. Ibid.

14. Tim D. White et al., "Pleistocene *Homo sapiens* from Middle Awash, Ethiopia," *Nature* 423 (2003): 742–47; J. Desmond Clark et al., "Stratigraphic, Chronological and Behavioural Contexts of Pleistocene *Homo sapiens* from Middle Awash, Ethiopia," *Nature* 423 (2003): 747–52.

15. Daniel E. Lieberman, Brandeis M. McBratney, and Gail Krovitz, "The Evolution and Development of Cranial Form in *Homo sapiens*," *Proceedings of the National Academy of Sciences, USA* 99 (2002): 1134–39; Erik Trinkaus, "Neandertal Faces Were Not Long; Modern Human Faces Are Short," *Proceedings of the National Academy of Sciences, USA* 100 (2003): 8142–45.

16. White et al., "Pleistocene *Homo sapiens*," 742–47; Clark et al., "Stratigraphic," 747–52.

17. Wieland and Sarfati, "Ethiopian 'Earliest Humans' Find."

18. Stringer and McKie, *African Exodus*, 195–96.

19. Klein with Edgar, *Dawn of Human Culture*, 230–37.

20. Richard G. Klein, *The Human Career: Human Biological and Cultural Origins*, 2nd ed. (Chicago: University of Chicago Press, 1999), 520–29; *Encyclopedia of Human Evolution and Prehistory*, ed. Eric Delson et al., 2nd ed. (New York: Garland, 2000), s.v. "late Paleolithic" and "later Stone Age."

21. Klein with Edgar, *Dawn of Human Culture*, 237–40.

22. Rachel Caspari and Sang-Hee Lee, "Older Age Becomes Common Late in Human Evolution," *Proceedings of the National Academy of Sciences, USA* 101 (2004): 10895–900; Karen Rosenberg, "Living Longer: Information Revolution, Population Expansion, and Modern Human Origins," *Proceedings of the National Academy of Sciences, USA* 101 (2004):

10847–48.

23. *Encyclopedia of Human Evolution and Prehistory*, 2nd ed., "late Paleolithic."

24. Klein with Edgar, *Dawn of Human Culture*, 11–15.

25. Klein, *Human Career*, 512–15.

26. Steven L. Kuhn et al., "Ornaments of the Earliest Upper Paleolithic: New Insights from the Levant," *Proceedings of the National Academy of Sciences, USA* 98 (2001): 7641–46.

27. Lewin, *Principles of Human Evolution*, 469–74.

28. Ibid.

29. Klein, *Human Career*, 545–53.

30. Ibid., 548.

31. Rex Dalton, "Lion Man Takes Pride of Place as Oldest Statue," *Nature News* (2003): http://www.nature.com/news/2003/030901/full/030901-6.html.

32. Nicholas J. Conard, "Palaeolithic Ivory Sculptures from Southwestern Germany and the Origins of Figurative Art," *Nature* 426 (2003): 830–32; Anthony Sinclair, "Archaeology: Art of the Ancients," *Nature* 426 (2003): 774–75.

33. *Encyclopedia of Human Evolution and Prehistory*, 2nd ed., "late Paleolithic."

34. Achim Schneider, "Ice-Age Musicians Fashioned Ivory Flute," *Nature News* (2004): doi:10.1038/news041213-14.

35. Tim Appenzeller, "Evolution or Revolution?," *Science* 282 (1998): 1451–54.

36. Michael Balter, "New Light on the Oldest Art," *Science* 283 (1999): 920–22; H. Valladas et al., "Paleolithic Paintings: Evolution of Prehistoric Cave Art," *Nature* 413 (2001): 479.

37. Sinclair, "Art of the Ancients," 774–75.

38. Ralf Kittler, Manfred Kayser, and Mark Stoneking, "Molecular Evolution of *Pediculus humanus* and the Origin of Clothing," *Current Biology* 13 (2003): 1414–17; J. Travis, "The Naked Truth? Lice Hint at a Recent Origin of Clothing," *Science News* 164 (2003): 118.

39. Klein, *Human Career*, 550–53.

40. Ibid.

41. Ibid., 551–52.

42. Klein with Edgar, *Dawn of Human Culture*, 261.

43. Ibid., 264–70.

44. Ibid.
45. Ibid., 270–72; Klein, *Human Career*, 589–91.
46. Klein with Edgar, *Dawn of Human Culture*, 270–72.
47. Steve Dorus et al., "Accelerated Evolution of Nervous System Genes in the Origin of *Homo sapiens*," *Cell* 119 (2004): 1027–40.
48. Klein with Edgar, *Dawn of Human Culture*, 240–45.
49. Ibid.
50. Christopher S. Henshilwood et al., "An Early Bone Tool Industry from the Middle Stone Age at Blombos Cave, South Africa: Implications for the Origins of Modern Human Behaviour, Symbolism and Language," *Journal of Human Evolution* 41 (2001): 631–78; Christopher S. Henshilwood et al., "Emergence of Modern Human Behavior: Middle Stone Age Engravings from South Africa," *Science* 295 (2002): 1278–80; Christopher S. Henshilwood et al., "Middle Stone Age Shell Beads from South Africa," *Science* 304 (2004): 404.
51. Richard Klein et al., "The Ysterfontein 1 Middle Stone Age Site, South Africa, and Early Human Exploitation of Coastal Resources," *Proceedings of the National Academy of Sciences, USA* 101 (2004): 5708–15.

Chapter 6: The Best Possible Time

1. Genesis 1:26–31; 9:1, 7; 11:7–8; Daniel 12:4; Matthew 28:18–20; Revelation 9:13–19; 18:11–18.
2. Kevin A. Maher and David J. Stevenson, "Impact Frustration of the Origin of Life," *Nature* 331 (1988): 612–14; Verne R. Oberbeck and Guy Fogleman, "Impacts and the Origin of Life," *Nature* 339 (1989): 434; Norman H. Sleep et al., "Annihilation of Ecosystems by Large Asteroid Impacts on the Early Earth," *Nature* 342 (1989): 139–42; Stephen J. Mojzsis, "Lithosphere-Hydrosphere Interactions on the Hadean (>4.0 Ga) Earth," *Astrobiology* 1 (2001): 382–83; Christopher Wills and Jeffrey Bada, *The Spark of Life: Darwin and the Primeval Soup* (Cambridge, MA: Perseus, 2000), 71–74; Richard A. Kerr, "Beating Up on a Young Earth, and Possibly Life," *Science* 290 (2000): 1677; B. A. Cohen, T. D. Swindle, and D. A. Kring, "Support for the Lunar Cataclysm Hypothesis for Lunar Meteorite Impact Melt Ages," *Science* 290 (2000): 1754–56.
3. Icko Iben Jr., "Stellar Evolution. I. The Approach to the Main Sequence," *Astrophysical Journal* 141 (1965): 993–1018, especially page 1000; G. Wuchterl and Ralf S. Klessen, "The First Million Years of the Sun: A Calculation of the Formation and Early Evolution of a Solar Mass

Star," *Astrophysical Journal Letters* 560 (2001): L185–L188; Frederick M. Walter and Don C. Barry, "Pre- and Main-Sequence Evolution of Solar Activity," in *The Sun in Time*, ed. C. P. Sonett, M. S. Giampapa, and M. S. Matthews (Tucson: University of Arizona Press, 1991), 633–57, note Table IV on page 653; David R. Soderblom, Burton F. Jones, and Debra Fischer, "Rotational Studies of Late-Type Stars. VII. M34 (NGC 1039) and the Evolution of Angular Momentum and Activity in Young Solar-Type Stars," *Astrophysical Journal* 563 (2001): 334–40.

4. Hugh Ross, "The Faint Sun Paradox," *Facts for Faith*, no. 10 (Q3 2002), 26–33; Fazale Rana and Hugh Ross, *Origins of Life: Biblical and Evolutionary Models Face Off* (Colorado Springs: NavPress, 2004), 218–21; Matthias Labrenz et al., "Formation of Sphalerite (ZnS) Deposits in Natural Biofilms of Sulfate-Reducing Bacteria," *Science* 290 (2000): 1744–47; Crisogono Vasconcelos and Judith A. McKenzie, "Sulfate Reducers—Dominant Players in a Low-Oxygen World?," *Science* 290 (2000): 1711–12.

5. Hugh Ross, *The Creator and the Cosmos: How the Greatest Scientific Discoveries of the Century Reveal God*, 3rd ed. (Colorado Springs: NavPress, 2001), 145–57.

6. Ibid., 145–57, 176–78, 188–89; Alister W. Graham, "An Investigation into the Prominence of Spiral Galaxy Bulges," *Astronomical Journal* 121 (2001): 820–40.

7. S. Chakrabarti, G. Laughlin, and F. H. Shu, "Branch, Spur, and Feather Formation in Spiral Galaxies," *Astrophysical Journal* 596 (2003): 220–39.

8. John Emsley, *The Elements*, 3rd ed. (Oxford, UK: Clarendon, 1998), 24, 40, 56, 58, 60, 62, 78, 102, 106, 122, 130, 138, 152, 160, 188, 198, 214, 222, 230.

9. Labrenz et al., "Formation of Sphalerite," 1744–47.

10. Vasconcelos and McKenzie, "Sulfate Reducers," 1711–12.

11. David Schwartzman and Tyler Volk, "Biotic Enhancement of Weathering and the Habitability of Earth," *Nature* 340 (1989): 457–60; Richard Monastersky, "Supersoil," *Science News* 136 (1989): 376–77.

12. Francesco Calura and Francesca Matteucci, "The Cosmic Evolution of the Galaxy Luminosity Density," *Astrophysical Journal* 596 (2003): 734–47.

13. Bernard E. J. Pagel, *Nucleosynthesis and Chemical Evolution of Galaxies* (Cambridge: Cambridge University Press, 1997), 205–6; D. Hardin et al., "Type Ia Supernova Rate at z ~ 0.1," *Astronomy and Astrophysics* 362 (2000): 419–25.

14. J. Goyette et al., "The History of the Local ISM: The Last 50 Million

Years," 198th Meeting of the American Astronomical Society, Session 65.01, *Bulletin of the American Astronomical Society* 33 (2001): 884; Thomas Preibisch et al., "Exploring the Full Stellar Population of the Upper Scorpius OB Association," *Astronomical Journal* 124 (2002): 404–16; Jesús Maíz-Apellániz, "The Origin of the Local Bubble," *Astrophysical Journal Letters* 560 (2001): L83–L86; Narciso Benítez, Jesús Maíz-Apellániz, and Matilde Canelles, "Evidence for Nearby Supernova Explosions," *Physical Review Letters* 88 (2002): http://arxiv.org/abs/astro-ph/0201018.

15. Benítez, Maíz-Apellániz, and Canelles, "Nearby Supernova Explosions"; Maíz-Apellániz, "Local Bubble," L83–L86.

16. Maíz-Apellániz, "Local Bubble," L83–L86.

17. Benítez, Maíz-Apellániz, and Canelles, "Nearby Supernova Explosions," http://arxiv.org/abs/astro-ph/0201018.

18. Ibid.

19. Peter L. Biermann et al., "The Last Gamma-Ray Burst in Our Galaxy? On the Observed Cosmic-Ray Excess at Particle Energy 10^{18} eV," *Astrophysical Journal Letters* 604 (2004): L29–L32.

20. D. H. Clark and F. R. Stephenson, *The Historical Supernovae* (New York: Pergamon, 1977); F. R. Stephenson and D. H. Clark, "Historical Supernovas," *Scientific American*, June 1976, 100–107; F. R. Stephenson and D. A. Green, *Historical Supernovae and Their Remnants* (Oxford, UK: Oxford University Press, 2002); "Supernovae Observed in the Milky Way: Historical Supernovae," *The Messier Catalog*, accessed November 11, 2003, http://messier.seds.org/more/mw_sn.html.

21. E. V. Gotthelf et al., "A 700-Year-Old Pulsar in the Supernova Remnant Kesteven 75," *Astrophysical Journal Letters* 542 (2000): L37–L40; F. Camilo et al., "PSR J1124-5916: Discovery of a Young Energetic Pulsar in the Supernova Remnant G292.0+1.8," *Astrophysical Journal Letters* 567 (2002): L71–L75; Cara E. Rukowski, John P. Hughes, and Patrick Slane, "Two New Ejecta-Dominated Galactic Supernova Remnants: G337.2-0.7 and G309.2-0.6," *Astrophysical Journal* 548 (2001): 258–68; David J. Helfand, Benjamin F. Collins, and E. V. Gotthelf, "*Chandra* X-Ray Imaging Spectroscopy of the Young Supernova Remnant Kesteven 75," *Astrophysical Journal* 582 (2003): 783–92; E. V. Gotthelf, "X-Ray Spectra of Young Pulsars and Their Wind Nebulae: Dependence on Spin-Down Energy Loss Rate," *Astrophysical Journal* 591 (2003): 361–65; Fronefield Crawford et al., "A Radio Supernova Remnant Associated with the Young

Pulsar J1119-6127," *Astrophysical Journal* 554 (2001): 152–60; V. M. Kaspi et al., "*Chandra* X-Ray Observations of G11.2-0.3: Implications for Pulsar Ages," *Astrophysical Journal* 560 (2001): 371–77; G. M. Dubner et al., "The Interstellar Medium around the Supernova Remnant G320.4-1.2," *Astronomical Journal* 123 (2002): 337–45.

22. A. A. Pavlov et al., "Passing through a Giant Molecular Cloud: 'Snowball' Glaciations Produced by Interstellar Dust," *Geophysical Research Letters* 32 (2005): doi:10.1029/2004GL021890.

23. D. O. Gough, "Solar Interior Structure and Luminosity Variations," *Solar Physics* 74 (1981): 21–34; Rudolf Kippenhahn and Alfred Weigert, *Stellar Structure and Evolution* (New York: Springer-Verlag, 1994), 162–64.

24. Since the luminosity of a star close to the solar mass depends on the 3.9 power of its mass (L ~ T3.9), even a little mass loss can dramatically lower the Sun's brightness. See Kippenhahn and Weigert, *Stellar Structure and Evolution*, 207–9.

25. I.-Juliana Sackmann and Arnold I. Boothroyd, "Our Sun. V. A Bright Young Sun Consistent with Helioseismology and Warm Temperatures on Ancient Earth and Mars," *Astrophysical Journal* 583 (2003): 1024–39.

26. Alan J. Kaufman and Shuhai Xiao, "High CO_2 Levels in the Proterozoic Atmosphere Estimated from Analyses of Individual Microfossils," *Nature* 425 (2003): 279–82; Stephen J. Mojzsis, "Global Change: Probing Early Atmospheres," *Nature* 425 (2003): 249–50.

27. Mercedes T. Richards et al., "Statistical Analysis of 5 Year Continuous Radio Flare Data from β Persei, V711 Tauri, δ Librae, and UX Arietis," *Astrophysical Journal Supplement* 147 (2003): 337–61.

28. M. W. Caffee et al., "Evidence in Meteorites for an Active Early Sun," *Astrophysical Journal Letters* 313 (1987): L31–L35; M. W. Caffee et al., "Irradiation Records in Meteorites," in *Meteorites and the Early Solar System*, ed. J. F. Kerridge and M. S. Matthews (Tucson: University of Arizona Press, 1988), 205–45; Daniel P. Whitmire et al., "A Slightly More Massive Young Sun as an Explanation for Warm Temperatures on Early Mars," *Journal of Geophysical Research* 100 (1995): 5457–64.

29. J. Geiss, "Solar Wind Composition and Implications about the History of the Solar System," in *Proceedings of the 13th International Cosmic Ray Conference*, vol. 5 (Denver: University of Denver Press, 1973), 3375–98; J. Geiss and P. Bochsler, "Long Time Variations in Solar Wind Properties: Possible Causes versus Observations," in *Sun in Time*, 98–117; J. F. Kerridge et al., "Long-Term Changes in Composition of Solar Particles

Implanted in Extraterrestrial Materials," in *Sun in Time*, 389–412.

30. Brian E. Wood et al., "Observational Estimates for the Mass-Loss Rates of α Centauri and Proxima Centauri Using *Hubble Space Telescope* Lyα Spectra," *Astrophysical Journal Letters* 547 (2001): L49–L52.

31. Richard R. Radick, "The Luminosity Variability of Solar-Type Stars," in *Sun in Time*, 805.

32. Ross, "Faint Sun Paradox," 26–33.

33. H. M. Antia, "Does the Sun Shrink with Increasing Magnetic Activity?," *Astrophysical Journal* 590 (2003): 567–72.

34. Q. R. Ahmad et al., "Measurement of the Rate $v_e + d \rightarrow p + p + e^-$ Interactions Produced by ^8B Solar Neutrinos at the Sudbury Neutrino Observatory," *Physical Review Letters* 87 (2001): 71301–5; A. B. Balantekin and H. Yüksel, "Do the KamLAND and Solar Neutrino Data Rule Out Solar Density Fluctuations?," *Physical Review D* 68 (2003): doi:10.1103/ physrevd.68.013006.

35. The Sun, though nearly 27 million times more massive, is so far away with respect to the Moon that its tidal torques are less than half the Moon's.

36. Perry G. Phillips, *Tidal Slowdown, Coral Growth, and the Age of the Earth* (Hatfield, PA: Interdisciplinary Biblical Research Institute, 1989); Alan Hayward, *Creation and Evolution: The Facts and the Fallacies* (London: Triangle Books, 1985), 95–96.

37. George Abell, *Exploration of the Universe* (New York: Holt, Rinehart and Winston, 1964), 195–209.

38. Ibid., 210–13.

39. F. W. Dyson, Arthur S. Eddington, and C. Davidson, "A Determination of the Deflection of Light by the Sun's Gravitational Field, from Observations Made at the Total Eclipse of May 29, 1919," *Philosophical Transactions of the Royal Society of London A* 220 (1920): 291–333.

40. Peter D. Ward and Donald Brownlee, *Rare Earth: Why Complex Life Is Uncommon in the Universe* (New York: Copernicus, 2000), 226.

41. Because the Moon's orbit is not perfectly circular, there are times when the Moon's distance from Earth is great enough that at the instant of a solar eclipse, the Moon's disk appears smaller than the Sun's. During such an eclipse, a ring of sunlight appears all around the Moon's disk and blazes so brightly that observation of the solar corona and adjacent stars proves impossible.

42. Patricia Barnes-Svarney, ed., *The New York Public Library Science Desk*

Reference (New York: Macmillan, 1995), 330.

43. Rana and Ross, *Origins of Life*, 84–87; Ross, "Faint Sun Paradox," 26–33.

44. J. S. Seewald, "Organic-Inorganic Interactions in Petroleum-Producing Sedimentary Basins," *Nature* 426 (2003): 327–33.

45. I. M. Head, D. M. Jones, and S. R. Larter, "Biological Activity in the Deep Subsurface and the Origin of Heavy Oil," *Nature* 426 (2003): 344–52.

46. N. White, M. Thompson, and T. Barwise, "Understanding the Thermal Evolution of Deep-Water Continental Margins," *Nature* 426 (2003): 334–43.

47. Richard H. Tedford and C. Richard Harington, "An Arctic Mammal Fauna from the Early Pliocene of North America," *Nature* 425 (2003): 388–90.

48. Spencer Weart, "The Discovery of Rapid Climate Change," *Physics Today*, August 2003, 30–36; Committee on Abrupt Climate Change, National Research Council, *Abrupt Climate Change: Inevitable Surprises* (Washington, DC: National Academy Press, 2002), accessed September 15, 2003, http://books.nap.edu/books/0309074347/html.

49. Dominik Fleitmann et al., "Holocene Forcing of the Indian Monsoon Recorded in a Stalagmite from Southern Oman," *Science* 300 (2003): 1737–39.

50. For an up-to-date listing of these windows and other design features necessary for the survival of advanced life, see the documents on Design Evidences, http://www.reasons.org/articles/rtb-design-compendium-2009, on the Reasons to Believe website, www.reasons.org.

Chapter 7: How the Fountain of Youth Ran Dry

1. Hugh Ross, *The Genesis Question: Scientific Advances and the Accuracy of Genesis*, 2nd ed. (Colorado Springs: NavPress, 2000), 117–18.

2. "The Origins of Writing," in *Heilbrunn Timeline of Art History*, Metrpolitan Museum of Art, accessed May 7, 2015, http://www.metmuseum.org/toah/hd/wrtg/hd_wrtg.htm.

3. For example, "Humans Could Live for Hundreds of Years," *Ananova.com*, accessed May 7, 2015, http://www.longecity.org/forum/topic/2076-humans-could-live-for-hundreds-of-years/.

4. Toren Finkel and Nikki J. Holbrook, "Oxidants, Oxidative Stress, and the Biology of Ageing," *Nature* 408 (2000): 239–47.

5. Sandeep Raha and Brian H. Robinson, "Mitochondria, Oxygen Free Radicals, Disease and Ageing," *Trends in Biochemistry* 25 (2000): 502–8.

6. Robert Arking, *Biology of Aging*, 2nd ed. (Sunderland, MA: Sinauer

Associates, 1998), 398–414; Finkel and Holbrook, "Oxidants, Oxidative Stress," 239–47.

7. Lubert Stryer, *Biochemistry*, 3rd ed. (New York: W. H. Freeman, 1988), 422.

8. Arking, *Biology of Aging*, 401–3.

9. Simon Melov et al., "Extension of Life Span with Superoxide Dismutase/Catalase Mimetics," *Science* 289 (2000): 1567–69.

10. Enzyme mimetics are synthetic compounds that catalyze the same chemical reactions as the enzymes after which they are named. For example, superoxide dismutase/catalase enzyme mimetics catalyze the decomposition of superoxide and hydrogen peroxide.

11. Oddly enough, the model systems used to study aging—yeast, nematodes, and fruit flies, for example—accurately reflect the mechanisms leading to senescence in humans. This stems from the fundamental unity of biochemistry among eukaryotic organisms (single- and multicellular organisms composed of complex cells—cells possessing a nucleus and internal membrane structures).

12. Melov et al., "Extension of Life Span," 1567–69.

13. Ruolan Liu et al., "Reversal of Age-Related Learning Deficits and Brain Oxidative Stress in Mice with Superoxide Dismutase/Catalase Mimetics," *Proceedings of the National Academy of Sciences, USA* 100 (2003): 8526–31.

14. Raha and Robinson, "Mitochondria, Oxygen Free-Radicals," 502–8.

15. Peng Huang et al., "Superoxide Dismutase as a Target for the Selective Killing of Cancer Cells," *Nature* 407 (2000): 390–95.

16. James Taub et al., "A Cytosolic Catalase Is Needed to Extend Adult Lifespan in *C. elegans daf-C* and *clk-1* Mutants," *Nature* 399 (1999): 162–66.

17. Jackob Moskovitz et al., "Overexpression of Peptide-Methionine Sulfoxide Reductase in *Saccharomyces cerevisiae* and Human T Cells Provides Them with High Resistance to Oxidative Stress," *Proceedings of the National Academy of Sciences, USA* 95 (1998): 14071–75.

18. Jackob Moskovitz et al., "Methionine Sulfoxide Reductase (MsrA) Is a Regulator of Antioxidant Defense and Lifespan in Mammals," *Proceedings of the National Academy of Sciences, USA* 98 (2001): 12920–25.

19. Arking, *Biology of Aging*, 313–27.

20. Luigi Fontana et al., "Long-Term Calorie Restriction Is Highly Effective in Reducing the Risk for Atherosclerosis in Humans," *Proceedings of the National Academy of Sciences, USA* 101 (2004): 6659–63.

21. Leonard Guarente and Cynthia Kenyon, "Genetic Pathways That Regulate Ageing in Model Organisms," *Nature* 408 (2000): 255–62.
22. Pierre-Antoine Defossez, Su-Ju Lin, and David S. McNabb, "Sound Silencing: The Sir2 Protein and Cellular Senescence," *Bioessays* 23 (2001): 327–32. A recent study (Matt Kaeberlein et al., "Sir2-Independent Life Span Extension by Calorie Restriction in Yeast," *PLoS Biology* 2 [2004]: e296) indicates that another mechanism, in addition to Sir2 activation, may be at work in caloric restriction. Researchers showed that combining caloric restriction with enhanced Sir2 activity extended life spans to a much greater degree than did either approach independently.
23. Jeffrey S. Smith et al., "A Phylogenetically Conserved NAD+-Dependent Protein Deacetylase Activity in the Sir2 Protein Family," *Proceedings of the National Academy of Sciences, USA* 97 (2000): 6658–63.
24. Su-Ju Lin et al., "Calorie Restriction Extends *Saccharomyces cerevisiae* Lifespan by Increasing Respiration," *Nature* 418 (2002): 344–48; Siu Sylvia Lee and Gary Ruvkun, "Don't Hold Your Breath," *Nature* 418 (2002): 287–88.
25. Defossez, Lin, and McNabb, "Sound Silencing," 327–32; Shin-Ichiro Imai et al., "Transcriptional Silencing and Longevity Protein Sir2 Is an NAD-Dependent Histone Deacetylase," *Nature* 403 (2000): 795–800; Joseph Landry et al., "The Silencing Protein SIR2 and Its Homologs Are NAD-Dependent Protein Deacetylases," *Proceedings of the National Academy of Sciences, USA* 97 (2000): 5807–11; Jason C. Tanny and Danesh Moazed, "Coupling of Histone Deacetylation to NAD Breakdown by the Yeast Silencing Protein Sir2: Evidence for Acetyl Transfer from Substrate to an NAD Breakdown Product," *Proceedings of the National Academy of Sciences, USA* 98 (2001): 415–20.
26. Defossez, Lin, and McNabb, "Sound Silencing," 327–32; Su-Ju Lin, Pierre-Antoine Defossez, and Leonard Guarente, "Requirement of NAD and *SIR2* for Life-Span Extension by Calorie Restriction in *Saccharomyces cerevisiae*," *Science* 289 (2000): 2126–28; Judith Campisi, "Aging, Cromatin, and Food Restriction—Connecting the Dots," *Science* 289 (2000): 2062–63; David A. Sinclair and Leonard Guarente, "Extrachromosomal rDNA Circles—A Cause of Aging in Yeast," *Cell* 91 (1997): 1033–42.
27. Antonio Bedalov et al., "Identification of a Small Molecule Inhibitor of Sir2p," *Proceedings of the National Academy of Sciences, USA* 98 (2001): 15113–18.

28. Toshiyuki Araki, Yo Sasaki, and Jeffrey Milbrandt, "Increased Nuclear NAD Biosynthesis and SIRT1 Activation Prevent Axonal Degeneration," *Science* 305 (2004): 1010–13.
29. Haim Y. Cohen et al., "Calorie Restriction Promotes Mammalian Cell Survival by Inducing the SIRT1 Deacetylase," *Science* 305 (2004): 390–92.
30. Heidi A. Tissenbaum and Leonard Guarente, "Increased Dosage of a *sir-2* Gene Extends Lifespan in *Caenorhabditis elegans*," *Nature* 410 (2001): 227–30; David Gems, "Ageing: Yeast Longevity Gene Goes Public," *Nature* 410 (2001): 154–55.
31. Konrad T. Howitz et al., "Small Molecule Activators of Sirtuins Extend *Saccharomyces cerevisiae* Lifespan," *Nature* 425 (2003): 191–96; Jason G. Wood et al., "Sirtuin Activators Mimic Caloric Restriction and Delay Ageing in Metazoans," *Nature* 430 (2004): 686–89.
32. Ken Yokoyama et al., "Extended Longevity of *Caenorhabditis elegans* by Knocking In Extra Copies of Hsp70F, a Homolog of Mot-2 (Mortalin)/Mthsp60/Grp75," *FEBS Letters* 516 (2002): 53–57; Ao-Lin Hsu, Coleen T. Murphy, and Cynthia Kenyon, "Regulation of Aging and Age-Related Disease by DAF-16 and Heat-Shock Factor," *Science* 300 (2003): 1142–43.
33. Alan G. Atherly, Jack R. Girton, and John F. McDonald, *The Science of Genetics* (Fort Worth, TX: Saunders College Publishing, 1999), 302–3.
34. Arking, *Biology of Aging*, 460–64.
35. For example, see Teruhiko Wakayama et al., "Ageing: Cloning of Mice to Six Generations," *Nature* 407 (2000): 318–19; Dean H. Betts et al., "Reprogramming of Telomerase Activity and Rebuilding of Telomere Length in Cloned Cattle," *Proceedings of the National Academy of Sciences, USA* 98 (2001): 1077–82.
36. Andrea G. Bodnar et al., "Extension of Life-Span by Introduction of Telomerase into Normal Human Cells," *Science* 279 (1998): 349–52.
37. Douglas Hanahan, "Cancer: Benefits of Bad Telomeres," *Nature* 406 (2000): 573–74.
38. For example, see Kee-Ho Lee et al., "Telomere Dysfunction Alters the Chemotherapeutic Profile of Transformed Cells," *Proceedings of the National Academy of Sciences, USA* 98 (2001): 3381–86; Jean-Louis Mergny et al., "Telomerase Inhibitors Based on Quadruplex Ligands Selected by a Fluorescence Assay," *Proceedings of the National Academy of Sciences, USA* 98 (2001): 3062–67.
39. Steven E. Artandi et al., "Telomere Dysfunction Promotes Non-Reciprocal Translocations and Epithelial Cancers in Mice," *Nature* 406 (2000):

641–45; Elizabeth H. Blackburn, "Telomere States and Cell Fates," *Nature* 408 (2000): 53–56.

40. Andrei Seluanov et al., "DNA End Joining Becomes Less Efficient and More Error-Prone during Cellular Senescence," *Proceedings of the National Academy of Sciences, USA* 101 (2004): 7624–29.

41. For example, see Junko Oshima, "The Werner Syndrome Protein: An Update," *Bioessays* 22 (2000): 894–901; George M. Martin and Junko Oshima, "Lessons from Human Progeroid Syndromes," *Nature* 408 (2000): 263–66.

42. Dan E. Arking et al., "Association of Human Aging with a Functional Variant of Klotho," *Proceedings of the National Academy of Sciences, USA* 99 (2002): 856–61.

43. Yi-Jyun Lin, Laurent Seroude, and Seymour Benzer, "Extended Life-Span and Stress Resistance in the *Drosophila* Mutant *methuselah*," *Science* 282 (1998): 943–46.

44. Anthony P. West Jr. et al., "Crystal Structure of the Ectodomain of Methuselah, a *Drosophila* G Protein-Coupled Receptor Associated with Extended Lifespan," *Proceedings of the National Academy of Sciences, USA* 98 (2001): 3744–49.

45. Elizabeth Pennisi, "Old Flies May Hold Secrets of Aging," *Science* 290 (2000): 2048; Blanka Rogina et al., "Extended Life-Span Conferred by Cotransporter Gene Mutations in *Drosophila*," *Science* 290 (2000): 2137–40.

46. John Travis, "Old Worms, New Aging Genes," *Science News* 164 (2003): 75–77; Marc Tatar, Andrzej Bartke, and Adam Antebi, "The Endocrine Regulation of Aging by Insulin-Like Signals," *Science* 299 (2003): 1346–51; Siegfried Hekimi and Leonard Guarente, "Genetics and the Specificity of the Aging Process," *Science* 299 (2003): 1351–54; Cynthia Kenyon, "A Conserved Regulatory System for Aging," *Cell* 105 (2001): 165–68.

47. Hekimi and Guarente, "Genetics," 1351–54.

48. Nuno Arantes-Oliveira, Jennifer R. Berman, and Cynthia Kenyon, "Healthy Animals with Extreme Longevity," *Science* 302 (2003): 611.

49. Elizabeth Pennisi, "Single Gene Controls Fruit Fly Life-Span," *Science* 282 (1998): 856.

50. A. D. Erlykin and A. W. Wolfendale, "A Single Source of Cosmic Rays in the Range 10^{15}–10^{16} eV," *Journal of Physics G: Nuclear and Particle Physics* 23 (1997): 979–89; A. D. Erlykin and A. W. Wolfendale, "High-Energy Cosmic Ray Mass Spectroscopy. II. Masses in the Range 10^{14}–10^{17}

eV," *Astroparticle Physics* 7 (1997): 203–11; A. D. Erlykin and A. W. Wolfendale, "'Fine Structure' in the Energy Spectrum, and Changes in the Mass Composition, of Cosmic Rays in the Energy Range 0.3–10 PeV," *Astronomy and Astrophysics Letters* 350 (1999): L1–L4; A. D. Erlykin and A. W. Wolfendale, "The Origin of PeV Cosmic Rays," *Astronomy and Astrophysics Letters* 356 (2000): L63–L65; A. D. Erlykin and A. W. Wolfendale, "Structure in the Cosmic Ray Spectrum: An Update," *Journal of Physics G: Nuclear and Particle Physics* 27 (2001): 1005–30; A. D. Erlykin and A. W. Wolfendale, "High-Energy Cosmic Gamma Rays from the 'Single Source,'" *Journal of Physics G: Nuclear and Particle Physics* 29 (2003): 709–18; A. D. Erlykin and A. W. Wolfendale, "Spectral Features and Masses in the PeV Region," *Nuclear Physics B - Proceedings Supplements* 122 (2003): 209–12.

51. Erlykin and Wolfendale, "Single Source," 979–89; Erlykin and Wolfendale, "Spectral Features and Masses," 209–12.

52. A. Erlykin and A. Wolfendale, "High-Energy Cosmic Ray Spectroscopy. I. Status and Prospects," *Astroparticle Physics* 7 (1997): 1–13; Peter L. Biermann, "Not-So-Cosmic Rays," *Nature* 388 (1997): 25.

53. R. Dodson et al., "The Vela Pulsar's Proper Motion and Parallax Derived from VLBI Observations," *Astrophysical Journal* 596 (2003): 1137–41.

54. B. Aschenback, R. Egger, and J. Trümper, "Discovery of Explosion Fragments outside the Vela Supernova Remnant Shock-Wave Boundary," *Nature* 373 (1995): 587–90; A. G. Lyne et al., "Very Low Braking Index for the Vela Pulsar," *Nature* 381 (1996): 497–98.

55. Erlykin and Wolfendale, "Spectral Features," 209–12.

56. Erlykin and Wolfendale, "High-Energy Cosmic Gamma Rays," 709–18.

Chapter 8: People on the Move

1. M. A. Jobling, M. E. Hurles, and C. Tyler-Smith, *Human Evolutionary Genetics: Origins, Peoples and Disease* (New York: Garland, 2004), 289.

2. Ornella Semino et al., "Ethiopians and Khosian Share the Deepest Clades of the Human Y-Chromosome Phylogeny," *American Journal of Human Genetics* 70 (2002): 265–68.

3. Jobling, Hurles, and Tyler-Smith, *Human Evolutionary Genetics*, 289–91.

4. Ibid., 289.

5. M. F. Hammer et al., "Out of Africa and Back Again: Nested Cladistic Analysis of Human Y Chromosome Variation," *Molecular Biology and Evolution* 15 (1998): 427–41; Fulvio Cruciani et al., "A Back Migration

from Asia to Sub-Saharan Africa Is Supported by High-Resolution Analysis of Human Y-Chromosome Haplotypes," *American Journal of Human Genetics* 70 (2002): 1197–214.

6. Jobling, Hurles, and Tyler-Smith, *Human Evolutionary Genetics*, 284–85.
7. Ibid.
8. Ibid., 289–91.
9. Ibid., 289–90; Martin Richards and Vincent Macaulay, "The Mitochondrial Gene Tree Comes of Age," *American Journal of Human Genetics* 68 (2001): 1315–20; Max Ingman et al., "Mitochondrial Genome Variation and the Origin of Modern Humans," *Nature* 408 (2000): 708–13.
10. Ingman et al., "Mitochondrial Genome Variation," 708–13.
11. Jobling, Hurles, and Tyler-Smith, *Human Evolutionary Genetics*, 290–91.
12. Ornella Semino et al., "The Genetic Legacy of Paleolithic *Homo sapiens sapiens* in Extant Europeans: A Y Chromosome Perspective," *Science* 290 (2000): 1155–59; Ann Gibbons, "Europeans Trace Ancestry to Paleolithic People," *Science* 290 (2000): 1080–81; Spencer Wells, *The Journey of Man: A Genetic Odyssey* (Princeton, NJ: Princeton University Press, 2002), 182–83.
13. Semino et al., "Genetic Legacy," 1155–59; Gibbons, "Europeans Trace Ancestry," 1080–81; Wells, *Journey of Man*, 182–83; Hugh Ross, *The Genesis Question: Scientific Advances and the Accuracy of Genesis*, 2nd ed. (Colorado Springs: NavPress, 2001), 185–87; Manfred Heun et al., "Site of Einkorn Wheat Domestication Identified by DNA Fingerprinting," *Science* 278 (1997): 1312–14; Jared Diamond, "Location, Location, Location: The First Farmers," *Science* 278 (1997): 1243–44; Melinda A. Zeder and Brian Hesse, "The Initial Domestication of Goats (*Capra hircus*) in the Zagros Mountains 10,000 Years Ago," *Science* 287 (2000): 2254–57.
14. Jobling, Hurles, and Tyler-Smith, *Human Evolutionary Genetics*, 284–86.
15. Ibid.
16. Li Jin and Bing Su, "Natives or Immigrants: Modern Human Origin in East Asia," *Nature Reviews: Genetics* 1 (2000): 126–33.
17. Jobling, Hurles, and Tyler-Smith, *Human Evolutionary Genetics*, 284–89.
18. V. V. Pitulko et al., "The Yana RHS Site: Humans in the Arctic before the Last Glacial Maximum," *Science* 303 (2004): 52–56; Richard Stone, "A Surprising Survival Story in the Siberian Arctic," *Science* 303 (2004): 33.
19. Jobling, Hurles, and Tyler-Smith, *Human Evolutionary Genetics*, 289–91.
20. Jin and Su, "Natives or Immigrants," 126–32.

21. L. Quintana-Murci et al., "Genetic Evidence of an Early Exit of *Homo sapiens sapiens* from Africa through Eastern Africa," *Nature Genetics* 23 (1999): 437–41.

22. Ibid.; Ingman et al., "Mitochondrial Genome Variation," 708–13.

23. Jobling, Hurles, and Tyler-Smith, *Human Evolutionary Genetics*, 289–91.

24. Ibid.; R. Thomson et al., "Recent Common Ancestry of Human Y Chromosomes: Evidence from DNA Sequence Data," *Proceedings of the National Academy of Sciences, USA* 97 (2000): 7360–65.

25. Christopher Stringer, "Palaeoanthropology: Coasting out of Africa," *Nature* 405 (2000): 24–27; Todd Disotell, "Human Evolution: The Southern Route to Asia," *Current Biology* 9 (1999): R925–R928.

26. Jobling, Hurles, and Tyler-Smith, *Human Evolutionary Genetics*, 286–87.

27. Ibid.; James M. Bowler et al., "New Ages for Human Occupation and Climatic Change at Lake Mungo, Australia," *Nature* 421 (2003): 837–40.

28. Jobling, Hurles, and Tyler-Smith, *Human Evolutionary Genetics*, 286–87.

29. Bowler et al., "New Ages for Human Occupation," 837–40.

30. Roger Lewin, *Principles of Human Evolution: A Core Textbook* (Malden, MA: Blackwell Science, 1998), 493–96.

31. Ibid.; Jobling, Hurles, and Tyler-Smith, *Human Evolutionary Genetics*, 286–87.

32. Lewin, *Principles of Human Evolution*, 493–96; Jobling, Hurles, and Tyler-Smith, *Human Evolutionary Genetics*, 286–87.

33. Lewin, *Principles of Human Evolution*, 493–96.

34. Richard Roberts et al., "Optical and Radiocarbon Dating at Jinmium Rock Shelter in Northern Australia," *Nature* 393 (1998): 358–62; Hugh Ross, "New Date for First Aussies," *Connections* 6 (2004), 2–3.

35. Yuehai Ke et al., "African Origin of Modern Humans in East Asia: A Tale of 12,000 Y Chromosomes," *Science* 292 (2001): 1151–53.

36. Shelia M. van Holst Pellekaan et al., "Mitochondrial Control-Region Sequence Variation in Aboriginal Australians," *American Journal of Human Genetics* 62 (1998): 435–49; Alan J. Redd and Mark Stoneking, "Peopling of Sahul: mtDNA Variation in Aboriginal Australian and Papua New Guinean Populations," *American Journal of Human Genetics* 65 (1999): 808–28.

37. Manfred Kayser et al., "Independent Histories of Human Y Chromosomes from Melanesia and Australia," *American Journal of Human Genetics* 68 (2001): 173–90; R. Spencer Wells et al., "The Eurasian Heartland: A Continental Perspective on Y-Chromosome Diversity," *Proceedings of the*

National Academy of Sciences, USA 98 (2001): 10244–49.

38. Wells, "Eurasian Heartland," 61–80.

39. Quintana-Murci et al., "Genetic Evidence," 437–41.

40. Van Holst Pellekaan et al., "Mitochondrial Control-Region," 435–49; Redd and Stoneking, "Peopling of Sahul," 808–28; Max Ingman and Ulf Gyllensten, "Mitochondrial Genome Variation and Evolutionary History of Australian and New Guinean Aborigines," *Genome Research* 13 (2003): 1600–1606.

41. Lewin, *Principles of Human Evolution*, 493–96; *Encyclopedia of Human Evolution and Prehistory*, ed. Eric Delson et al., 2nd ed. (New York: Garland, 2000), s.v. "Australia."

42. Lewin, *Principles of Human Evolution*, 493–96.

43. Ibid., 485.

44. Jobling, Hurles, and Tyler-Smith, *Human Evolutionary Genetics*, 343–45.

45. Tom D. Dillehay, "Palaeoanthropology: Tracking the First Americans," *Nature* 425 (2003): 23–24.

46. Rolando González-José et al., "Craniometric Evidence for Palaeoamerican Survival in Baja California," *Nature* 425 (2003): 62–65.

47. Lewin, *Principles of Human Evolution*, 492–94; Richard Monastersky, "The Killing Fields: What Robbed the Americas of Their Most Charismatic Mammals?," *Science News* 156 (1999): 360–61; John Alroy, "A Multispecies Overkill Simulation of the End-Pleistocene Megafaunal Mass Extinction," *Science* 292 (2001): 1893–96.

48. Jobling, Hurles, and Tyler-Smith, *Human Evolutionary Genetics*, 345–48; Lewin, *Principles of Human Evolution*, 488–90.

49. Eliot Marshall, "Clovis First," *Science* 291 (2001): 1732.

50. Lewin, *Principles of Human Evolution*, 488–90.

51. Eliot Marshall, "Pre-Clovis Sites Fight for Acceptance," *Science* 291 (2001): 1730–32; Terrence Falk, "Wisconsin Dig Seeks to Confirm Pre-Clovis Americans," *Science* 305 (2004): 590.

52. Jobling, Hurles, and Tyler-Smith, *Human Evolutionary Genetics*, 348.

53. Ibid.

54. Ibid., 349.

55. Ibid.

56. Ibid., 349–51; P. Forster et al., "Origin and Evolution of Native American mtDNA Variation: A Reappraisal," *American Journal of Human Genetics* 59 (1996): 1864–81; Anne C. Stone and Mark Stoneking, "mtDNA Analysis of a Prehistoric Oneota Population: Implications for the

Peopling of the New World," *American Journal of Human Genetics* 62 (1998): 1153–70; Maere Reidla et al., "Origin and Diffusion of mtDNA Haplogroup X," *American Journal of Human Genetics* 73 (2003): 1178–90.

57. Jobling, Hurles, and Tyler-Smith, *Human Evolutionary Genetics*, 349–51; A. Torroni et al., "Mitochondrial DNA 'Clock' for the Amerinds and Its Implications for Timing Their Entry into North America," *Proceedings of the National Academy of Sciences, USA* 91 (1994): 1158–62; S. L. Bonatto and F. M. Salzano, "Diversity and Age of the Four Major mtDNA Haplogroups, and Their Implications for the Peopling of the New World," *American Journal of Human Genetics* 61 (1997): 1413–23; W. A. Silva Jr. et al., "Mitochondrial Genome Diversity of Native Americans Supports a Single Early Entry of Founder Populations into America," *American Journal of Human Genetics* 71 (2002): 187–92.

58. Jobling, Hurles, and Tyler-Smith, *Human Evolutionary Genetics*, 349–52; Torroni et al., "Mitochondrial DNA 'Clock,'" 1158–62.

59. D. A. Merriwether et al., "mtDNA Variation Indicates Mongolia May Have Been the Source for the Founding Populations for the New World," *American Journal of Human Genetics* 59 (1996): 204–12; C. J. Kolman, N. Sambuughin, and E. Bermingham, "Mitochondrial DNA Analysis of Mongolian Populations and Implications for the Origin of New World Founders," *Genetics* 142 (1996): 1321–34; Silva et al., "Mitochondrial Genome Diversity," 187–92.

60. Jobling, Hurles, and Tyler-Smith, *Human Evolutionary Genetics*, 352–53.

61. Ibid.; A. Ruiz-Linares et al., "Microsatellites Provide Evidence for Y Chromosome Diversity among the Founders of the New World," *Proceedings of the National Academy of Sciences, USA* 96 (1999): 6312–17; T. M. Karafet et al., "Ancestral Asian Source(s) of New World Y-Chromosome Founder Haplotypes," *American Journal of Human Genetics* 64 (1999): 817–31.

62. Jobling, Hurles, and Tyler-Smith, *Human Evolutionary Genetics*, 352–53.

63. Lewin, *Principles of Human Evolution*, 486–87.

64. Scott A. Elias et al., "Life and Times of the Bering Land Bridge," *Nature* 382 (1996): 60–63.

65. Lewin, *Principles of Human Evolution*, 486–87.

66. Richard Monastersky, "Drowned Land Holds Clue to First Americans," *Science News* 157 (2000): 85; Daryl W. Fedje and Heiner Josenhans, "Drowned Forests and Archaeology on the Continental Shelf of British Columbia, Canada," *Geology* 28 (2000): 99–102.

67. For example, see Hansjürgen T. Agostini et al., "Asian Genotypes of JC Virus in Native Americans and in a Pacific Island Population: Markers of Viral Evolution and Human Migration," *Proceedings of the National Academy of Sciences, USA* 94 (1997): 14542–46; Chie Sugimoto et al., "Evolution of Human Polyomavirus JC: Implications for the Population History of Humans," *Journal of Molecular Evolution* 54 (2002): 285–97; Angelo Pavesi, "African Origin of Polyomavirus JC and Implications for Prehistoric Human Migrations," *Journal of Molecular Evolution* 56 (2003): 564–72; Chandrabali Ghose et al., "East Asian Genotypes of *Helicobacter pylori* Strains in Amerindians Provide Evidence for Its Ancient Human Carriage," *Proceedings of the National Academy of Sciences, USA* 99 (2002): 15107–11; Daniel Falush et al., "Traces of Human Migrations in *Helicobacter pylori* Populations," *Science* 299 (2003): 1582–85; Jianbing Mu et al., "Chromosome-Wide SNPs Reveal an Ancient Origin for *Plasmodium falciparum*," *Nature* 418 (2002): 323–26; Deirdre A. Joy et al., "Early Origin and Recent Expansion of *Plasmodium falciparum*," *Science* 300 (2003): 318–21; Ralf Kittler, Manfred Kayser, and Mark Stoneking, "Molecular Evolution of *Pediculus humanus* and the Origin of Clothing," *Current Biology* 13 (2003): 1414–17.

Chapter 9: Is Human Evolution a Fact?

1. Niles Eldredge, *The Triumph of Evolution and the Failure of Creationism* (New York: W. H. Freeman, 2000), 24. For a book review and response, see Fazale R. Rana's review of *The Triumph of Evolution and the Failure of Creationism*, in *Facts for Faith*, no. 3 (Q3 2000), 60–61.
2. Eldredge, *Triumph of Evolution*, 25–60.
3. Phillip E. Johnson, *Darwin on Trial*, 2nd ed. (Downers Grove, IL: InterVarsity, 1993), 113–24.
4. Roger Lewin, *Principles of Human Evolution: A Core Textbook* (Malden, MA: Blackwell Science, 1998), 117–18; "The Primate Fossil Record," in *The Cambridge Encyclopedia of Human Evolution*, ed. Steve Jones, Robert Martin, and David Pilbeam (Cambridge: Cambridge University Press, 1992), 197–98.
5. Lewin, *Principles of Human Evolution*, 165–66.
6. Ibid., 175.
7. Philip L. Reno et al., "Sexual Dimorphism in *Australopithecus afarensis* Was Similar to That of Modern Humans," *Proceedings of the National Academy of Sciences, USA* 100 (2003): 9404–9.

8. Ibid.; Clark Spencer Larsen, "Equality for the Sexes in Human Evolution? Early Hominid Sexual Dimorphism and Implications for Mating Systems and Social Behavior," *Proceedings of the National Academy of Sciences, USA* 100 (2003): 9103–4.

9. Meave G. Leakey et al., "New Hominin Genus from Eastern Africa Shows Diverse Middle Pliocene Lineages," *Nature* 410 (2001): 433–40; Daniel E. Lieberman, "Another Face in Our Family Tree," *Nature* 410 (2001): 419–20.

10. B. Bower, "Fossil Skull Diversifies Family Tree," *Science News* 159 (2001): 180; Michael Balter, "Fossil Tangles Roots of Human Family Tree," *Science* 291 (2001): 2289–91.

11. Tim D. White, "Early Hominids—Diversity or Distortion?," *Science* 299 (2003): 1994–97; B. Bower, "Ancestral Bushwhack: Hominid Tree Gets Trimmed Twice," *Science News* 163 (2003): 275.

12. Jeffrey H. Schwartz, "Another Perspective on Hominid Diversity," *Science* 301 (2003): 763.

13. Lewin, *Principles of Human Evolution*, 298–300.

14. Ibid.

15. Camilo J. Cela-Conde and Francisco J. Ayala, "Genera of the Human Lineage," *Proceedings of the National Academy of Sciences, USA* 100 (2003): 7684–89.

16. Lewin, *Principles of Human Evolution*, 281–96.

17. Bernard Wood and Mark Collard, "The Human Genus," *Science* 284 (1999): 65–71; B. Bower, "Redrawing the Human Line," *Science News* 155 (1999): 267.

18. Leakey et al., "New Hominin Genus," 433–40.

19. Robert J. Blumenschine et al., "Late Pliocene *Homo* and Hominid Land Use from Western Olduvai Gorge, Tanzania," *Science* 299 (2003): 1217–21; Phillip V. Tobias, "Encore Olduvai," *Science* 299 (2003): 1193–94.

20. Lewin, *Principles of Human Evolution*, 306; Bernard Wood, "Evolution of Australopithecines," in *Cambridge Encyclopedia of Human Evolution*, 240.

21. Jean de Heinzelin et al., "Environment and Behavior of 2.5-Million-Year-Old Bouri Hominids," *Science* 284 (1999): 625–29; Berhane Asfaw et al., "*Australopithecus garhi*: A New Species of Early Hominid from Ethiopia," *Science* 284 (1999): 572–73; B. Bower, "African Fossils Flesh Out Humanity's Past," *Science News* 155 (1999): 262.

22. Michel Brunet et al., "A New Hominid from the Upper Miocene of Chad, Central Africa," *Nature* 418 (2002): 145–51; Patrick Vignaud et

al., "Geology and Paleontology of the Upper Miocene Toros-Menalla Hominid Locality, Chad," *Nature* 418 (2002): 152–55.

23. Mark Collard and Bernard Wood, "How Reliable Are Human Phylogenetic Hypotheses?," *Proceedings of the National Academy of Sciences, USA* 97 (2000): 5003–6.

24. Ibid.

25. Aapo T. Kangas et al., "Nonindependence of Mammalian Dental Characters," *Nature* 432 (2004): 211–14.

26. For example, see Lewin, *Principles of Human Evolution*, 300–302; Robert Foley, "Striking Parallels in Early Hominid Evolution," *Trends in Ecology and Evolution* 8 (1993): 196–97; Melanie A. McCollum, "The Robust Australopithecine Face: A Morphogenetic Perspective," *Science* 284 (1999): 301–5; Leslea J. Hlusko, "Integrating the Genotype and Phenotype in Hominid Paleontology," *Proceedings of the National Academy of Sciences, USA* 101 (2004): 2653–57.

27. T. C. Partridge et al., "Lower Pliocene Hominid Remains from Sterkfontein," *Science* 300 (2003): 607–12; Ann Gibbons, "Great Age Suggested for South African Hominids," *Science* 300 (2003): 562.

28. John Whitfield, "Oldest Member of Human Family Found," *Nature News*, posted July 11, 2002, http://www.nature.com/news/2002/020711/full/news020708-12.html; Bernard Wood, "Hominid Revelations from Chad," *Nature* 418 (2002): 133–35.

29. Wood, "Hominid Revelations from Chad," 133–35.

30. Yohannes Haile-Selassie, Gen Suwa, and Tim D. White, "Late Miocene Teeth from Middle Awash, Ethiopia, and Early Hominid Dental Evolution," *Science* 303 (2004): 1503–5; David R. Begun, "The Earliest Hominins—Is Less More?," *Science* 303 (2004): 1478–80.

31. Brandon Carter, "The Anthropic Principle and Its Implications for Biological Evolution," *Philosophical Transactions of the Royal Astronomical Society A* 370 (1983): 347–60; John D. Barrow and Frank J. Tipler, *The Anthropic Cosmological Principle* (New York: Oxford University Press, 1986), 510–73.

32. Barrow and Tipler, *Anthropic Cosmological Principle*, 557–66.

33. Quoted by Frank J. Tipler in "Intelligent Life in Cosmology," *International Journal of Astrobiology* 2 (2003): 142.

Chapter 10: Bipedalism and Brain Size

1. Roger Lewin, *Principles of Human Evolution: A Core Textbook* (Malden,

MA: Blackwell Science, 1998).

2. John G. Fleagle, "Primate Locomotion and Posture," in *The Cambridge Encyclopedia of Human Evolution*, ed. Steve Jones, Robert Martin, and David Pilbeam (Cambridge: Cambridge University Press, 1992), 75–85.

3. *Encyclopedia of Human Evolution and Prehistory*, ed. Eric Delson et al., 2nd ed. (New York: Garland, 2000), s.v. "locomotion"; B. Bower, "African Fossils Flesh Out Humanity's Past," *Science News* 155 (1999): 262; Elizabeth Culotta, "A New Human Ancestor?," *Science* 284 (1999): 572–73; Jean de Heinzelin et al., "Environment and Behavior of 2.5-Million-Year-Old Bouri Hominids," *Science* 284 (1999): 625–29; Berhane Asfaw et al., "*Australopithecus garhi*: A New Species of Early Hominid from Ethiopia," *Science* 284 (1999): 629–35.

4. Lewin, *Principles of Human Evolution*, 219–22.

5. Ibid., 227.

6. Ibid., 224–26; Dennis M. Bramble and Daniel E. Lieberman, "Endurance Running and the Evolution of *Homo*," *Nature* 432 (2004): 345–52.

7. Fleagle, "Primate Locomotion and Posture," 75–78.

8. Lewin, *Principles of Human Evolution*, 227.

9. Ibid., 218; Robert Martin, "Walking on Two Legs," in *Cambridge Encyclopedia of Human Evolution*, 78; Fred Spoor, Bernard Wood, and Frans Zonneveld, "Implications of Early Hominid Labyrinthine Morphology for Evolution of Human Bipedal Locomotion," *Nature* 369 (1994): 645–49.

10. Meave G. Leakey et al., "New Four-Million-Year-Old Hominid Species from Kanapoi and Allia Bay, Kenya," *Nature* 376 (1995): 565–71.

11. Meave G. Leakey et al., "New Specimens and Confirmation of an Early Age for *Australopithecus anamensis*," *Nature* 393 (1998): 62–66; B. Bower, "Early Hominid Rises Again," *Science News* 153 (1998): 315; Sileshi Semaw et al., "Early Pliocene Hominids from Gona, Ethiopia," *Nature* 433 (2005): 301–5.

12. Tim D. White, Gen Suwa, and Berhane Asfaw, "*Australopithecus ramidus*, a New Species of Early Hominid from Aramis, Ethiopia," *Nature* 371 (1994): 306–12; Henry Gee, "New Hominid Remains Found in Ethiopia," *Nature* 373 (1995): 272; Tim D. White, Gen Suwa, and Berhane Asfaw, "Corrigendum: *Australopithecus ramidus*, a New Species of Early Hominid from Aramis, Ethiopia," *Nature* 375 (1995): 88.

13. Yohannes Haile-Selassie, "Late Miocene Hominids from the Middle Awash, Ethiopia," *Nature* 412 (2001): 178–81; Henry Gee, "Palaeontology:

Return to the Planet of the Apes," *Nature* 412 (2001): 131–32; Michael Balter and Ann Gibbons, "Human Evolution: Another Emissary from the Dawn of Humanity," *Science* 293 (2001): 187–89.

14. Michael Balter, "Scientists Spar over Claims of Earliest Human Ancestor," *Science* 291 (2001): 1460–61; Ann Gibbons, "In Search of the First Hominids," *Science* 295 (2002): 1214–19; K. Galik et al., "External and Internal Morphology of the BAR 1002'00 *Orrorin tugenensis* Femur," *Science* 305 (2004): 1450–53.

15. Michel Brunet et al., "A New Hominid from the Upper Miocene of Chad, Central Africa," *Nature* 418 (2002): 145–51; Bernard Wood, "Palaeoanthropology: Hominid Revelations from Chad," *Nature* 418 (2002): 133–35; Ann Gibbons, "First Member of Human Family Uncovered," *Science* 297 (2002): 171–72.

16. Meave G. Leakey and Alan Walker, "Early Hominid Fossils from Africa," *Scientific American*, June 1997, 74–79; Clark Spencer Larsen, Robert M. Matter, and Daniel L. Gebo, *Human Origins: The Fossil Record*, 3rd ed. (Prospect Heights, IL: Waveland Press, 1998), 46; Giday WoldeGabriel et al., "Ecological and Temporal Placement of Early Pliocene Hominids at Aramis, Ethiopia," *Nature* 371 (1994): 330–33; Giday WoldeGabriel et al., "Geology and Palaeontology of the Late Miocene Middle Awash Valley, Afar Rift, Ethiopia," *Nature* 412 (2001): 175–78; Gibbons, "In Search of First Hominids," 1214–19; Patrick Vignaud et al., "Geology and Palaeontology of the Upper Miocene Toros-Menalla Hominid Locality, Chad," *Nature* 418 (2002): 152–55; Semaw et al., "Early Pliocene Hominids," 301–5.

17. Lewin, *Principles of Human Evolution*, 266–69.

18. Michel Brunet et al., "The First Australopithecine 2,500 Kilometres West of the Rift Valley (Chad)," *Nature* 378 (1995): 273–75.

19. Meave G. Leakey et al., "New Hominin Genus from Eastern Africa Shows Diverse Middle Pliocene Lineages," *Nature* 410 (2001): 433–40.

20. Balter and Gibbons, "Human Evolution," 187–89.

21. Lewin, *Principles of Human Evolution*, 222.

22. Mark A. Cane and Peter Molnar, "Closing of the Indonesian Seaway as a Precursor to East African Aridification around 3–4 Million Years Ago," *Nature* 411 (2001): 157–62.

23. Craig Stanford, *Upright: The Evolutionary Key to Becoming Human* (Boston: Houghton Mifflin, 2003), 104–22.

24. François Marchal, "A New Morphometric Analysis of the Hominid Pelvic

Bone," *Journal of Human Evolution* 38 (2000): 347–65.

25. Niles Eldredge, *Reinventing Darwin: The Great Debate at the High Table of Evolutionary Theory* (New York: Wiley, 1995), 78–81.
26. Lewin, *The Principles of Human Evolution*, 448–50; Terrence W. Deacon, "The Human Brain," in *Cambridge Encyclopedia of Human Evolution*, 115–23.
27. Terrence W. Deacon, "Impressions of Ancestral Brains," in *Cambridge Encyclopedia of Human Evolution*, 116.
28. *Encyclopedia of Human Evolution and Prehistory*, 2nd ed., s.v. "brain."
29. Deacon, "Impressions of Ancestral Brains," 116.
30. G. C. Conroy, M. W. Vannier, and P. V. Tobias, "Endocranial Features of *Australopithecus africanus* Revealed by 2- and 3-D Computed Tomography," *Science* 247 (1990): 838–41.
31. G. C. Conroy and M. W. Vannier, "Noninvasive Three-Dimensional Computer Imaging of Matrix-Filled Fossil Skulls by High-Resolution Computed Tomography," *Science* 226 (1984): 456–58; G. C. Conroy et al., "Endocranial Capacity in an Early Hominid Cranium from Sterkfontein, South Africa," *Science* 280 (1998): 1730–31; Kate Wong, "Face Off: Three-Dimensional Imaging Stands In for Fossils," *Scientific American*, July 1998, 21–22; Dean Falk, "Hominid Brain Evolution: Looks Can Be Deceiving," *Science* 280 (1998): 1714.
32. Conroy et al., "Endocranial Capacity," 1730–31.
33. C. A. Lockwood and W. H. Kimbel, "Endocranial Capacity of Early Hominids," *Science* 283 (1999): 9; J. Hawks and M. H. Wolpoff, "Endocranial Capacity of Early Hominids," *Science* 283 (1999): 9; G. C. Conroy et al., "Response: Endocranial Capacity of Early Hominids," *Science* 283 (1999): 9. For the full text of these comments, see http://www.sciencemag.org/cgi/content/full/283/5398/9b.
34. Conroy et al., "Endocranial Capacity," 1730–31.
35. Falk, "Hominid Brain Evolution," 1714.
36. Tim White, "No Surprises?" *Science* 281 (1998): 45; Dean Falk, "Response to 'No Surprises?'," *Science* 281 (1998): 45.
37. R. L. Holloway, "Hominid Brain Volume," *Science* 283 (1999): 34.
38. G. C. Conroy et al., "Response: Hominid Brain Volume," *Science* 283 (1999): 34.
39. Elizabeth Culotta, "Anthropologists Probe Bones, Stones, and Molecules," *Science* 284 (1999): 1109–11.

Chapter 11: Who Was Turkana Boy?

1. Roger Lewin, *Principles of Human Evolution: A Core Textbook* (Malden, MA: Blackwell Science, 1998), 329–32.
2. Ibid., 335–36, 448–50. For an accessible description of *Homo erectus* anatomy, biogeography, etc., see Richard G. Klein with Blake Edgar, *The Dawn of Human Culture: A Bold New Theory on What Sparked the "Big Bang" of Human Consciousness* (New York: Wiley, 2002), 91–131.
3. Berhane Asfaw et al., "Remains of *Homo erectus* from Bouri, Middle Awash, Ethiopia," *Nature* 416 (2002): 317–20; J. Pickrell, "Unified *Erectus*: Fossil Suggests Single Human Ancestor," *Science News* 161 (2002): 179; Ann Gibbons, "African Skull Points to One Human Ancestor," *Science* 295 (2002): 2192–93.
4. Richard Potts et al., "Small Mid-Pleistocene Hominin Associated with East African Acheulean Technology," *Science* 305 (2004): 75–78; Jeffrey H. Schwartz, "Getting to Know *Homo erectus*," *Science* 305 (2004): 53–54.
5. Schwartz, "Getting to Know," 53–54.
6. Lewin, *Principles of Human Evolution*, 325–41; C. C. Swisher III et al., "Age of the Earliest Known Hominids in Java, Indonesia," *Science* 263 (1994): 1118–21; Ann Gibbons, "Rewriting—and Redating—Prehistory," *Science* 263 (1994): 1087–88; R. X. Zhu et al., "Earliest Presence of Humans in Northeast Asia," *Nature* 413 (2001): 413–17; Roy Larick et al., "Early Pleistocene ^{40}Ar/^{39}Ar Ages for Bapang Formation Hominins, Central Jawa, Indonesia," *Proceedings of the National Academy of Sciences, USA* 98 (2001): 4866–71; Leo Gabunia et al., "Earliest Pleistocene Hominid Cranial Remains from Dmanisi, Republic of Georgia: Taxonomy, Geological Setting, and Age," *Science* 288 (2000): 1019–25; Abesalom Vekua et al., "A New Skull of Early *Homo* from Dmanisi, Georgia," *Science* 297 (2002): 85–89; Michael Balter and Ann Gibbons, "A Glimpse of Humans' First Journey out of Africa," *Science* 288 (2000): 948–49.
7. Lewin, *Principles of Human Evolution*, 325–41.
8. Ibid., 386–89.
9. Ibid., 392–97.
10. Milford H. Wolpoff et al., "Modern Human Ancestry at the Peripheries: A Test of the Replacement Theory," *Science* 291 (2001): 293–97; Elizabeth Pennisi, "Skull Study Targets Africa-Only Origins," *Science* 291 (2001): 231.
11. Pennisi, "Skull Study," 231.
12. M. A. Jobling, M. E. Hurles, and C. Tyler-Smith, *Human Evolutionary*

Genetics: Origins, Peoples and Disease (New York: Garland, 2004), 289–92; Li Jin and Bing Su, "Natives or Immigrants: Modern Human Origin in East Asia," *Nature Reviews: Genetics* 1 (2000): 126–33.

13. Yuehai Ke et al., "African Origins of Modern Humans in East Asia: A Tale of 12,000 Y Chromosomes," *Science* 292 (2001): 1151–53; Ann Gibbons, "Modern Men Trace Ancestry to African Migrants," *Science* 292 (2001): 1051.

14. Naoyuki Takahata, Sang-Hee Lee, and Yoko Satta, "Testing Multiregionality of Modern Human Origins," *Molecular Biology and Evolution* 18 (2001): 172–83.

15. Jin and Su, "Natives or Immigrants," 126–33.

16. Lewin, *Principles of Human Evolution*, 233–36.

17. Ibid., 337–40.

18. Adrienne Zihlman, Debra Bolter, and Christophe Boesch, "Wild Chimpanzee Dentition and Its Implications for Assessing Life History in Immature Hominin Fossils," *Proceedings of the Natural Academy of Sciences, USA* 101 (2004): 10541–43.

19. University of California, Santa Cruz, "Growth Study of Wild Chimpanzees Challenges Assumptions about Early Humans," *ScienceDaily*, posted July 14, 2004, http://www.sciencedaily.com/releases/2004/07/040714090708.htm.

20. Christopher Dean et al., "Growth Processes in Teeth Distinguish Modern Humans from *Homo erectus* and Earlier Hominins," *Nature* 414 (2001): 628–31; Helen Pearson, "Ancestors Skip Adolescence," *Nature News* (2001): doi:10.1038/news011206-10; Jacopo Moggi-Cecchi, "Human Evolution: Questions of Growth," *Nature* 414 (2001): 595–96; B. Bower, "Human Evolution Put Brakes on Tooth Growth," *Science News* 160 (2001): 357.

21. H. Coqueugniot et al., "Early Brain Growth in *Homo erectus* and Implications for Cognitive Ability," *Nature* 431 (2004): 299–302.

22. Lewin, *Principles of Human Evolution*, 343–49; Klein with Edgar, *Dawn of Human Culture*, 91–131.

23. Steve Weiner et al., "Evidence for the Use of Fire at Zhoukoudian, China," *Science* 281 (1998): 251–53.

24. B. Bower, "Ancient Fire Use Flickers Inside Cave," *Science News* 154 (1998): 22.

25. *Encyclopedia of Human Evolution and Prehistory*, ed. Eric Delson et al., 2nd ed. (New York: Garland, 2000), s.v. "fire."

26. Berhane Asfaw et al., "*Australopithecus garhi*: A New Species of Early Hominid from Ethiopia," *Science* 284 (1999): 629–35.

27. Lewin, *Principles of Human Evolution*, 309–21; Klein with Edgar, *Dawn of Human Culture*, 63–89.

28. P. Brown et al., "A New Small-Bodied Hominid from the Late Pleistocene of Flores, Indonesia," *Nature* 431 (2004): 1055–61; M. J. Morwood et al., "Archaeology and Age of a New Hominin from Flores in Eastern Indonesia," *Nature* 431 (2004): 1087–91.

29. Dean Falk et al., "The Brain of LB1, *Homo floresiensis*," *Science* 308 (2005): 242–45.

30. Chris Stringer, "A Stranger from Flores," *Nature News* (2004): doi:10.1038/news041025-3.

31. Marta Mirazón Lahr and Robert Foley, "Palaeoanthropology: Human Evolution Writ Small," *Nature* 431 (2004): 1043–44.

32. Morwood et al., "Archaeology and Age," 1087–91.

33. Naama Goren-Inbar et al., "Evidence of Hominin Control of Fire at Gesher Benot Ya'aqov, Israel," *Science* 304 (2004): 725–27.

34. Michael Balter, "Earliest Signs of Human-Controlled Fire Uncovered in Israel," *Science* 304 (2004): 663–64.

Chapter 12: Who Were the Neanderthals?

1. Roger Lewin, *Principles of Human Evolution: A Core Textbook* (Malden, MA: Blackwell Science, 1998), 373–82.

2. William L. Straus Jr. and A. J. E. Cave, "Pathology and the Posture of Neanderthal Man," *Quarterly Review of Biology* 32 (1957): 348–63.

3. Lewin, *Principles of Human Evolution*, 365.

4. Ibid.

5. *Encyclopedia of Human Evolution and Prehistory*, ed. Eric Delson et al., 2nd ed. (New York: Garland, 2000), s.v. "Neanderthals."

6. For accessible descriptions of Neanderthal anatomy, see Christopher Stringer and Robin McKie, *African Exodus: The Origins of Modern Humanity* (New York: Henry Holt, 1996), 85–114; Richard G. Klein with Blake Edgar, *The Dawn of Human Culture: A Bold New Theory on What Sparked the "Big Bang" of Human Consciousness* (New York: Wiley, 2002), 172–80.

7. Lewin, *Principles of Human Evolution*, 137–40.

8. Timothy D. Weaver, "The Shape of the Neandertal Femur Is Primarily the Consequence of a Hyperpolar Body Form," *Proceedings of the National*

Academy of Sciences, USA 100 (2003): 6926–29.

9. For the story behind this discovery, see Stringer and McKie, *African Exodus*, 85–89; Yoel Rak, W. H. Kimbel, and E. Hovers, "A Neandertal Infant from Amud Cave," *Journal of Human Evolution* 26 (1994): 313–24.

10. Katerina Harvati, Stephen R. Frost, and Kieran P. McNulty, "Neanderthal Taxonomy Reconsidered: Implications of 3D Primate Models of Intra- and Interspecific Differences," *Proceedings of the National Academy of Sciences, USA* 101 (2004): 1147–52.

11. Ibid.

12. Klein with Edgar, *Dawn of Human Culture*, 176.

13. Matthias Krings et al., "Neandertal DNA Sequences and the Origin of Modern Humans," *Cell* 90 (1997): 19–30. For commentaries on this work, see Ryk Ward and Chris Stringer, "A Molecular Handle on the Neanderthals," *Nature* 388 (1997): 225–26; Patricia Kahn and Ann Gibbons, "DNA from an Extinct Human," *Science* 277 (1997): 176–78.

14. Matthias Krings et al., "DNA Sequence of the Mitochondrial Hypervariable Region II from the Neandertal Type Specimen," *Proceedings of the National Academy of Sciences, USA* 96 (1999): 5581–85.

15. Krings et al., "Neandertal DNA Sequences," 19–30; Krings et al., "DNA Sequence," 5581–85.

16. Alan Cooper et al., "Letters: Neandertal Genetics," *Science* 277 (1997): 1021–24; G. A. Clark, "Letters: Neandertal Genetics," *Science* 277 (1997): 1025–26; Kate Wong, "Ancestral Quandary," *Scientific American*, January 1998, 30–31.

17. Anders J. Hansen et al., "Statistical Evidence for Miscoding Lesions in Ancient DNA Templates," *Molecular Biology and Evolution* 18 (2001): 262–65.

18. Matthias Höss, "Ancient DNA: Neanderthal Population Genetics," *Nature* 404 (2000): 453–54; Igor V. Ovchinnikov et al., "Molecular Analysis of Neanderthal DNA from the Northern Caucasus," *Nature* 404 (2000): 490–93.

19. Matthias Krings et al., "A View of Neandertal Genetic Diversity," *Nature Genetics* 26 (2000): 144–46; Ralf W. Schmitz et al., "The Neandertal Type Site Revisited: Interdisciplinary Investigations of Skeletal Remains from the Neander Valley, Germany," *Proceedings of the National Academy of Sciences, USA* 99 (2002): 13342–47; David Serre et al., "No Evidence of Neandertal mtDNA Contribution to Early Modern Humans," *PLoS Biology* 2 (2004): e57, doi:10.1371/journal.pbio.0020057.

20. For example, see John H. Relethford, *Reflections of Our Past: How Human History Is Revealed in Our Genes* (Boulder, CO: Westview, 2003), 75–99.

21. Gregory J. Adcock et al., "Mitochondrial DNA Sequence in Ancient Australians: Implications for Modern Human Origins," *Proceedings of the National Academy of Sciences, USA* 98 (2001): 390–91; Constance Holden, "Oldest Human DNA Reveals Aussie Oddity," *Science* 291 (2001): 230–31.

22. James M. Bowler et al., "New Ages for Human Occupation and Climatic Change at Lake Mungo, Australia," *Nature* 421 (2003): 837–40.

23. David Caramelli et al., "Evidence for a Genetic Discontinuity between Neandertals and 24,000-Year-Old Anatomically Modern Europeans," *Proceedings of the National Academy of Sciences, USA* 100 (2003): 6593–97.

24. Oliva Handt et al., "Molecular Genetic Analyses of the Tyrolean Ice Man," *Science* 264 (1994): 1775–78; Giulietta Di Benedetto et al., "Mitochondrial DNA Sequences in Prehistoric Human Remains from the Alps," *European Journal of Human Genetics* 8 (2000): 669–77.

25. To carry out their analysis, the research team computed (using multivariate statistics) numerical parameters for each mitochondrial-DNA sequence included in their study. These parameters concisely described the entire DNA sequence. When compared with one another, the parameters measured "genetic" distances among the sequences. Genetic distance collectively reflected the number, type, and locations of individual base pair differences.

26. Michael Scholz et al., "Genomic Differentiation of Neanderthals and Anatomically Modern Man Allows a Fossil-DNA-Based Classification of Morphologically Indistinguishable Hominid Base," *American Journal of Human Genetics* 66 (2000): 1927–32.

27. E. M. Geigl, "Inadequate Use of Molecular Hybridization to Analyze DNA in Neanderthal Fossils," *American Journal of Human Genetics* 68 (2001): 287–90; Lutz Bachmann, "Reply to Geigl," *American Journal of Human Genetics* 68 (2001): 290–91.

28. Constance Holden, "Ancient Child Burial Uncovered in Portugal," *Science* 283 (1999): 169.

29. B. Bower, "Fossil May Expose Humanity's Hybrid Roots," *Science News* 155 (1999): 295; Cidália Duarte et al., "The Early Upper Paleolithic Human Skeleton from the Abrigo do Lagar Velho (Portugal) and Modern Human Emergence in Iberia," *Proceedings of the National Academy of Sciences, USA* 96 (1999): 7604–9.

30. Ian Tattersall and Jeffrey H. Schwartz, "Hominids and Hybrids: The

Place of Neanderthals in Human Evolution," *Proceedings of the National Academy of Sciences, USA* 96 (1999): 7117–19.

31. Ibid.

32. Bower, "Fossil May Expose," 295.

33. Tattersall and Schwartz, "Hominids and Hybrids," 7117–19.

34. Ibid.

35. Ibid.

36. Erik Trinkaus et al., "An Early Modern Human from Pe tera cu Oase, Romania," *Proceedings of the National Academy of Sciences, USA* 100 (2003): 11231–36.

37. Serre et al., "No Evidence," e57.

38. Mathias Currat and Laurent Excoffier, "Modern Humans Did Not Admix with Neanderthals during Their Range Expansion into Europe," *PLoS Biology* 2 (2004): e421, doi:10.1371/journal.pbio.0020421.

39. Marcia S. Ponce de León and Christoph P. E. Zollikofer, "Neanderthal Cranial Ontogeny and Its Implications for Late Hominid Diversity," *Nature* 412 (2001): 534–38; B. Bower, "Neandertals, Humans May Have Grown Apart," *Science News* 160 (2001): 71.

40. Fernando V. Ramirez Rozzi and José Maria Bermúdez de Castro, "Surprisingly Rapid Growth in Neanderthals," *Nature* 428 (2004): 936–39; Jay Kelley, "Palaeoanthropology: Neanderthal Teeth Lined Up," *Nature* 428 (2004): 904–5.

41. Hartmut Thieme, "Lower Palaeolithic Hunting Spears from Germany," *Nature* 385 (1997): 807–10; Robin Dennell, "The World's Oldest Spears," *Nature* 385 (1997): 767–68; John J. Shea, "Neandertal and Early Modern Human Behavioral Variability: A Regional-Scale Approach to Lithic Evidence for Hunting in the Levantine Mousterian," *Current Anthropology* 39, Supplemental (1998): S45–S78.

42. Lewin, *Principles of Human Evolution*, 368–72.

43. Klein with Edgar, *Dawn of Human Culture*, 180.

44. Wesley A. Niewoehner, "Behavioral Inferences from the Skhul/Qafzeh Early Modern Human Hand Remains," *Proceedings of the National Academy of Sciences, USA* 98 (2001): 2979–84; Steve E. Churchill, "Hand Morphology, Manipulation, and Tool Use in Neandertals and Early Modern Humans of the Near East," *Proceedings of the National Academy of Sciences, USA* 98 (2001): 2953–55; Wesley A. Niewoehner et al., "Digital Analysis: Manual Dexterity in Neanderthals," *Nature* 422 (2003): 395.

45. Michael P. Richards et al., "Stable Isotope Evidence for Increasing Dietary

Breadth in the European Mid-Upper Paleolithic," *Proceedings of the National Academy of Sciences, USA* 98 (2001): 6528–32.

46. Lewin, *Principles of Human Evolution*, 457–61; Stringer and McKie, *African Exodus*, 94–95.

47. Lewin, *Principles of Human Evolution*, 460–61.

48. Richard F. Kay, Matt Cartmill, and Michelle Balow, "The Hypoglossal Canal and the Origin of Human Vocal Behavior," *Proceedings of the National Academy of Sciences, USA* 95 (1998): 5417–19.

49. David DeGusta, W. Henry Gilbert, and Scott P. Turner, "Hypoglossal Canal Size and Hominid Speech," *Proceedings of the National Academy of Sciences, USA* 96 (1999): 1800–1804; Philip Lieberman, "Silver-Tongued Neandertals?," *Science* 283 (1999): 175; William L. Jungers et al., "Hypoglossal Canal Size in Living Hominoids and the Evolution of Human Speech," *Human Biology* 75 (2003): 473–84.

50. Lewin, *Principles of Human Evolution*, 460.

51. Richard G. Klein, "Whither the Neanderthals?," *Science* 299 (2003): 1525–27.

52. Klein with Edgar, *Dawn of Human Culture*, 192–96.

53. Ibid.; *Encyclopedia of Human Evolution and Prehistory*, 2nd ed., s.v. "musical instruments."

54. Lewin, *Principles of Human Evolution*, 368–72.

55. Klein with Edgar, *Dawn of Human Culture*, 192–94.

56. Lewin, *Principles of Human Evolution*, 368–72; Klein with Edgar, *Dawn of Human Culture*, 192–94.

57. Lewin, *Principles of Human Evolution*, 368–72.

58. Christoph P. E. Zollikofer et al., "Evidence for Interpersonal Violence in the St. Césaire Neanderthal," *Proceedings of the National Academy of Sciences, USA* 99 (2002): 6444–48.

59. Alban Defleur et al., "Neanderthal Cannibalism at Moula-Guercy, Ardèche, France," *Science* 286 (1999): 128–31; B. Bower, "Cave Finds Revive Neandertal Cannibalism," *Science News* 156 (1999): 213.

60. *Encyclopedia of Human Evolution and Prehistory*, 2nd ed., s.v. "ritual."

61. Jean-Jacques Hublin et al., "A Late Neanderthal Associated with Upper Palaeolithic Artifacts," *Nature* 381 (1996): 224–26; Jeffrey Brainard, "Giving Neandertals Their Due: Similarities with Modern Humans Shift the Image of the Caveman Brute," *Science News* 154 (1998): 72–74.

62. Brainard, "Giving Neandertals Their Due," 72–74; Klein, "Whither the Neanderthals?," 1525–27.

63. Emiliano Bruner, Giorgio Manzi, and Juan Luis Arsuaga, "Encephalization and Allometric Trajectories in the Genus *Homo*: Evidence from the Neandertal and Modern Lineages," *Proceedings of the National Academy of Sciences, USA* 100 (2003): 15335–40; Emiliano Bruner, "Geometric Morphometrics and Paleoneurology: Brain Shape Evolution in the Genus *Homo*," *Journal of Human Evolution* 47 (2004): 279–303.

64. Andrew Newberg, Eugene G. D'Aquili, and Vince Rause, *Why God Won't Go Away: Brain Science and the Biology of Belief* (New York: Ballantine Books, 2002).

Chapter 13: What about Chimpanzees?

1. Kevin Davies, *Cracking the Genome: Inside the Race to Unlock Human DNA* (New York: Free Press, 2001), 169.

2. Mary-Claire King and A. C. Wilson, "Evolution at Two Levels in Humans and Chimpanzees," *Science* 188 (1975): 107–16.

3. Davies, *Cracking the Genome*, 169.

4. Charles Darwin, *The Descent of Man, and Selection in Relation to Sex*, 2nd ed., Great Minds Series (1874; repr., Amherst, NY: Prometheus Books, 1998), 5–26, 632.

5. Jonathan Marks, *What It Means to Be 98% Chimpanzee: Apes, People, and Their Genes* (Berkeley: University of California Press, 2002), 58–61.

6. Robert Martin, "Classification of Primates," in *The Cambridge Encyclopedia of Human Evolution*, ed. Steve Jones, Robert Martin, and David Pilbeam (New York: Cambridge University Press, 1994), 20.

7. Alan G. Atherly, Jack R. Girton, and John F. McDonald, *The Science of Genetics* (Fort Worth, TX: Saunders College Publishing, 1999), 55–56.

8. Robert C. Bohinski, *Modern Concepts in Biochemistry*, 4th ed. (Boston: Allyn and Bacon, 1983), 86–87.

9. Harvey Lodish et al., *Molecular Cell Biology*, 4th ed. (New York: W. H. Freeman, 2000), 54–60.

10. Ibid., 51–54.

11. Ibid., 52.

12. Ibid., 101–5.

13. Atherly, Girton, and McDonald, *Science of Genetics*, 57.

14. Ibid., 293–99.

15. Jorge J. Yunis, J. R. Sawyer, and K. Dunham, "The Striking Resemblance of High-Resolution G-Banded Chromosomes of Man and Chimpanzee,"

Science 208 (1980): 1145–48; Jorge J. Yunis and Om Prakash, "The Origin of Man: A Chromosomal Pictorial Legacy," *Science* 215 (1982): 1525–30.

16. Jonathan Marks, "Chromosomal Evolution in Primates," in *Cambridge Encyclopedia of Human Evolution*, 298–302.

17. For some recent examples, see Florence Richard, Martine Lombard, and Bernard Dutrillaux, "Phylogenetic Origin of Human Chromosomes 7, 16, and 19 and Their Homologs in Placental Mammals," *Genome Research* 10 (2000): 644–51; Jeffrey A. Bailey et al., "Human-Specific Duplication and Mosaic Transcripts: The Recent Paralogous Structure of Chromosome 22," *American Journal of Human Genetics* 70 (2002): 83–100; Hildegard Kehrer-Sawatzki et al., "Molecular Characterization of the Pericentric Inversion That Causes Differences between Chimpanzee Chromosome 19 and Human Chromosome 17," *American Journal of Human Genetics* 71 (2002): 375–88.

18. Marks, "Chromosomal Evolution in Primates," 298–302; Yunis and Prakash, "Origin of Man," 1525–30.

19. For a detailed list of references, see Charles G. Sibley and Jon E. Ahlquist, "The Phylogeny of the Hominoid Primates, as Indicated by DNA-DNA Hybridization," *Journal of Molecular Evolution* 20 (1984): 2–15.

20. Charles G. Sibley, "The DNA Hybridisation Technique," in *Cambridge Encyclopedia of Human Evolution*, 314.

21. Charles G. Sibley and Jon E. Ahlquist, "DNA Hybridization Evidence of Hominoid Phylogeny: Results from an Expanded Data Set," *Journal of Molecular Evolution* 26 (1987): 99–121; Adalgisa Caccone and Jeffrey R. Powell, "DNA Divergence among Hominoids," *Evolution* 43 (1989): 925–42; Charles G. Sibley, "DNA-DNA Hybridisation in the Study of Primate Evolution," in *Cambridge Encyclopedia of Human Evolution*, 313–15.

22. For a detailed account of this controversy, see Michael H. Brown, *The Search for Eve: Have Scientists Found the Mother of Us All?* (New York: Harper and Row, 1990), 125–35. Also see Carl W. Schmid and Jonathan Marks, "DNA Hybridization as a Guide to Phylogeny: Chemical and Physical Limits," *Journal of Molecular Evolution* 30 (1990): 237–46.

23. King and Wilson, "Evolution at Two Levels," 107–16; Morris Goodman, "Reconstructing Human Evolution from Proteins," in *Cambridge Encyclopedia of Human Evolution*, 307–12.

24. Marks, *What It Means*, 32–33.

25. Derek E. Wildman et al., "Implications of Natural Selection in Shaping 99.4% Nonsynonymous DNA Identity between Humans and

Chimpanzees: Enlarging Genus *Homo*," *Proceedings of the National Academy of Sciences, USA* 100 (2003): 7181–88.

26. Morris Goodman, "The Genomic Record of Humankind's Evolutionary Roots," *American Journal of Human Genetics* 64 (1999): 31–39; Joseph G. Hacia, "Genome of the Apes," *Trends in Genetics* 17 (2001): 637–45.

27. Feng-Chi Chen and Wen-Hsiung Li, "Genomic Divergences between Humans and Other Hominoids and the Effective Population Size of the Common Ancestor of Humans and Chimpanzees," *American Journal of Human Genetics* 68 (2001): 444–56; Hacia, "Genome of the Apes," 637–45.

28. Roderic D. M. Page and Edward C. Holmes, *Molecular Evolution: A Phylogenetic Approach* (Malden, MA: Blackwell Science, 1998), 251–61.

29. Vincent M. Sarich and Allan Wilson, "Immunological Time Scale for Hominid Evolution," *Science* 158 (1967): 1200–1203.

30. John H. Relethford, *Reflections of Our Past: How Human History Is Revealed in Our Genes* (Boulder, CO: Westview, 2003), 31–36.

31. Sibley and Ahlquist, "Phylogeny of the Hominoid," 2–15; Sibley and Ahlquist, "DNA Hybridization Evidence," 99–121; Caccone and Powell, "DNA Divergence among Hominoids," 925–42.

32. Pascal Gagneux et al., "Mitochondrial Sequences Show Diverse Evolutionary Histories of African Hominoids," *Proceedings of the National Academy of Sciences, USA* 96 (1999): 5077–82; Satoshi Horai et al., "Recent African Origin of Modern Humans Revealed by Complete Sequences of Hominoid Mitochondrial DNAs," *Proceedings of the National Academy of Sciences, USA* 92 (1995): 532–36; Naoyuki Takahata and Yoko Satta, "Evolution of Primate Lineage Leading to Modern Humans: Phylogenetic and Demographic Inferences from DNA Sequences," *Proceedings of the National Academy of Sciences, USA* 94 (1997): 4811–15; Chen and Li, "Genomic Divergences," 444–56; Wildman et al., "Implications of Natural Selection," 7181–88; Jinxiu Shi et al., "Divergence of the Genes on Human Chromosome 21 between Human and Other Hominoids and Variation of Substitution Rates among Transcription Units," *Proceedings of the National Academy of Sciences, USA* 100 (2003): 8331–36.

33. Asao Fujiyama et al., "Construction and Analysis of a Human-Chimpanzee Comparative Clone Map," *Science* 295 (2002): 131–34.

34. Ingo Ebersberger et al., "Genomewide Comparison of DNA Sequences between Humans and Chimpanzees," *American Journal of Human Genetics* 70 (2002): 1490–97.

35. Fujiyama et al., "Constructions and Analysis," 131–34.
36. Roy J. Britten, "Divergence between Samples of Chimpanzee and Human DNA Sequences Is 5%, Counting Indels," *Proceedings of the National Academy of Sciences, USA* 99 (2002): 13633–35.
37. Tatsuya Anzai et al., "Comparative Sequencing of Human and Chimpanzee MHC Class 1 Regions Unveils Insertions/Deletions as the Major Path to Genomic Divergence," *Proceedings of the National Academy of Sciences, USA* 100 (2003): 7708–13.
38. Kelly A. Frazer et al., "Genomic DNA Insertions and Deletions Occur Frequently between Humans and Nonhuman Primates," *Genome Research* 13 (2003): 341–46; Elizabeth Pennisi, "Jumbled DNA Separates Chimps and Humans," *Science* 298 (2002): 719–21.
39. The International Chimpanzee Chromosome 22 Consortium, "DNA Sequence and Comparative Analysis of Chimpanzee Chromosome 22," *Nature* 429 (2004): 382–88; Jean Weissenbach, "Genome Sequencing: Differences with the Relatives," *Nature* 429 (2004): 353–55.
40. J. W. Thomas et al., "Comparative Analyses of Multi-Species Sequences from Targeted Genomic Regions," *Nature* 424 (2003): 788–93.
41. Ulfur Arnason, Xiufeng Xu, and Anette Gullberg, "Comparison between the Complete Mitochondrial DNA Sequences of *Homo* and the Common Chimpanzee Based on Nonchimeric Sequences," *Journal of Molecular Evolution* 42 (1996): 145–52.
42. Immo E. Scheffler, *Mitochondria* (New York: Wiley, 1999), 273–325.
43. Elaine A. Muchmore, Sandra Diaz, and Ajit Varki, "A Structural Difference between the Cell Surfaces of Humans and Great Apes," *American Journal of Physical Anthropology* 107 (1998): 187–98.
44. Joseph Alper, "Sugar Separates Humans from Apes," *Science* 291 (2001): 2340.
45. Ann Gibbons, "Which of Our Genes Makes Us Human?," *Science* 281 (1998): 1432–34.
46. Ibid.; Alper, "Sugar Separates," 2340; Hsun-Hua Chou et al., "A Mutation in Human CMP-Sialic Acid Hydroxylase Occurred after the *Homo-Pan* Divergence," *Proceedings of the National Academy of Sciences, USA* 95 (1998): 11751–56.
47. Toshiyuki Hayakawa et al., "*Alu*-Mediated Inactivation of the Human CMP-*N*-Acetylneuraminic Acid Hydroxylase Gene," *Proceedings of the National Academy of Sciences, USA* 98 (2001): 11399–404.
48. Hsun-Hua Chou et al., "Inactivation of CMP-*N*-Acetylneuraminic

Acid Hydroxylase Occurred Prior to Brain Expansion during Human Evolution," *Proceedings of the National Academy of Sciences, USA* 99 (2002): 11736–41.

49. Wolfgang Enard et al., "Molecular Evolution of *FOXP2*, a Gene Involved in Speech and Language," *Nature* 418 (2002): 869–72; Michael Balter, "'Speech Gene' Tied to Modern Humans," *Science* 297 (2002): 1105.

50. Cecilia S. L. Lai et al., "A Forkhead-Domain Gene Is Mutated in a Severe Speech and Language Disorder," *Nature* 413 (2001): 519–23; Steven Pinker, "Talk of Genetics and Vice Versa," *Nature* 413 (2001): 465–66; John Whitfield, "Language Gene Found," Institute for Oriental Study, Thane, posted June 5, 2002, http://orientalthane.com/science/news_2004_04_08.htm.

51. Enard et al., "Molecular Evolution of *FOXP2*," 869–72.

52. Ibid.

53. Patrick D. Evans et al., "Adaptive Evolution of *ASPM*, a Major Determinant of Cerebral Cortical Size in Humans," *Human Molecular Genetics* 13 (2004): 489–94; Jianzhi Zhang, "Evolution of the Human *ASPM* Gene, A Major Determinant of Brain Size," *Genetics* 165 (2003): 2063–70; Natalay Kouprina et al., "Accelerated Evolution of the *ASPM* Gene Controlling Brain Size Begins Prior to Human Brain Expansion," *PLoS Biology* 2 (2004): e126, doi:10.1371/journal.pbio.0020126.

54. Jacquelyn Bond et al., "Protein-Truncating Mutations in *ASPM* Cause Variable Reduction in Brain Size," *American Journal of Human Genetics* 73 (2003): 1170–77.

55. Andrew G. Clark et al., "Inferring Nonneutral Evolution from Human-Chimp-Mouse Orthologous Gene Trios," *Science* 302 (2003): 1960–63; Elizabeth Pennisi, "Genome Comparisons Hold Clues to Human Evolution," *Science* 302 (2003): 1876–77.

56. International Chimpanzee Chromosome 22 Consortium, "DNA Sequence," 382–88; Weissenbach, "Genome Sequencing," 353–55.

57. Marks, "What It Means," 7–50.

58. Ibid., 29.

59. Mouse Genome Sequencing Consortium, "Initial Sequencing and Comparative Analysis of the Mouse Genome," *Nature* 420 (2002): 520–62; John Whitfield, "Plans of Mice and Men," *Nature News* (2002): http://www.nature.com/news/2002/021202/full/021202-9.html.

60. Dennis Normile, "Gene Expression Differs in Human and Chimp Brains," *Science* 292 (2001): 44–45; Wolfgang Enard et al., "Intra- and Interspecific

Variation in Primate Gene Expression Patterns," *Science* 296 (2002): 340–43; Elizabeth Pennisi, "Gene Activity Clocks Brain's Fast Evolution," *Science* 296 (2002): 233–34; Jianying Gu and Yun Gu, "Induced Gene Expression in Human Brain after the Split from Chimpanzee," *Trends in Genetics* 19 (2003): 63–65.

61. Normile, "Gene Expression Differs," 44–45.

62. Mazen W. Karaman et al., "Comparative Analysis of Gene-Expression Patterns in Human and African Great Ape Cultured Fibroblasts," *Genome Research* 13 (2003): 1619–30.

63. Ibid.

64. Mario Cáceres et al., "Elevated Gene Expression Levels Distinguish Human from Non-Human Primate Brains," *Proceedings of the National Academy of Sciences, USA* 100 (2003): 13030–35.

65. Monica Uddin et al., "Sister Grouping of Chimpanzees and Humans as Revealed by Genome-Wide Phylogenetic Analysis of Brain Gene Expression Profiles," *Proceedings of the National Academy of Sciences, USA* 101 (2004): 2957–62.

66. Philipp Khaitovich et al., "Regional Patterns of Gene Expression in Human and Chimpanzee Brains," *Genome Research* 14 (2004): 1462–73.

67. International Chimpanzee Chromosome 22 Consortium, "DNA Sequence," 382–88; Weissenbach, "Genome Sequencing," 353–55.

68. Wolfgang Enard et al., "Differences in DNA Methylation Patterns between Humans and Chimpanzees," *Current Biology* 14 (2004): R148.

69. Peter A. Jones and Daiya Takai, "The Role of DNA Methylation in Mammalian Epigentics," *Science* 293 (2001): 1068–70.

70. Todd M. Preuss et al., "Human Brain Evolution: Insights from Microarrays," *Nature Reviews Genetics* 5 (2004): 850–60.

71. Susan E. Ptak et al., "Absence of the TAP2 Human Recombination Hotspot in Chimpanzees," *PLoS Biology* 2 (2004): e155, doi:10.1371/journal.pbio.0020155; Wendy Winckler et al., "Comparison of Fine-Scale Recombination Rates in Humans and Chimpanzees," *Science* 308 (2005): 107–11.

72. Rosaleen Gibbons et al., "Distinguishing Humans from Great Apes with AluYb8 Repeats," *Journal of Molecular Biology* 339 (2004): 721–29.

Chapter 14: What about "Junk" DNA?

1.   Genesis 1:31.

2.   Edward E. Max, "Plagiarized Errors and Molecular Genetics: Another

Argument in the Evolution-Creation Controversy," *Creation/Evolution*, 1986, accessed August 12, 2003, http://www.talkorigins.org/faqs/molgen/.

3. Wen-Hsiung Li, *Molecular Evolution* (Sunderland, MA: Sinauer Associates, 1998), 395–99.

4. Max, "Plagiarized Errors," http://www.talkorigins.org/faqs/molgen/.

5. The classic work that describes this evolutionary argument is Max's "Plagiarized Errors," http://www.talkorigins.org/faqs/molgen/.

6. Roderic D. M. Page and Edward C. Holmes, *Molecular Evolution: A Phylogenetic Approach* (Malden, MA: Blackwell Science, 1998), 56–57.

7. Max, "Plagiarized Errors," http://www.talkorigins.org/faqs/molgen/.

8. Ibid.; Morimitsu Nishikimi, Toshihide Kawai, and Kunio Yagi, "Guinea Pigs Possess a Highly Mutated Gene for L-Gulono-Gamma-Lactone Oxidase, the Key Enzyme for L-Ascorbic Acid Biosynthesis Missing in This Species," *Journal of Biological Chemistry* 267 (1992): 21967–72; Morimitsu Nishikimi et al., "Cloning and Chromosomal Mapping of the Human Nonfunctional Gene for L-Gulono-Gamma-Lactone Oxidase, the Enzyme for L-Ascorbic Acid Biosynthesis Missing in Man," *Journal of Biological Chemistry* 269 (1994): 13685–88.

9. Yuriko Ohta and Morimitsu Nishikimi, "Random Nucleotide Substitutions in Primate Nonfunctional Gene for L-Gulono-Gamma-Lactone Oxidase, the Missing Enzyme in L-Ascorbic Acid Biosynthesis," *Biochimica et Biophysica Acta* 1472 (1999): 408–11.

10. See Max, "Plagiarized Errors," http://www.talkorigins.org/faqs/molgen/.

11. Page and Holmes, *Molecular Evolution*, 56–57.

12. See Max, "Plagiarized Errors," http://www.talkorigins.org/faqs/molgen/.

13. Harvey Lodish et al., *Molecular Cell Biology*, 4th ed. (New York: W. H. Freeman, 2000), 125–34.

14. Ibid., 410–22.

15. Page and Holmes, *Molecular Evolution*, 56–57.

16. See Max, "Plagiarized Errors," http://www.talkorigins.org/faqs/molgen/.

17. Page and Holmes, *Molecular Evolution*, 80–85.

18. Ibid.

19. Ibid.

20. Max, "Plagiarized Errors," http://www.talkorigins.org/faqs/molgen/; Ikuhisa Sawada et al., "Evolution of Alu Family Repeats since the Divergence of Human and Chimpanzee," *Journal of Molecular Evolution* 22 (1985): 316–22.

21. Page and Holmes, *Molecular Evolution*, 80–85.

22. For a recent example, see Abdel-Halim Salem et al., "Alu Elements and Hominid Phylogenetics," *Proceedings of the National Academy of Sciences, USA* 100 (2003): 12787–91.

23. Michael J. Pelczar Jr. and E. C. S. Chan, *Elements of Microbiology* (New York: McGraw-Hill, 1981), 180–212.

24. Alan G. Atherly, Jack R. Girton, and John F. McDonald, *The Science of Genetics* (Fort Worth, TX: Saunders College Publishing, 1999), 597–604.

25. Page and Holmes, *Molecular Evolution*, 80–85.

26. For example, see T. I. Bonner, C. O'Connell, and M. Cohen, "Cloned Endogenous Retroviral Sequences from Human DNA," *Proceedings of the National Academy of Sciences, USA* 79 (1982): 4709–13; Patrik Medstrand and Dixie L. Mager, "Human-Specific Integrations of the HERV-K Endogenous Retrovirus Family," *Journal of Virology* 72 (1998): 9782–87; Max, "Plagiarized Errors," http://www.talkorigins.org/faqs/molgen/.

27. Shinji Hirotsune et al., "An Expressed Pseudogene Regulates the Messenger-RNA Stability of Its Homologous Coding Gene," *Nature* 423 (2003): 91–96.

28. Ibid.

29. Evgeniy S. Balakirev and Francisco J. Ayala, "Pseudogenes: Are They 'Junk' or Functional DNA?," *Annual Review of Genetics* 37 (2003): 123–51.

30. Hirotsune et al., "An Expressed Pseudogene," 91–96; Shinji Hirotsune et al., "Addendum: An Expressed Pseudogene Regulates the Messenger-RNA Stability of Its Homologous Coding Gene," *Nature* 426 (2003): 100; Sergei A. Korneev, Ji-Ho Park, and Michael O'Shea, "Neuronal Expression of Neural Nitric Oxide Synthase (nNOS) Protein Is Suppressed by an Antisense RNA Transcribed from an NOS Pseudogene," *Journal of Neuroscience* 19 (1999): 7711–20.

31. Esther Betrán et al., "Evolution of the *Phosphoglycerate mutase* Processed Gene in Human and Chimpanzee Revealing the Origin of a New Primate Gene," *Molecular Biology and Evolution* 19 (2002): 654–63.

32. Christopher B. Marshall, Garth L. Fletcher, and Peter L. Davies, "Hyperactive Antifreeze Protein in a Fish," *Nature* 429 (2004): 153.

33. Wen-Man Liu et al., "Cell Stress and Translational Inhibitors Transiently Increase the Abundance of Mammalian SINE Transcripts," *Nucleic Acids Research* 23 (1995): 1758–65; Tzu-Huey Li et al., "Physiological Stresses Increase Mouse Short Interspersed Element (SINE) RNA Expression *in vivo*," *Gene* 239 (1999): 367–72; Richard H. Kimura, Prabhakara V. Choudary, and Carl W. Schmid, "Silk Worm Bm1 SINE RNA Increases

Following Cellular Insults," *Nucleic Acids Research* 27 (1999): 3380–87.

34. Wen-Ming Chu et al., "Potential Alu Function: Regulation of the Activity of Double- Stranded RNA-Activated Kinase PKR," *Molecular and Cellular Biology* 18 (1998): 58–68.

35. Wen-Man Liu et al., "Alu Transcripts: Cytoplasmic Localisation and Regulation by DNA Methylation," *Nucleic Acids Research* 22 (1994): 1087–95; Wen-Man Liu et al., "Proposed Roles for DNA Methylation in Alu Transcriptional Repression and Mutational Inactivation," *Nucleic Acids Research* 21 (1993): 1351–59; Carol M. Rubin et al., "Alu Repeated DNAs Are Differentially Methylated in Primate Germ Cells," *Nucleic Acids Research* 22 (1994): 5121–27; Igor N. Chesnokov and Carl W. Schmid, "Specific Alu Binding Protein from Human Sperm Chromatin Prevents DNA Methylation," *Journal of Biological Chemistry* 270 (1995): 18539–42; Utha Hellmann-Blumberg et al., "Developmental Differences in Methylation of Human Alu Repeats," *Molecular and Cellular Biology* 13 (1993): 4523–30.

36. Carl W. Schmid, "Does SINE Evolution Preclude Alu Function?," *Nucleic Acids Research* 26 (1998): 4541–50.

37. Jeffrey A. Bailey et al., "Molecular Evidence for a Relationship between LINE-1 Elements and X Chromosome Inactivation: The Lyon Repeat Hypothesis," *Proceedings of the National Academy of Sciences, USA* 97 (2000): 6634–39.

38. Edith Heard, Philippe Clerc, and Philip Avner, "X-Chromosome Inactivation in Mammals," *Annual Review of Genetics* 31 (1997): 571–610.

39. Jack J. Pasternak, *An Introduction to Human Molecular Genetics: Mechanisms of Inherited Diseases* (Bethesda, MD: Fitzgerald Science Press, 1999), 31–32.

40. Mary F. Lyon, "LINE-1 Elements and X Chromosome Inactivation: A Function for 'Junk' DNA?," *Proceedings of the National Academy of Sciences, USA* 97 (2000): 6248–49.

41. Elena Allen et al., "High Concentrations of Long Interspersed Nuclear Element Sequence Distinguish Monoallelically Expressed Genes," *Proceedings of the National Academy of Sciences, USA* 100 (2003): 9940–45.

42. Jerzy Jurka, "Subfamily Structure and Evolution of the Human L1 Family of Repetitive Sequences," *Journal of Molecular Evolution* 29 (1989): 496–503.

43. Atherly, Girton, and McDonald, *Science of Genetics*, 597–608.

44. Jurka, "Subfamily Structure and Evolution," 496–503; Atherly, Girton, and

McDonald, *Science of Genetics*, 597–608.

45. For example, see Greg Towers et al., "A Conserved Mechanism of Retrovirus Restriction in Mammals," *Proceedings of the National Academy of Sciences, USA* 97 (2000): 12295–99; Jonathan P. Stoye, "An Intracellular Block to Primate Lentivirus Replication," *Proceedings of the National Academy of Sciences, USA* 99 (2002): 11549–51; Caroline Besnier, Yasuhiro Takeuchi, and Greg Towers, "Restriction of Lentivirus in Monkeys," *Proceedings of the National Academy of Sciences, USA* 99 (2002): 11920–25.

46. Theodora Hatziioannou et al., "Restriction of Multiple Divergent Retroviruses by Lv1 and Ref1," *EMBO Journal* 22 (2003): 385–94.

47. Clare Lynch and Michael Tristem, "A Co-Opted *gypsy*-Type LTR-Retrotransposon Is Conserved in the Genomes of Humans, Sheep, Mice, and Rats," *Current Biology* 13 (2003): 1518–23.

48. Vera Schramke and Robin Allshire, "Hairpin RNAs and Retrotransposon LTRs Effect RNAi and Chromatin-Based Gene Silencing," *Science* 301 (2003): 1069–74; Wenhu Pi et al., "The LTR Enhancer of ERV-9 Human Endogenous Retrovirus Is Active in Oocytes and Progenitor Cells in Transgenic Zebrafish and Humans," *Proceedings of the National Academy of Sciences, USA* 101 (2004): 805–10; Catherine A. Dunn, Patrik Medstrand, and Dixie L. Mager, "An Endogenous Retroviral Long Terminal Repeat Is the Dominant Promoter for Human β1,3-Galactosyltransferase 5 in the Colon," *Proceedings of the National Academy of Sciences, USA* 100 (2003): 12841–46.

49. François Mallet et al., "The Endogenous Retroviral Locus ERVWE1 Is a Bona Fide Gene Involved in Hominoid Placental Physiology," *Proceedings of the National Academy of Sciences, USA* 101 (2004): 1731–36; Anne Dupressoir et al., "Syncytin-A and Syncytin-B, Two Fusogenic Placenta-Specific Murine Envelope Genes of Retroviral Origin Conserved in Muridae," *Proceedings of the National Academy of Sciences, USA* 102 (2005): 725–30.

50. Lynch and Tristem, "Co-Opted *gypsy*-Type LTR-Retrotransposon," 1518–23; Matthew P. Hare and Stephen R. Palumbi, "High Intron Sequence Conservation across Three Mammalian Orders Suggests Functional Constraints," *Molecular Biology and Evolution* 20 (2003): 969–78; J. W. Thomas et al., "Comparative Analyses of Multi-Species Sequences from Targeted Genomic Regions," *Nature* 424 (2003): 788–93; Nicholas J. Kaplinsky et al., "Utility and Distribution of Conserved Noncoding Sequences in the Grasses," *Proceedings of the National Academy of*

Sciences, USA 99 (2002): 6147–51; Emmanouil T. Dermitzakis et al., "Evolutionary Discrimination of Mammalian Conserved Non-Genic Sequences (CNGs)," *Science* 302 (2003): 1033–35; Gill Bejerano et al., "Ultraconserved Elements in the Human Genome," *Science* 304 (2004): 1321–25; International Chicken Genome Sequencing Consortium, "Sequence and Comparative Analysis of the Chicken Genome Provide Unique Perspectives on Vertebrate Evolution," *Nature* 432 (2004): 695–716; Adam Woolfe et al., "Highly Conserved Non-Coding Sequences Are Associated with Vertebrate Development," *PLoS Biology* (2005): e7, doi:10.1371/journal.pbio.0030007; Jeremy Schmutz et al., "The DNA Sequence and Comparative Analysis of Human Chromosome 5," *Nature* 431 (2004): 268–74.

Chapter 17: Better Dates for Humanity's Genesis

1. Elizabeth Pennisi, "Tracking the Sexes by Their Genes," *Science* 291 (2001): 1733–34; Carl Zimmer, "After You, Eve," *Natural History*, March 2001, 32–35.
2. Phillip Endicott et al., "Evaluating the Mitochondrial Timescale of Human Evolution, *Trends in Ecology and Evolution* 24 (2009): 515–21.
3. Aylwyn Scally and Richard Durbin, "Revising the Human Mutation Rate: Implications for Understanding Human Evolution," *Nature Reviews Genetics* 13 (2012): 745–53.
4. Qiaomei Fu et al., "A Revised Timescale for Human Evolution Based on Ancient Mitochondrial Genomes," *Current Biology* 23 (2013): 553–59.
5. Adrien Rieux et al., "Improved Calibration of the Human Mitochondrial Clock Using Ancient Genomes," *Molecular Biology and Evolution* 31 (2014): 2780–92.
6. Qiaomei Fu et al., "Genome Sequence of a 45,000-Year-Old Modern Human from Western Siberia," *Nature* 514 (2014): 445–49.
7. Fulvio Cruciani et al., "A Revised Root for the Human Y Chromosomal Phylogenetic Tree: The Origin of Patrilineal Diversity in Africa," *American Journal of Human Genetics* 88 (2011): 814–18; Wei Wei et al., "A Calibrated Human Y-Chromosomal Phylogeny Based on Resequencing," *Genome Research* 23 (2013): 388–95; Rebecca L. Cann, "Y Weigh In Again on Modern Humans," *Science* 341 (2013): 465–67; G. David Poznik et al., "Sequencing Y Chromosomes Resolves Discrepancy in Time to Common Ancestor of Males versus Females," *Science* 341 (2013): 562–65; Paolo Francalacci et al., "Low-Pass DNA Sequencing of 1200 Sardinians

Reconstructs European Y-Chromosome Phylogeny," *Science* 341 (2013): 565–69.

8. Fernando L. Mendez et al., "An African American Paternal Lineage Adds an Extremely Ancient Root to the Human Y Chromosome Phylogenetic Tree," *American Journal of Human Genetics* 92 (2013): 1454–59.

9. Eran Elhaik et al., "The 'Extremely Ancient' Chromosome That Isn't: A Forensic Bioinformatic Investigation of Albert Perry's X-Degenerate Portion of the Y Chromosome," *European Journal of Human Genetics* 22 (2014): 1111–16.

10. Poznik et al., "Sequencing Y Chromosomes," 562–65.

11. Hugh Ross, *Navigating Genesis: A Scientist's Journey through Genesis 1–11* (Covina, CA: RTB Press, 2014), 96–100, 145–60.

12. Quentin D. Atkinson, "Phonemic Diversity Supports a Serial Founder Effect Model of Language Expansion from Africa," *Science* 332 (2011): 346–49.

Chapter 18: When Did Modern Human Behavior Begin?

1. Christopher S. Henshilwood et al., "Emergence of Modern Human Behavior: Middle Stone Age Engravings from South Africa," *Science* 295 (2002): 1278–80; Christopher Henshilwood et al., "Middle Stone Age Shell Beads from South Africa," *Science* 304 (2004): 404; Lyn Wadley, Tamaryn Hodgskiss, and Michael Grant, "Implications for Complex Cognition from the Hafting of Tools with Compound Adhesives in the Middle Stone Age, South Africa," *Proceedings of the National Academy of Sciences, USA* 106 (2009): 9590–94; Kyle S. Brown et al., "Fire as an Engineering Tool of Early Modern Humans," *Science* 325 (2009): 859–62; Vincent Mourre, Paola Villa, and Christopher S. Henshilwood, "Early Use of Pressure Flaking on Lithic Artifacts at Blombos Cave, South Africa," *Science* 330 (2010): 659–62; Pierre-Jean Texier et al., "A Howiesons Poort Tradition of Engraving Ostrich Eggshell Containers Dated to 60,000 Years Ago at Diepkloof Rock Shelter, South Africa," *Proceedings of the National Academy of Sciences, USA* 107 (2010): 6180–85; Lyn Wadley et al., "Middle Stone Age Bedding Construction and Settlement Patterns at Sibudu, South Africa," *Science* 334 (2011): 1388–91.

2. Kyle S. Brown et al., "An Early and Enduring Advanced Technology Originating 71,000 Years Ago in South Africa," *Nature* 491 (2012): 590–93.

3. M. Aubert et al., "Pleistocene Cave Art from Sulawesi, Indonesia," *Nature* 514 (2014): 223–27.

4. Paul S. C. Tacon et al., "The Global Implications of the Early Surviving Rock Art of Greater Southeast Asia," *Antiquity* 88 (2014): 1050–64.

5. Pallab Ghosh, "Cave Paintings Change Ideas about the Origin of Art," *BBC News*, October 8, 2014, http://www.bbc.com/news/science-environment-29415716.

6. Adrien Rieux et al., "Improved Calibration of the Human Mitochondrial Clock Using Ancient Genomes," *Molecular Biology and Evolution* 31 (2014): 2780–92.

7. Chris Stringer, *Lone Survivors: How We Came to Be the Only Humans on Earth* (New York: Times Books / Henry Holt, 2012), 108–41.

8. Marian Vanhaeren et al., "Middle Paleolithic Shell Beads in Israel and Algeria," *Science* 312 (2006): 1785–88.

9. Erella Hovers et al., "An Early Case of Color Symbolism: Ochre Use by Modern Humans in Qafzeh Cave," *Current Anthropology* 44 (2003): 491–522.

10. Curtis W. Marean et al., "Early Human Use of Marine Resources and Pigment in South Africa during the Middle Pleistocene," *Nature* 449 (2007): 905–8.

11. John Shea, "*Homo sapiens* Is as *Homo sapiens* Was," *Current Anthropology* 52 (2011): 1–35; Michael Balter, "Archaeologist Hammers Away at 'Modern' Behavior," *Science* 339 (2013): 642–43.

Chapter 19: New Hominid Fossils Provide Model Tests

1. Brooks Hanson, "Light on the Origin of Man," *Science* 326 (2009): 60–61.

2. Tim D. White et al., "*Ardipithecus ramidus* and the Paleobiology of Early Hominids," *Science* 326 (2009): 64, 75–86; Giday WoldeGabriel et al., "The Geological, Isotopic, Botanical, Invertebrate, and Lower Vertebrate Surroundings of *Ardipithecus ramidus*," *Science* 326 (2009): 65, 65n1–65n5; Antoine Louchart et al., "Taphonomic, Avian, and Small-Vertebrate Indicators of *Ardipithecus ramidus* Habitat," *Science* 326 (2009): 66, 66e1–66e4; Tim D. White et al., "Macrovertebrate Paleontology and the Pliocene Habitat of *Ardipithecus ramidus*," *Science* 326 (2009): 67, 87–93; Gen Suwa et al., "The *Ardipithecus ramidus* Skull and Its Implications for Hominid Origins," *Science* 326 (2009): 68, 68e1–68e7; Gen Suwa et al., "Paleobiological Implications of the *Ardipithecus ramidus* Dentition," *Science* 326 (2009): 69, 94–99; C. Owen Lovejoy et al., "Careful Climbing in the Miocene: The Forelimbs of *Ardipithecus ramidus* and Humans Are Primitive," *Science* 326 (2009): 70, 70e1–70e8; C. Owen Lovejoy et

al., "The Pelvis and Femur of *Ardipithecus ramidus*: The Emergence of Upright Walking," *Science* 326 (2009): 71, 71e1–71e6; C. Owen Lovejoy et al., "The Great Divides: *Ardipithecus ramidus* Reveals the Postcrania of Our Last Common Ancestors with African Apes," *Science* 326 (2009): 73, 100–106; C. Owen Lovejoy, "Reexamining Human Origins in Light of *Ardipithecus ramidus*," *Science* 326 (2009): 74, 74e1–74e8.

3. Yoel Rak, Avishag Ginzburg, and Eli Geffen, "Gorilla-Like Anatomy on *Australopithecus afarensis* Mandibles Suggests *Au. afarensis* Link to Robust Australopiths," *Proceedings of the National Academy of Sciences, USA* 104 (2007): 6568–72.

4. Yohannes Haile-Selassie et al., "An Early *Australopithecus afarensis* Postcranium from Woranso-Mille, Ethiopia," *Proceedings of the National Academy of Sciences, USA* 107 (2010): 12121–26.

5. Carol V. Ward, William H. Kimbel, and Donald C. Johanson, "Complete Fourth Metatarsal and Arches in the Foot of *Australopithecus afarensis*," *Science* 331 (2011): 750–53.

6. Robin H. Crompton et al., "Human-Like External Function of the Foot, and Fully Upright Gait, Confirmed in the 3.66 Million Year Old Laetoli Hominin Footprints by Topographic Statistics, Experimental Footprint-Formation and Computer Simulation," *Journal of the Royal Society: Interface* 9 (2012): 707–19.

7. Martin Häusler and Peter Schmid, "Comparison of the Pelves of Sts 14 and AL288-1: Implications for Birth and Sexual Dimorphism in Australopithecines," *Journal of Human Evolution* 29 (1995): 363–83.

8. Robert G. Tague and C. Owen Lovejoy, "AL 288-1—Lucy or Lucifer: Gender Confusion in the Pliocene," *Journal of Human Evolution* 35 (1998): 75–94.

9. These two articles summarize a series of papers published in *Science* by Lee Berger and collaborators: Fred Spoor, "Palaeoanthropology: Malapa and the Genus *Homo*," *Nature* 478 (2011): 44–45; Ann Gibbons, "Skeletons Present an Exquisite Paleo-Puzzle," *Science* 333 (2011): 1370–72. These papers are the original scientific studies: Kristian J. Carlson et al., "The Endocast of MH1, *Australopithecus sediba*," *Science* 333 (2011): 1402–7; Job M. Kibii et al., "A Partial Pelvis of *Australopithecus sediba*," *Science* 333 (2011): 1407–11; Tracy L. Kivell et al., "*Australopithecus sediba* Hand Demonstrates Mosaic Evolution of Locomotor and Manipulative Abilities," *Science* 333 (2011): 1411–17; Bernhard Zipfel et al., "The Foot and Ankle of *Australopithecus sediba*," *Science* 333 (2011): 1417–20;

Robyn Pickering et al., "*Australopithecus sediba* at 1.977 Ma and Implications for the Origins of the Genus *Homo*," *Science* 333 (2011): 1421–23.

10. Lee R. Berger et al., "*Australopithecus sediba*: A New Species of *Homo*-Like Australopith from South Africa," *Science* 328 (2010): 195–204.

11. Pickering et al., "*Australopithecus sediba* at 1.977 Ma," 1421–23.

12. D. Curnoe, "A Review of Early *Homo* in Southern Africa Focusing on Cranial, Mandibular and Dental Remains, with the Description of a New Species (*Homo gautengensis* sp. nov.)," *HOMO - Journal of Comparative Human Biology* 61 (2010): 151–77.

13. Richard J. Sherwood, Steven C. Ward, and Andrew Hill, "The Taxonomic Status of the Chemeron Temporal (KNM-BC 1)," *Journal of Human Evolution* 42 (2002): 153–84; William H. Kimbel et al., "Late Pliocene *Homo* and Oldowan Tools from the Hadar Formation (Kada Hadar Member), Ethiopia," *Journal of Human Evolution* 31 (1996): 549–61; William H. Kimbel, Donald C. Johanson, and Yoel Rak, "Systematic Assessment of a Maxilla of *Homo* from Hadar, Ethiopia," *American Journal of Physical Anthropology* 103 (1997): 235–62.

14. F. Spoor et al., "Implications of New Early *Homo* Fossils from Ileret, East of Lake Turkana, Kenya," *Nature* 448 (2007): 688–91.

15. David Lordkipanidze et al., "A Complete Skull from Dmanisi, Georgia, and the Evolutionary Biology of Early *Homo*," *Science* 342 (2013): 326–31; Ann Margvelashvili et al., "Tooth Wear and Dentoalveolar Remodeling Are Key Factors of Morphological Variation in the Dmanisi Mandibles," *Proceedings of the National Academy of Sciences, USA* 110 (2013): 17278–83.

16. University of Zurich, "Unique Skull Find Rebuts Theories on Species Diversity in Early Humans," *ScienceDaily*, posted October 17, 2013, http://www.sciencedaily.com/releases/2013/10/131017173906.htm.

17. F. Spoor et al., "Implications," 688–91.

18. E. Carbonell et al., "An Early Pleistocene Hominin Mandible from Atapuerca-TD6, Spain," *Proceedings of the National Academy of Sciences, USA* 102 (2005): 5674–78.

19. J. M. Bermúdez de Castro et al., "A Hominid from the Lower Pleistocene of Atapuerca, Spain: Possible Ancestor to Neandertals and Modern Humans," *Science* 276 (1997): 1392–95.

20. J. L. Arsuaga et al., "Neandertal Roots: Cranial and Chronological Evidence from Sima de los Huesos," *Science* 344 (2014): 1358–63.

21. Michael Balter, "RIP for a Key *Homo* Species?," *Science* 345 (2014): 129.

22. Darren Curnoe et al., "Human Remains from the Pleistocene-Holocene Transition of Southwest China Suggest a Complex Evolutionary History for East Asians," *PLoS ONE* 7 (2012): e31918, doi:10.1371/journal.pone.0031918.

23. Chimpanzee Sequencing and Analysis Consortium, "Initial Sequence of the Chimpanzee Genome and Comparison with the Human Genome," *Nature* 437 (2005): 69–87.

24. Sally McBrearty and Nina Jablonski, "First Fossil Chimpanzee," *Nature* 437 (2005): 105–8.

25. Michael Hopkin, "First Chimp Fossil Unearthed," *Nature News* (2005): doi:10.1038/news050829-10.

Chapter 20: Are Neanderthals Similar to Humans?

1. Aida Gómez-Robles et al., "No Known Hominin Species Matches the Expected Dental Morphology of the Last Common Ancestor of Neanderthals and Modern Humans," *Proceedings of the National Academy of Sciences, USA* 110 (2013): 18196–201.

2. Indiana University, "No Known Hominin Is Common Ancestor of Neanderthals and Modern Humans, Study Suggests," *ScienceDaily*, posted October 21, 2013, http://www.sciencedaily.com/releases/2013/10/131021153202.htm.

3. Matthias Meyer et al., "A Mitochondrial Genome Sequence of a Hominin from Sima de los Huesos," *Nature* 505 (2014): 403–6.

4. Ewen Callaway, "Hominin DNA Baffles Experts," *Nature* 504 (2013): 16–17.

5. Tanya M. Smith et al., "Dental Evidence for Ontogenetic Differences between Modern Humans and Neanderthals," *Proceedings of the National Academy of Sciences, USA* 107 (2010): 20923–28.

6. Isabelle Crevecoeur et al., "The Spy VI Child: A Newly Discovered Neandertal Infant," *Journal of Human Evolution* 59 (2010): 641–56.

7. Philipp Gunz et al., "Brain Development after Birth Differs between Neanderthals and Modern Humans," *Current Biology* 20 (2010): R921–R922.

8. Eiluned Pearce, Chris Stringer, and R. I. M. Dunbar, "New Insights into Differences in Brain Organization between Neanderthals and Anatomically Modern Humans," *Proceedings of the Royal Society B* 280 (2013): doi:10.1098/rspb.2013.0168.

9. Richard E. Green et al., "A Complete Neandertal Mitochondrial Genome Sequence Determined by High-Throughput Sequencing," *Cell* 134 (2008):

416–26.

10. Adrian W. Briggs et al., "Targeted Retrieval and Analysis of Five Neandertal mtDNA Genomes," *Science* 325 (2009): 318–21.

11. Richard E. Green et al., "Analysis of One Million Base Pairs of Neanderthal DNA," *Nature* 444 (2006): 330–36; James P. Noonan et al., "Sequencing and Analysis of Neanderthal Genomic DNA," *Science* 314 (2006): 1113–18.

12. Richard E. Green et al., "A Draft Sequence of the Neandertal Genome," *Science* 328 (2010): 710–22.

13. Kay Prüfer et al., "The Complete Genome Sequence of a Neanderthal from the Altai Mountains," *Nature* 505 (2014): 43–49.

14. Sergi Castellano et al., "Patterns of Coding Variation in the Complete Exomes of Three Neandertals," *Proceedings of the National Academy of Sciences, USA* 111 (2014): 6666–71.

15. David Gokhmam et al., "Reconstructing the DNA Methylation Maps of the Neandertal and the Denisovan," *Science* 344 (2014): 523–27.

16. Carles Lalueza-Fox et al., "A Melanocortin 1 Receptor Allele Suggests Varying Pigmentation among Neanderthals," *Science* 318 (2007): 1453–55.

17. M. Sazzini et al., "Searching for Signatures of Cold Adaptations in Modern and Archaic Humans: Hints from the Brown Adipose Tissue Genes," *Heredity* 113 (2014): 259–67.

18. Carles Lalueza-Fox et al., "Bitter Taste Perception in Neanderthals through the Analysis of the *TAS2R38* Gene," *Biology Letters* 5 (2009): 809–11.

19. Johannes Krause et al., "The Complete Mitochondrial DNA Genome of an Unknown Hominin from Southern Siberia," *Nature* 464 (2008): 894–97.

20. David Reich et al., "Genetic History of an Archaic Hominin Group from Denisova Cave in Siberia," *Nature* 468 (2010): 1053–60; Matthias Meyer et al., "A High-Coverage Genome Sequence from an Archaic Denisovan Individual," *Science* 338 (2012): 222–26.

Chapter 21: That Messy Interbreeding Problem

1. Patrick D. Evans et al., "Evidence that the Adaptive Allele of the Brain Size Gene *Microcephalin* Introgressed into *Homo sapiens* from an Archaic *Homo* Lineage," *Proceedings of the National Academy of Sciences, USA* 103 (2006): 18178–83.

2. Martina Lari et al., "The *Microcephalin* Ancestral Allele in a Neanderthal Individual," *PLoS ONE* 5 (2010): e10648, doi:10.1371/journal.pone.0010648.
3. Daniel Garrigan et al., "Evidence for Archaic Asian Ancestry on the Human X Chromosome," *Molecular Biology and Evolution* 22 (2005): 189–92; Daniel Garrigan et al., "Deep Haplotype Divergence and Long-Range Linkage Disequilibrium at Xp21.1 Provide Evidence That Humans Descend from a Structured Ancestral Population," *Genetics* 170 (2005): 1849–56; Michael F. Hammer et al., "Genetic Evidence for Archaic Admixture in Africa," *Proceedings of the National Academy of Sciences, USA* 108 (2011): 15123–28; Joseph Lachance et al., "Evolutionary History and Adaptation from High-Coverage Whole-Genome Sequences of Diverse African Hunter-Gatherers," *Cell* 150 (2012): 457–69.
4. Lachance et al., "Evolutionary History and Adaptation," 457–69.
5. Ibid.
6. James P. Noonan et al., "Sequencing and Analysis of Neanderthal Genomic DNA," *Science* 314 (2006): 1113–18; Richard E. Green et al., "Analysis of One Million Base Pairs of Neanderthal DNA," *Nature* 444 (2006): 330–36.
7. Elizabeth Pennisi, "The Dawn of Stone Age Genomics," *Science* 314 (2006): 1068–71.
8. Elizabeth Pennisi, "No Sex Please, We're Neandertals," *Science* 316 (2007): 967.
9. Jeffrey D. Wall and Sung K. Kim, "Inconsistencies in Neanderthal Genomic DNA Sequences," *PLoS Genetics* 3 (2007): e175, doi:10.1371/journal.pgen.0030175.
10. Richard E. Green, "A Draft Sequence of the Neandertal Genome," *Science* 328 (2010): 710–22.
11. Sriram Sankararaman et al., "The Date of Interbreeding between Neandertals and Modern Humans," *PLoS Genetics* 8, (2012): e1002947, doi:10.1371/journal.pgen.1002947.
12. David Reich et al., "Genetic History of an Archaic Hominin Group from Denisova Cave in Siberia," *Nature* 468 (2010): 1053–60; Matthias Meyer et al., "A High-Coverage Genome Sequence from an Archaic Denisovan Individual," *Science* 338 (2012): 222–26; David Reich et al., "Denisova Admixture and the First Modern Human Dispersals into Southeast Asia and Oceania," *American Journal of Human Genetics* 89 (2011): 516–28.
13. Kay Prüfer et al., "The Complete Genome Sequence of a Neanderthal from the Altai Mountains," *Nature* 505 (2014): 43–49.

14. Qiaomei Fu et al., "DNA Analysis of an Early Modern Human from Tianyuan Cave, China," *Proceedings of the National Academy of Sciences, USA* 110 (2013): 2223–27.

15. Andaine Seguin-Orlando et al., "Genomic Structure in Europeans Dating Back at Least 36,200 Years," *Science* 346 (2014): 1113–18.

16. Qiaomei Fu et al., "Genome Sequence of a 45,000-Year-Old Modern Human from Western Siberia," *Nature* 514 (2014): 445–49.

17. Israel Hershkovitz et al., "Levantine Cranium from Manot Cave (Israel) Foreshadows the First European Modern Humans," *Nature Letters* (2015): doi:10.1038/nature14134.

18. Sriram Sankararaman et al., "The Genomic Landscape of Neanderthal Ancestry in Present-Day Humans," *Nature* 507 (2014): 354–57; Benjamin Vernot and Joshua M. Akey, "Resurrecting Surviving Neandertal Lineages from Modern Human Genomes," *Science* 343 (2014): 1017–21.

19. Svante Pääbo, *Neanderthal Man: In Search of Lost Genomes* (New York: Basic Books, 2014), 172.

20. Laurent Abi-Rached et al., "The Shaping of Modern Human Immune Systems by Multiregional Admixture with Archaic Humans," *Science* 334 (2011): 89–94.

21. Sebastian Temme et al., "A Novel Family of Human Leukocyte Antigen Class II Receptors May Have Its Origin in Archaic Human Species," *Journal of Biological Chemistry* 289 (2014): 639–53.

22. Qiliang Ding, Ya Hu, and Li Jin, "Non-Neanderthal Origin of the HLA-DPB1*0401," *Journal of Biological Chemistry* 289 (2014): 10252.

23. Qiliang Ding et al., "Neanderthal Introgression at Chromosome 3p21.31 Was under Positive Natural Selection in East Asians," *Molecular Biology and Evolution* 31 (2014): 683–95.

24. Sankararaman et al., "Genomic Landscape," 354–57; Vernot and Akey, "Resurrecting Surviving Neandertal Lineages," 1017–21.

25. Sandra Beleza et al., "The Timing of Pigmentation Lightening in Europeans," *Molecular Biology and Evolution* 30 (2013): 24–35.

26. Iñigo Olalde et al., "Derived Immune and Ancestral Pigmentation Alleles in a 7,000-Year-Old Mesolithic European," *Nature* 507 (2014): 225–28.

27. Chris Stringer, *Lone Survivors: How We Came to Be the Only Humans on Earth* (New York: Times Book, 2012), 198–99.

28. Ekaterina E. Khrameeva et al., "Neanderthal Ancestry Drives Evolution of Lipid Catabolism in Contemporary Europeans," *Nature Communications* 5 (2014): doi:10.1038/ncomms4584.

29. Sankararaman et al., "Genomic Landscape," 354–57.
30. Emilia Huerta-Sánchez et al., "Altitude Adaptation in Tibetans Caused by Introgression of Denisovan-Like DNA," *Nature* 512 (2014): 194–97.
31. Felipe R. Lorenzo et al., "A Genetic Mechanism for Tibetan High-Altitude Adaptation," *Nature Genetics* 46 (2014): 951–56.
32. Mathias Currat and Laurent Excoffier, "Strong Reproductive Isolation between Humans and Neanderthals Inferred from Observed Patterns of Introgression," *Proceedings of the National Academy of Sciences, USA* 108 (2011): 15129–34; Sankararaman et al., "Genomic Landscape," 354–57; Vernot and Akey, "Resurrecting Surviving Neandertal Lineages," 1017–21.
33. Adrian W. Briggs et al., "Targeted Retrieval and Analysis of Five Neandertal mtDNA Genomes," *Science* 325 (2009): 318–21; Prüfer et al., "Complete Genome Sequence," 43–49; Sergi Castellano et al., "Patterns of Coding Variation in the Complete Exomes of Three Neandertals," *Proceedings of the National Academy of Sciences, USA* 111 (2014): 6666–71.
34. Stringer, *Lone Survivors*, 183.
35. Jeffrey C. Long, Jie Li, and Meghan E. Healy, "Human DNA Sequences: More Variation and Less Race," *American Journal of Physical Anthropology* 139 (2009): 23–34.
36. Ian Tattersall, *Masters of the Planet: The Search for Our Human Origins* (New York: Palgrave Macmillian, 2012), 168.
37. Sankararaman et al., "Genomic Landscape," 354–57; Vernot and Akey, "Resurrecting Surviving Neandertal Lineages," 1017–21.
38. Ewen Callaway, "Modern Human Genomes Reveal Our Inner Neanderthal," *Nature News* (2014): doi:10.1038/nature.2014.14615.

Chapter 22: Did Neanderthals Have the Smarts?
1. Dennis M. Sandgathe et al., "The Roc de Marsal Neandertal Child: A Reassessment of Its Status as a Deliberate Burial," *Journal of Human Evolution* 61 (2011): 243–53.
2. Ibid.
3. Michael Balter, "Did Neandertals Truly Bury Their Dead?," *Science* 337 (2012): 1443–44.
4. William Rendu et al., "Evidence Supporting an Intentional Neandertal Burial at La Chapelle-aux-Saints," *Proceedings of the National Academy of Sciences, USA* 111 (2014): 81–86.
5. For a survey of some of these discoveries, see Paola Villa and Wil Roebroeks, "Neandertal Demise: An Archaeological Analysis of the Modern

Human Superiority Complex," *PLoS ONE* 9 (2014): e96424, doi:10.1371/journal.pone.0096424.

6. Amanda G. Henry, Alison S. Brooks, and Dolores R. Piperno, "Microfossils in Calculus Demonstrate Consumption of Plants and Cooked Foods in Neanderthal Diets (Shanidar III, Iraq; Spy I and II, Belgium)," *Proceedings of the National Academy of Sciences, USA* 108 (2011): 486–91.

7. Matthew J. Collins and Les Copeland, "Ancient Starch: Cooked or Just Old?," *Proceedings of the National Academy of Sciences, USA* 108 (2011): E145.

8. Karen Hardy et al., "Neanderthal Medics? Evidence for Food, Cooking, and Medicinal Plants Entrapped in Dental Calculus," *Naturwissenschaften* 99 (2012): 617–26.

9. Shrivastava Rounak, Khare Apoorva, and Agrawal Shweta, "Zoopharmacognosy (Animal Self Medication): A Review," *International Journal of Research in Ayurveda and Pharmacy* 2 (2011): 1510–12.

10. A. W. G. Pike et al., "U-Series Dating of Paleolithic Art in 11 Caves in Spain," *Science* 336 (2012): 1409–13.

11. Ibid.

12. Tom Higham et al., "The Timing and Spatiotemporal Patterning of Neanderthal Disappearance," *Nature* 512 (2014): 306–9.

13. Tom Higham et al., "The Earliest Evidence for Anatomically Modern Humans in Northwestern Europe," *Nature* 479 (2011): 521–24; Stefano Benazzi et al., "Early Dispersal of Modern Humans in Europe and Implications for Neanderthal Behavior," *Nature* 479 (2011): 525–28.

14. Joaquín Rodríguez-Vidal et al., "A Rock Engraving Made by Neanderthals in Gibraltar," *Proceedings of the National Academy of Sciences, USA* 111 (2014): 13301–6.

15. Eugène Morin and Véronique Laroulandie, "Presumed Symbolic Use of Diurnal Raptors by Neanderthals," *PLoS ONE* 7 (2012): e32856, doi:10.1371/journal.pone.0032856.

16. Wil Roebroeks et al., "Use of Red Ochre by Early Neandertals," *Proceedings of the National Academy of Sciences, USA* 109 (2012): 1889–94.

17. Ibid., 1893.

18. João Zilhão et al., "Symbolic Use of Marine Shells and Mineral Pigments by Iberian Neandertals," *Proceedings of the National Academy of Sciences, USA* 107 (2010): 1023–28.

19. Marco Peresani et al., "An Ochered Fossil Marine Shell from the Mousterian of Fumane Cave, Italy," *PLoS ONE* 8 (2013): e68572, doi:10.1371/

journal.pone.0068572.

20. Ian Tattersall and Jeffrey H. Schwartz, "Evolution of the Genus *Homo*," *Annual Review of Earth and Planetary Sciences* 37 (2009): 81.

21. Josephine C. A. Joordens et al., "*Homo erectus* at Trinil on Java Used Shells for Tool Production and Engraving," *Nature* 518 (2015): 228–31.

22. Steven L. Kuhn and Mary C. Stiner, "What's a Mother to Do? The Division of Labor among Neandertals and Modern Humans in Eurasia," *Current Anthropology* 47 (2006): 953–80.

23. Thomas Higham et al., "Chronology of the Grotte du Renne (France) and Implications for the Context of Ornaments and Human Remains within the Châtelperronian," *Proceedings of the National Academy of Sciences, USA* 107 (2010): 20234–39.

24. Johannes Krause et al., "The Derived *FOXP2* Variant of Modern Humans Was Shared with Neandertals," *Current Biology* 17 (2007): 1908–12.

25. Wolfgang Enard et al., "Molecular Evolution of *FOXP2*, a Gene Involved in Speech and Language," *Nature* 418 (2002): 869–72.

26. Jianzhi Zhang, David M. Webb, and Ondrej Podlaha, "Accelerated Protein Evolution and Origins of Human-Specific Features: FOXP2 as an Example," *Genetics* 162 (2002): 1825–35.

27. Sriram Sankararaman et al., "The Genomic Landscape of Neanderthal Ancestry in Present-Day Humans," *Nature* 507 (2014): 354–57; Benjamin Vernot and Joshua M. Akey, "Resurrecting Surviving Neandertal Lineages from Modern Human Genomes," *Science* 343 (2014): 1017–21.

28. Ian Tattersall, *Masters of the Planet: The Search for Our Human Origins* (New York: Palgrave Macmillian, 2012), 209–10.

29. Johan J. Bolhuis et al., "How Could Language Have Evolved?" *PLoS Biology* 12 (2014): e1001934, doi:10.1371/journal.pbio.1001934.

30. Ibid.

31. Vitor A. Nóbrega and Shigeru Miyagawa, "The Precedence of Syntax in the Rapid Emergence of Human Language in Evolution as Defined by the Integration Hypothesis," *Frontiers in Psychology* 6 (2015): doi: 10.3389/fpsyg2015.00271.

32. Massachusetts Institute of Technology, "The Rapid Rise of Human Language," *ScienceDaily*, posted March 31, 2015, http://www.sciencedaily.com/releases/2015/03/150331131324.htm.

Chapter 23: Comparing Chimp and Hominid Behaviors

1. Iowa State University, "Chimps Have Been Found Using Caves for

Shelter," *ScienceDaily*, posted April 12, 2007, http://www.sciencedaily.com/releases/2007/04/070412082939.htm.

2. David R. Samson and Kevin D. Hunt, "Chimpanzees Preferentially Select Sleeping Platform Construction Tree Species with Biomechanical Properties that Yield Stable, Firm, but Compliant Nests," *PLoS ONE* 9 (2014): e104024, doi:10.1371/journal.pone.0104024.

3. Jill D. Pruetz and Paco Bertolani, "Savanna Chimpanzees, *Pan troglodytes verus*, Hunt with Tools," *Current Biology* 17 (2007): 412–17.

4. Crickette M. Sanz and David B. Morgan, "Chimpanzee Tool Technology in the Goualougo Triangle, Republic of Congo," *Journal of Human Evolution* 52 (2007): 420–33.

5. Julio Mercader et al., "4,300-Year-Old Chimpanzee Sites and the Origins of Percussive Stone Technology," *Proceedings of the National Academy of Sciences, USA* 104 (2007): 3043–48.

6. Ibid.

7. Thomas Suddendorf, *The Gap: The Science of What Separates Us from Other Animals* (New York: Basic Books, 2013), 2–3.

8. Dora Biro et al., "Chimpanzee Mothers at Bossou, Guinea Carry the Mummified Remains of Their Dead Infants," *Current Biology* 20 (2010): R351–R352.

9. James R. Anderson, Alasdair Gillies, and Louise C. Lock, "*Pan* Thanatology," *Current Biology* 20 (2010): R349–R351; Biro et al., "Chimpanzee Mothers at Bossou," R351–R352.

10. Hugh Ross, *Hidden Treasures in the Book of Job: How the Oldest Book in the Bible Answers Today's Scientific Questions* (Grand Rapids, MI: Baker Books, 2011), 119–74.

Chapter 24: Trying on the Genes

1. Chimpanzee Sequencing and Analysis Consortium, "Initial Sequence of the Chimpanzee Genome and Comparison with the Human Genome," *Nature* 437 (2005): 69–87.

2. Kay Prüfer et al., "The Bonobo Genome Compared with the Chimpanzee and Human Genomes," *Nature* 486 (2012): 527–31.

3. Aylwyn Scally et al., "Insights into Hominid Evolution from the Gorilla Genome Sequence," *Nature* 483 (2012): 169–75; Kay Prüfer et al., "The Bonobo Genome Compared with the Chimpanzee and Human Genomes," *Nature* 486 (2012): 527–31.

4. For example, see Ning Fu et al., "Comparison of Protein and mRNA

Expression Evolution in Humans and Chimpanzees," *PLoS ONE* 2, (2007): e216, doi:10.1371/journal.pone.0000216; Ralph Haygood et al., "Promoter Regions of Many Neural- and Nutrition-Related Genes Have Experienced Positive Selection during Human Evolution," *Nature Genetics* 39 (2007): 1140–44.

5. John A. Calarco et al., "Global Analysis of Alternate Splicing Differences between Humans and Chimpanzees," *Genes and Development* 21 (2007): 2963–75.

6. Maria C. N. Marchetto et al., "Differential L1 Regulation in Pluripotent Stem Cells of Humans and Apes," *Nature* 503 (2013): 525-29.

Chapter 25: Is It Time to Scrap Junk DNA?

1. ENCODE Project Consortium, "Identification and Analysis of Functional Elements in 1% of the Human Genome by the ENCODE Pilot Project," *Nature* 447 (2007): 799–816.

2. ENCODE Project Consortium, "An Integrated Encyclopedia of DNA Elements in the Human Genome," *Nature* 489 (2012): 57–74.

3. For a more detailed discussion of the function of *Alu* sequences, see the excellent six-part series of articles written by biochemist Patricia (Fanning) Babin entitled "'Junk' DNA: An Outdated Concept" at reasons.org.

4. Paz Polak and Eytan Domany, "Alu Elements Contain Many Binding Sites for Transcription Factors and May Play a Role in Regulation of Developmental Processes," *BMC Genomics* 7 (2006): 133–47; Chenguang Gong and Lynne E. Maquat, "lncRNAs Transactivate STAU1-Mediated mRNA Decay by Duplexing with 3' UTRs via Alu Elements," *Nature* 470 (2011): 284–88.

5. Yoshiaki Tanaka et al., "Effects of Alu Elements on Global Nucleosome Positioning in the Human Genome," *BMC Genomics* 11 (2010): 309–19.

6. Pierre-Étienne Jacques, Justin Jeyakani, and Guillaume Bourque, "The Majority of Primate-Specific Regulatory Sequences Are Derived from Transposable Elements," *PLoS Genetics* 9 (2013): e1003504, doi:10.1371/journal.pgen.1003504.

7. Rui M. M. Branca et al., "HiRIEF LC-MS Enables Deep Proteome Coverage and Unbiased Proteogenomics," *Nature Methods* 11 (2014): 59–62.

8. Karolinska Institutet, "Protein Coding 'Junk Genes' May Be Linked to Cancer," *ScienceDaily*, posted November 17, 2013, http:/www.sciencedaily.com/releases/2013/11/131117155500.htm.

9. Laura Poliseno et al., "A Coding-Independent Function of Gene and

Pseudogene mRNAs Regulates Tumour Biology," *Nature* 465 (2010): 1033–38.

10. Yan-Zi Wen et al., "Pseudogene-Derived Small Interference RNAs Regulate Gene Expression in African *Trypanosoma brucei*," *Proceedings of the National Academy of Sciences, USA* 108 (2011): 8345–50.

11. Ana C. Marques, Jennifer Tan, and Chris P. Ponting, "Wrangling for microRNAs Provokes Much Crosstalk," *Genome Biology* 12 (2011): 132; Leonardo Salmena et al., "A *ceRNA* Hypothesis: The Rosetta Stone of a Hidden RNA Language?," *Cell* 146 (2011): 353–58.

12. Ana C. Marques et al., "Evidence for Conserved Post-Transcriptional Roles of Unitary Pseudogenes for Frequent Bifunctionality of mRNAs," *Genome Biology* 13 (2012): R102, doi:10.1186/gb-2012-13-11-r102.

13. NIH/National Human Genome Research Institute, "First Holistic View of How Human Genome Actually Works: ENCODE Study Produces Massive Data Set," *ScienceDaily*, posted September 5, 2012, http://www.http.com/releases/2012/09/120905140913.htm.

Chapter 26: Criticisms of RTB's Human Origins Model

1. For example, see Dennis Venema and Darrel Falk, "Does Genetics Point to a Single Primal Couple?," *Biologos Forum* (blog), posted April 5, 2010, http://biologos.org/blog/does-genetics-point-to-a-single-primal-couple.

2. For a recent example, see Nuha Elhassan et al., "The Episode of Genetic Drift Defining the Migration of Humans out of Africa Is Derived from a Large East African Population Size," *PLoS ONE* 9 (2014): e97674, doi:10.1371/journal.pone.0097674.

3. For example, see Venema and Falk, "Single Primal Couple?," http://biologos.org/blog/does-genetics-point-to-a-single-primal-couple.

4. Lev A. Zhivotovsky, Noah A Rosenberg, and Marcus W. Feldman, "Features of Evolution and Expansion of Modern Humans, Inferred from Genomewide Microsatellite Markers," *American Journal of Human Genetics* 72 (2003): 1171–86.

5. Lev A. Zhivotovsky et al., "Human Population Expansion and Microsatellite Variation," *Molecular Biology and Evolution* 17 (2000): 757–67.

6. Renaud Kaeuffer et al., "Unexpected Heterozygosity in an Island Mouflon Population Founded by a Single Pair of Individuals," *Proceedings of the Royal Society B: Biological Sciences* 274 (2007): 527–33; Hiroki Goto et al., "A Massively Parallel Sequencing Approach Uncovers Ancient Origins and High Genetic Variability of Endangered Przewalski's Horses,"

Genome Biology and Evolution 3 (2011): 1096–106; S. Elizabeth Alter, Seth D. Newsome, and Stephen R. Palumni, "Pre-Whaling Genetic Diversity and Population Ecology in Eastern Pacific Gray Whales: Insights from Ancient DNA and Stable Isotopes," *PLoS ONE* 7 (2012): e35039, doi:10.1371/journal.pone.0035039.

7. Kaeuffer et al., "Unexpected Heterozygosity," 527–33.
8. For example, see Eric Bazin, Sylvain Glémin, and Nicolas Galtier, "Population Size Does Not Influence Mitochondrial Genetic Diversity in Animals," *Science* 312 (2006): 570–72; Benoit Nabholz et al., "Determination of Mitochondrial Genetic Diversity in Mammals," *Genetics* 178 (2008): 351–61; Benoit Nabholz, Sylvain Glémin, and Nicolas Galtier, "The Erratic Mitochondrial Clock: Variations of Mutation Rate, Not Population Size, Affect mtDNA Diversity across Birds and Mammals," *BMC Evolutionary Biology* 9 (2009): 54, doi:10.1186/1471-2148-9-54; Gwenael Piganeau and Adam Eyre-Walker, "Evidence for Variation in the Effective Population Size of Animal Mitochondrial DNA," *PLoS ONE* 4 (2009): e4396, doi:10.1371/journal.pone.0004396; Hans Ellegren, "Is Genetic Diversity Really Higher in Large Populations?," *Journal of Biology* 8 (2009): 41, doi:10.1186/jbiol135; Robin S. Waples, "A Bias Correction for Estimates of Effective Population Size Based on Linkage Disequilibrium at Unlinked Gene Loci," *Conservation Genetics* 7 (2006): 167–84.
9. Ellegren, "Genetic Diversity Really Higher?," 41.
10. Quentin D. Atkinson, Russell D. Gray, and Alexei J. Drummond, "mtDNA Variation Predicts Population Size in Humans and Reveals a Major Southern Asian Chapter in Human Prehistory," *Molecular Biology and Evolution* 25 (2008): 468–74.
11. Chiara Batini and M. A. Jobling, "The Jigsaw Puzzle of Our African Ancestry: Unsolved, or Unsolvable?," *Genome Biology* 12 (2011): 118, doi:10.1186/gb-2011-12-6-118.
12. The centromere is a region of the DNA molecule near the center of the chromosome that serves as the point of attachment for the mitotic spindle during the cell division process. Telomeres are DNA sequences located at the tip ends of chromosomes designed to stabilize the chromosome preventing it from undergoing degradation.
13. J. W. IJdo et al., "Origin of Human Chromosome 2: An Ancestral Telomere-Telomere Fusion," *Proceedings of the National Academy of Sciences, USA* 88 (1991): 9051–55; Rosamaria Avarello et al., "Evidence for an Ancestral Alphoid Domain on the Long Arm of Human Chromosome 2,"

Human Genetics 89 (1992): 247–49.

14. Roger Lewin, *Principles of Human Evolution: A Core Textbook* (Malden, MA: Blackwell Science, 1998), 499–508; M. A. Jobling, M. E. Hurles, and C. Tyler-Smith, *Human Evolutionary Genetics: Origins, Peoples and Disease* (New York: Garland, 2004), 452.

15. For example, see P. Thomas Schoenemann, "Hominid Brain Evolution," in *A Companion to Paleoanthropology*, ed. David R. Begun (Oxford: Wiley-Blackwell, 2013): 136–64.

16. Lewin, *Principles of Human Evolution*, 499–508; Jobling, Hurles, and Tyler-Smith, *Human Evolutionary Genetics*, 300–338.

17. Dolores R. Piperno et al., "Processing of Wild Cereal Grains in the Upper Palaeolithic Revealed by Starch Grain Analysis," *Nature* 430 (2004): 670–73.

18. Anna Revedin et al., "Thirty Thousand-Year-Old Evidence of Plant Food Processing," *Proceedings of the National Academy of Sciences, USA* 107 (2010): 18815–19.

19. Michael Balter, "Seeking Agriculture's Ancient Roots," *Science* 316 (2007): 1830–35.

20. Tom D. Dillehay et al., "Preceramic Adoption of Peanut, Squash, and Cotton in Northern Peru," *Science* 316 (2007): 1890–93.

21. Yuriko Igarashi et al., "New Method for Estimation of Adult Skeletal Age at Death from the Morphology of the Auricular Surface of the Ilium," *American Journal of Physical Anthropology* 128 (2005): 324–39.

22. For example, see Mehmet Yaşar İşcan, ed., *Age Markers in the Human Skeleton* (Springfield, IL: Charles C. Thomas, 1989).

23. Hugh Ross, *Navigating Genesis: A Scientist's Journey through Genesis 1–11* (Covina, CA: RTB Press, 2014), 122–30, 138–44.

Chapter 27: Three New Questions

1. Christopher Stringer, *Lone Survivors: How We Came to Be the Only Humans on Earth* (New York: Henry Holt and Company, 2012), 185–86.

2. Ibid., 185–90.

3. Steven W. Wilhelm and Curtis A. Suttle, "Viruses and Nutrient Cycles in the Sea: Viruses Play Critical Roles in the Structure and Function of Aquatic Food Webs," *Bioscience* 49 (1999): 781–88.

4. Nathalie Cartier et al., "Hematopoietic Stem Cell Gene Therapy with a Lentiviral Vector in X-Linked Adrenoleukodystrophy," *Science* 326 (2009): 818–23.

5. Peter J. Hudson, Andrew P. Dobson, and Kevin D. Lafferty, "Is a Healthy Ecosystem One That Is Rich in Parasites?," *Trends in Ecology and Evolution* 21 (2006): 381–85.
6. Junjie Qin et al., "A Human Gut Microbial Gene Catalogue Established by Metagenomic Sequencing," *Nature* 464 (2010): 59–65.
7. Yuping Lai et al., "Commensal Bacteria Regulate Toll-Like Receptor 3–Dependent Inflammation after Skin Injury," *Nature Medicine* 15 (2009): 1377–82.
8. Peter J. Turnbaugh et al., "An Obesity-Associated Gut Microbiome with Increased Capacity for Energy Harvest," *Nature* 444 (2006): 1027–31; Ruth E. Ley et al., "Microbial Ecology: Human Gut Microbes Associated with Obesity," *Nature* 444 (2006): 1022–23.
9. Francisco Guarner et al., "Mechanisms of Disease: The Hygiene Hypothesis Revisited," *Nature Reviews Gastroenterology and Hepatology* 3 (2006): 275–84; Thomas W. McDade et al., "Early Origins of Inflammation: Microbial Exposures in Infancy Predict Lower Levels of C-Reactive Protein in Adulthood," *Proceedings of the Royal Society B: Biological Sciences* 277 (2010): 1129–37.
10. Bethan V. Lowder et al., "Recent Human-to-Poultry Host Jump, Adaptation, and Pandemic Spread of *Staphylococcus aureus*," *Proceedings of the National Academy of Sciences, USA* 106 (2009): 19545–50.
11. Nicolaas Rupke, *Richard Owen: Biology without Darwin*, rev. ed. (Chicago: University of Chicago Press, 2009), 90–140.
12. Richard Owen, *On the Nature of Limbs: A Discourse*, ed. Ron Amundson (Chicago: University of Chicago Press, 2007).
13. Richard Owen, *On the Archetype and Homologies of the Vertebrate Skeleton* (London: Richard and John E. Taylor, 1848), quoted in Rupke, *Richard Owen*, 120.
14. Owen, *Nature of Limbs*, 38.
15. Ibid.
16. Dennis Venema and Darrel Falk, "Signature in the Synteny," *Biologos Forum* (blog), posted April 19, 2010, http://biologos.org/blog/signature-in-the-synteny.
17. Byrappa Venkatesh et al., "Survey Sequencing and Comparative Analysis of the Elephant Shark (*Callorhinchus milii*) Genome," *PLoS Biology* 5 (2007): e101, doi:10.1371/journal.pbio.0050101.
18. Matthew V. Rockman, Sonja S. Skrovanek, and Leonid Kruglyak, "Selection at Linked Sites Shapes Heritable Phenotypic Variation in *C. elegans*,"

Science 330 (2010): 372–76.

19. Asaf Levy, Schraga Schwartz, and Gil Ast, "Large-Scale Discovery of Insertion Hotspots and Preferential Integration Sites of Human Transposed Elements," *Nucleic Acids Research* 38 (2010): 1515–30; Wenli Li et al., "Extensive, Recent Intron Gains in *Daphnia* Populations," *Science* 326 (2009): 1260–62; Richard J. A. Buggs et al., "Rapid, Repeated, and Clustered Loss of Duplicate Genes in Allopolyploid Plant Populations of Independent Origin," *Current Biology* 22 (2012): 248–52.

20. Alessandro Ambrosi, Claudia Cattoglio, and Clelia Di Serio, "Retroviral Integration Process in the Human Genome: Is It Really Non-Random? A New Statistical Approach," *PLoS Computational Biology* 4 (2008): e1000144, doi:10.1371/journal.pcbi.1000144.

21. Cheryl P. Andam, David Williams, and J. Peter Gogarten, "Biased Gene Transfer Mimics Patterns Created through Shared Ancestry," *Proceedings of the National Academy of Sciences, USA* 107 (2010): 10679–84; Clement Gilbert et al., "A Role for Host-Parasite Interactions in the Horizontal Transfer of Transposons across Phyla," *Nature* 464 (2010): 1347–50; Pernilla Vallenback, Lena Ghatnekar, and Bengt O. Bengtsson, "Structure of the Natural Transgene *PgiC2* in the Common Grass *Festuca ovina*," *PLoS ONE* 5 (2010): e13529, doi:10.1371/journal.pone.0013529; Ulfar Bergthorsson et al., "Widespread Horizontal Transfer of Mitochondrial Genes in Flowering Plants," *Nature* 424 (2003): 197–201; Sandra Stegemann et al., "Horizontal Transfer of Chloroplast Genomes between Plant Species," *Proceedings of the National Academy of Sciences, USA* 109 (2012): 2434–38.

Chapter 28: Where Does the RTB Model Stand?

1. Hugh Ross, *Navigating Genesis: A Scientist's Journey through Genesis 1–11* (Covina, CA: RTB Press, 2014), 75, 96–100, 156–60.

Index

gray whales 351
great apes 36–37, 56, 205, 221–226, 228–229, 250–252, 259–260, 285, 327–332, 375
Great Rift Valley 288
Green, Eric 348
greenhouse gases 106–107
guanine 211

haplotypes 64–65, 130–135, 138–139, 302
heavy elements 102
Hebrew words
    'āb 50
    āśâ 47, 52–53, 227–228
    bārā 47, 52–53
    bēn 50
    yāṣar 52
Helicobacter pylori 76–77, 141, 367
helium 106
hemoglobin 308–309
heteroduplexes 212
heteroplasmy 67–68
heterozygosity 351
histones 119
historical contingency 26–27
holotype 282–283
hominid environments 164–165
hominid reclassification 150–155
hominids 84, 146–147, 258–259, 277
    australopithecines 31, 90, 151, 153, 166, 168, 178
    Australopithecus aethiopicus 150, 152, 154
    Australopithecus afarensis 38, 40, 148–150, 152, 154, 164, 279–281
    Australopithecus africanus 28, 38, 41, 150, 152, 154, 170–171, 279
    Australopithecus anamensis 37, 40–41, 150, 154–155, 163, 279, 281
    Australopithecus bahrelghazali 38, 150, 154, 165
    Australopithecus boisei 150, 152, 154
    Australopithecus garhi 41, 150, 152, 180
    Australopithecus ramidus 164, 279, 281
    Australopithecus robustus 150, 152, 154

About the Authors

Fazale Rana attended West Virginia State College and then Ohio University, where he earned a PhD in chemistry. His postdoctoral work was conducted at the Universities of Virginia and Georgia. He was a presidential scholar, elected into two honor societies, and won the Donald Clippinger Research Award twice at Ohio University. Dr. Rana worked for seven years as a senior scientist in product development for Procter & Gamble before joining Reasons to Believe, where he now serves as vice president of research and apologetics.

He has published articles in peer-reviewed scientific journals, delivered presentations at international scientific meetings, and addressed church and university audiences in the United States and abroad. Dr. Rana also coauthored a chapter on antimicrobial peptides for *Biological and Synthetic Membranes* in addition to contributing numerous feature articles to Christian magazines. He appears on reasons.org podcasts and gives frequent radio interviews.

He and his wife, Amy, live in Southern California.

Hugh Ross is founder and president of Reasons to Believe, an organization that researches and communicates how God's revelation in the words of the Bible harmonizes with the facts of nature.

With a degree in physics from the University of British Columbia and a grant from the National Research Council of Canada, Dr. Ross earned a PhD in astronomy from the University of Toronto. For several years he continued his research on quasars and galaxies as a postdoctoral fellow at the California Institute of Technology. His writings include journal and magazine articles and numerous books—*Navigating Genesis, Hidden Treasures in the Book of Job, Why the Universe Is the Way It Is*, and more. He has spoken on hundreds of university campuses as well as at conferences and churches around the world.

He lives in Southern California with his wife, Kathy.

About Reasons to Believe

Uniquely positioned within the science-faith discussion since 1986, Reasons to Believe (RTB) communicates that science and faith are, and always will be, allies, not enemies. Distinguished for integrating science and faith respectfully and with integrity, RTB welcomes dialogue with both skeptics and believers. Addressing topics such as the origin of the universe, the origin of life, and the history and destiny of humanity, RTB's website offers a vast array of helpful resources. Through their books, blogs, podcasts, and speaking events, RTB scholars present powerful reasons from science to trust in the reliability of the Bible and the message it conveys about creation and redemption.

For more information, contact us via:
www.reasons.org
818 S. Oak Park Rd.
Covina, CA 91724
(855) REASONS / (855) 732-7667
ministrycare@reasons.org

WHAT DID FIRST LIFE LOOK LIKE?

When did it appear and how did it get here?

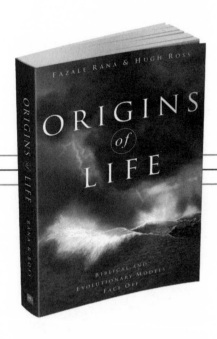

Imagine primordial earth, a churning cauldron of liquefied rock. Steaming, seething—a vast desolate wasteland, inhospitable to life. Yet somehow first life appeared. Maybe chemicals in a primordial soup spontaneously spawned a single-celled creature that continued to evolve. Or, perhaps a transcendent Creator formed and nurtured the initial life-forms.

To determine what really happened requires a framework to evaluate the evidence. Dr. Rana and Dr. Ross present a scientific model for the creation of first life on Earth—a model based on the Bible. They present testable predictions for this life origins scenario and for the competing naturalistic scenarios. Which model withstands the rigorous scrutiny of science and the tests of time?

HOW LONG WERE THE CREATION DAYS OF GENESIS—HOURS OR EPOCHS?

Does belief in an old earth equate to believe in evolution? Was there any kind of death before the fall?

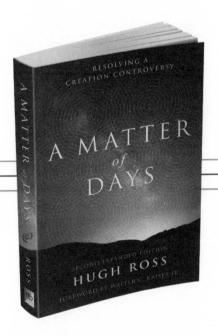

The length of the creation days in Genesis sparks a storm of controversy. At the core of this dissension lie key questions, the answers to which provide hope for resolution. Hugh Ross addresses these questions as he explores how the creation-day controversy developed.

Updated edition with over 50 pages of new content!

Discover other books by

FAZALE RANA

What Darwin Didn't Know

The Cell's Design: How Chemistry Reveals the Creator's Artistry

Creating Life in the Lab

Discover other books by

HUGH ROSS

Navigating Genesis: A Scientist's Journey through Genesis 1–11

*Hidden Treasures in the Book of Job: How the Oldest Book
in the Bible Answers Today's Scientific Questions*

More Than a Theory: Revealing a Testable Model for Creation